4-2-63

PRACTICAL
QUALITY CONTROL
FOR CONCRETE

PRACTICAL
QUALITY CONTROL
FOR CONCRETE

JOSEPH J. WADDELL

*Construction Materials Engineer; Chief Materials
Engineer, Soil Testing Services, Inc.,
Chicago, Illinois*

McGRAW-HILL BOOK COMPANY, INC.

New York   Toronto   London

PRACTICAL QUALITY CONTROL FOR CONCRETE

II

67641

Preface

Because so many variables must interact to produce the material we call concrete, it has earned a reputation among some circles as the least predictable of construction materials. The aggregates used are natural products, obtained locally and subject to wide variations of composition and form. Other factors upon which the quality of the end product depends—such as water, admixtures, weather, mixing methods, placing techniques, curing conditions—are also subject to a wide range of variations. However, many engineers and architects realize that, under proper conditions of design, construction, and inspection, concrete is one of the most versatile and dependable of construction materials. Consequently, engineers and architects are beginning to appreciate the vital importance of quality control, and they are beginning to apply it to design and construction by incorporating requirements for such control in construction specifications.

The object of quality control is the construction, at minimum practicable cost, of structures in which quality is uniform and sufficient to assure satisfactory service throughout the intended operating life. The need for a comprehensive manual of preventive and corrective methods of quality control for concrete prompted the writing of this book.

There are numerous papers and reports in the literature discussing specific instances of concrete failure and distress. These papers are a rich source of information for the solution of problems which continually arise when one is dealing with concrete. To know the solutions and corrections applied by others can frequently be of great help even though the situation at hand may not necessarily be identical with the ones previously solved. However, to find the specific answer to a certain problem may be difficult, entailing an extensive search through many references before the report of a similar experience is found. To expedite the solution of perplexing problems by the elimination of such a search is one of the objectives of this book. It is obvious that the whole vast field of concrete experience cannot be covered in a single volume. Nevertheless, it is the hope of the author that this book, by bringing together some of these experiences, will present to the field man a representative range of effective solutions of similar problems—problems that have arisen before and that will arise again as long as concrete is used as a construction material.

The second objective of the present volume is to offer to field engineers and inspectors practical advice on how to apply quality control measures to the everyday business of concrete construction, to the end that the full potential durability and beauty of concrete can be realized.

Joseph J. Waddell

Contents

Chapter 6. *Watertightness* 80

Chapter 7. *Cracking* 87

Chapter 8. *Concrete Surfaces* 105

Part III. CONSTRUCTION AND INSPECTION

Chapter 9. *Inspection Fundamentals* 121

Chapter 10. Materials for Concrete

Part IV. TESTS AND CONTROL

PART ONE

Characteristics

CHAPTER 1 *Basic Considerations*

1-1. DEVELOPMENT OF CONCRETE

Concrete as it is known today is a relatively new construction material. True, there are authentic examples of construction several thousand years old, using cementing materials to join together the parts of masonry construction. The ancient Egyptians, for instance, calcined limestone and gypsum to produce common lime and plaster. The Romans produced a crude hydraulic lime which, when combined with natural pozzolans and water, made an excellent cementing material. But all such construction, until late in the nineteenth century, was of masonry cemented together with some type of mortar.

It was in 1824 that Joseph Aspdin, a bricklayer of Leeds, England, made the discovery that led to the production of what we now call portland cement. The first kiln for the production of portland cement in the United States was erected in Copley, Pennsylvania, about 1875. With the great industrial expansion of the late nineteenth and early twentieth centuries, concrete as a material of construction developed rapidly, assuming a more and more important position in the industry. One of the earliest examples of monolithic building construction was the Leland Stanford University Museum, erected in 1893. It is interesting to note that this building came through the 1906 San Francisco earthquake virtually unscathed.

Today we find concrete one of the most important materials for construction. It is used in heavy-duty construction such as highways, bridges, and dams as well as in artistic details of fine buildings. Millions of cubic yards are produced every year. Its manufacture has progressed from a wheelbarrow and shovel basis in the hands of relatively unskilled laborers into a highly technical branch of engineering science, requiring the attention of skilled technicians and engineers for the proper control of its production. Great strides have been made in the design and manufacture of machinery to produce this concrete, and we today have

3

automatic batching and mixing plants that can produce hundreds of cubic yards of concrete per hour.

1-2. PROPERTIES OF CONCRETE

An understanding of the properties of concrete is necessary before one can analyze the failures and distress of concrete. These properties can be divided into two main groups: (1) properties of fresh concrete, while it is still in the plastic state, and (2) properties of hardened concrete.

Properties of Fresh Concrete

Properties of fresh concrete are workability, cohesiveness, plasticity, and consistency. Workability is the most important, as the other traits are subordinate to and form a part of it. No completely adequate test has yet been devised to measure these properties. The slump cone, flow trough, and flow table are the most common instruments in use today. A penetration ball was introduced several years ago and has gained great popularity because of its simplicity and accuracy.[1.1] The slump cone is the most widely used, owing at least in part to its convenience. In the end, the ease with which concrete can be placed is the real measure of its workability. But the designer must not yield to the temptation to obtain what passes for workability by following the easy path of rich and wet mixes. The requirements of economy, strength, and durability demand that the cement content and water-cement ratio be kept as low as reasonably possible. The use of overly fluid or wet mixes that flow into place with insufficient vibration is not the answer to difficult placing. Frequently, the fault is not with the concrete but with the placing technique or equipment.

Workability of the concrete is affected by the shape and surface texture of the aggregate, grading of the aggregate, amount of entrained air, amount of cement and water in the mix, and the maximum size of aggregate. Mixes that are too dry or too wet lack cohesiveness and are harsh. The addition of fine particles, such as sand, cement, powdered admixture, or entrained air makes a mix more cohesive.

Properties of Hardened Concrete

Properties of hardened concrete are durability, strength, modulus of elasticity, watertightness, and density. Volume change, creep, extensibility, and thermal properties are of importance in some cases. Fortunately,

* Superscript figures refer to chapter and reference number. The references are found at the end of each chapter.

most of the desirable properties will be present if concrete of adequate strength and durability is made.

Durability consists of resistance to weathering (freezing and thawing, wetting and drying, temperature fluctuations), resistance to erosion and impact, and resistance to chemical attack, both internal (alkali-aggregate reaction) and external (corrosion and leaching). It is difficult to separate durability from the other properties of concrete. Again and again one finds that workability, strength, and other properties are intimately related to durability, hence the accent on durability as probably the most important property.

Of prime importance for good durability is a concrete surface that is resistant to penetration of water, obtained by good formwork and consolidation, low water-cement ratio, entrained air, and adequate curing. Selection of proper raw materials is very important.

In this connection, it should be remembered that the overall cost during the life of the structure far overshadows the first cost of materials. Cheapest in the beginning may not be cheapest in the long run. In those cases in which it becomes expedient to make use of a certain substance or method to minimize a deficiency or weakness, recognition should always be given to possible side effects that may be detrimental to other properties of the concrete. Addition of more water makes concrete fluid and easy to place, but is detrimental to strength, durability, and other desirable properties. Addition of clay would probably stop bleeding, but what of the undesirable side effects? Such questions should be carefully weighed and the answers determined before plunging blindly ahead in the first course that appears to lead the way out of a dilemma.

1-3. AGENCIES OF DESTRUCTION

Many old structures have served useful lives, and some are still serving after many years; some, on the other hand, have succumbed to the ravages of time and exposure. What are the deficiencies that have marred the appearance or impaired the safety of some of these structures? Cracking, spalling, settlement, and erosion are among the evidences of surrender to the agencies of destruction. These agencies are at work to some extent at all times and in all places. They may be classified into four general categories:

1. Deficiencies or weaknesses of the concrete itself, resulting from failure to follow the five fundamentals of good concrete construction. (These five fundamentals will be discussed later.) Such weaknesses, while not actually acting to damage the concrete, may be the opening wedge for serious damage by actual attack. For example, low strength resulting from impurities in the mixing water or aggregates could con-

tribute to failure by attack by any of the forces in the three following categories.

2. Cyclic forces of the weather. Examples of these forces are cycles of freezing and thawing, or wetting and drying, which create disruptive stresses in the concrete, producing cracking, spalling, or worse. Some concrete, such as that inside of buildings, is not normally exposed to this attack.

3. Chemical or mechanical attack by outside agencies other than weather cycles. A great multitude of agencies can be listed under this group. Among them are attack by sulfates (alkalies) in the soil, erosion caused by running water, and foundation failures.

4. Reaction between the constituents of the concrete itself. One example of this is the alkali-aggregate reaction in which certain siliceous portions of the aggregates react with alkalies in the cement to produce a gel. This gel, in attempting to expand, creates a powerful expansive force which causes a characteristic pattern cracking. Another example is thermal incompatibility, in which a portion of the aggregate is of such composition that its coefficient of thermal expansion is of a different magnitude from the rest. This will produce unequal expansion on heating whereby the concrete is caused to crack. These activities are usually aggravated in the presence of water.

Briefly, such are the agencies of destruction. Steps necessary to protect the concrete from these attacking agencies appear obvious. Where there is the danger of deficiencies in the concrete itself, care must be taken to provide the best concrete possible commensurate with requirements of the exposure; where there are cyclic weather forces, good concrete must be provided, and it should be protected as much as possible; where there is attack by outside agencies, good concrete is necessary, and the attacking forces must be neutralized; and where there is danger of reaction between the constituents, others must be provided, or they must be neutralized in order to make good concrete. In all cases, the starting point is good, durable concrete. To provide this kind of concrete requires care from the time a structure is first conceived and throughout its life.

1-4. FIVE FUNDAMENTALS OF GOOD CONCRETE CONSTRUCTION

This care is implemented by the five fundamentals of concrete construction, which are (1) investigation of the site, (2) design of the structure, (3) selection of materials and mix, (4) workmanship in handling materials and concrete, and (5) maintenance of the structure throughout its life. Let us now consider each of these five fundamentals and determine how each of them can help to obtain good, durable concrete.

Investigation of the Site

Some sort of site investigation is made for any structure, regardless of how insignificant it may be. This investigation is important for proper design of the structure and has a significant influence on selection of the materials and mix. An intelligent design cannot be made, nor can logical use be made of the available materials, without a thorough investigation of all features at the site. Proper evaluation of the site means a three-way approach involving (1) an investigation of the fitness of the location to suit the requirements of the structure; (2) an investigation of the competence of the foundation to carry expected loads safely; and (3) an investigation of the existence of forces or substances that may attack the concrete.

Investigation of the fitness of the location includes economic considerations as well as engineering. These questions should be answered:

Is the structure really necessary, or can the problem be solved by improvements or adjustments to existing facilities?

Is the project economically and financially sound? Have the necessary financial studies been made whereby the ratio of benefit to cost has been found to be favorable?

Is use being made of the best location, considering accessibility, availability of construction materials, right-of-way costs, foundation adequacy, type of structure, etc.?

Have geological and engineering studies shown that the site is capable of supporting the structure and construction facilities both during and after construction?

Finally, will the structure be aesthetically compatible with its surroundings?

Concurrent with the study of the above questions is the investigation to determine the presence of agencies that may attack or damage the concrete. A full discussion of destructive agencies and methods of preventing or correcting damage is included in Chap. 5.

Ground and surface waters must be analyzed. It should be remembered that the quality of water may vary at different seasons of the year, hence care must be taken to obtain samples at the most unfavorable time. Among the commonest substances that are dangerous are sulfates leached out of the ground or from manufacturing plant waste; organic acids from sewage or decaying organic matter, such as in swamps; leachings such as might come from storage of coal or cinders nearby; sulfides in swamps or marshes, carbon dioxide in water; and atmospheric gases from certain manufacturing processes.

Concrete for construction of food-processing plants is vulnerable to attack by certain organic substances. For instance, lactic acid, produced in some fermentation processes as well as being present in dairies, actively attacks concrete and requires that good, dense concrete be provided, made with cement low in lime and iron, or that protective coatings be applied.

In this investigation one is concerned with chemical or mechanical attack by outside agencies. Chemical attack is aggravated in the presence of water, principally because the water is a vehicle for bringing the substances into intimate contact with the concrete, even to the extent of transporting them into the concrete through cracks, honeycombs, or pores in the surface.

Cyclic forces of the weather may be destructive in two ways: first, by alternately expanding and contracting the concrete, whereby the concrete is stressed to the point where it cracks, and second, by the entrance of destructive solutions into the cracks thus produced.

Design of the Structure

Design of the structure is the second fundamental. It is obvious that design of a structure must be adequate, accomplished by competent engineers in accordance with accepted safe practices. A structure cannot be designed by a cut-and-dried process requiring only the ability to read a table of values or take off a quantity from a graph. It requires intelligence and experience to design a structure adequately and to make certain that everything possible has been done to assure the safety and economy of the design, based on results of the investigation. Failure or distress may range from small tension cracks to complete failure of the entire structure. There is not much that can be done for a structure that shows signs of distress because of poor design, other than makeshift expedients that will shore it up and provide additional support. Design should include a consideration of the capabilities of men and machines and should aim to facilitate formwork and other construction procedures.

Drainage is most important. Horizontal surfaces should be sloped slightly to prevent the formation of puddles of water resulting from rain or any other cause. If at all possible, runoff or seepage should not be allowed to run over concrete surfaces or to collect on or against them. Weeps should be provided, and they should drain away from concrete surfaces. Whenever possible, the structure should be given an adequate earth covering.

Hydraulic structures, such as sea walls, irrigation canals, or other structures exposed to water or used for conveying water, should be given special care in designing as well as construction.

A detailed consideration of the theory and practice of design is beyond the scope of this treatise, and the reader is referred to the many excellent books on the subject of concrete structural design.

Selection of Materials and Mix

Principle number three is selection of materials and mix. Many cases of distress have been traced to faulty materials or improper mix proportions. For example, poor proportioning may require so much water to achieve a workable mix that the durability of the concrete will be impaired, or chemical reaction between aggregates and cement may cause cracking. In most cases materials that are available have been used for making concrete for a number of years. If such is the case, histories of these materials and of the structures built with them should be examined. Information gained by such a study will reveal whether or not the materials under consideration are suitable. In any such investigation, one should keep in mind the fact that poor concrete can result even when good materials are used if insufficient care is taken in proportioning and handling the materials and concrete. Many times, especially for structures built years ago, there is a lack of accurate information about the materials and methods used. Even so, the reputation of the local materials should be given careful consideration.

For large and important works, and if historical data for other cases are lacking, it is necessary to determine suitability of materials by tests. These tests should not be used as an inflexible criterion for acceptance or rejection of the material since they require sound engineering judgment in their interpretation and application.

Ordinarily, there should be no trouble with cement if it complies with standard specifications, but it should be tested as a matter of record. Potable water is usually safe for concrete; any clean water, reasonably free of mineral salts and organic matter, is satisfactory. Aggregate tests should include those to determine soundness, resistance to abrasion, presence of unsatisfactory or contaminating materials, reactivity with cement, and other properties which would tend to produce unsatisfactory concrete. A petrographic examination will disclose the presence of unsatisfactory rock types such as reactive opal or unsound chert. Specifications and tests for materials are provided by the American Society for Testing and Materials, American Concrete Institute, American Association of State Highway Officials, governmental agencies, and others. The user of concrete should be familiar with these requirements and should set up his own standards in accordance with them. Appropriate specifications and test methods are listed in the appendix.

Aggregates must be structurally sound, relatively nonabsorbent, properly graded, and inert. The different rock types should possess similar physical properties; they should have good bonding properties, be free of coatings, and possess a surface that is not smooth and glossy.

Cement should be fresh but not still hot from the mill, conforming to the requirements of ASTM Designation: C 150. It should be low in tricalcium aluminate (not over 5 per cent for sulfate-resistant or low-heat cement, and not over 12 per cent for others) and low in sulfur trioxide. If a reactive aggregate is suspected, the cement should be low-alkali type. It should be free of premature stiffening tendencies.

Water should be clean, free from organic materials, mud, or other contaminating substances, such as alkalies. Some agencies permit use of sea water for mixing in certain cases, while others prohibit its use entirely. Due to the presence of chlorides in sea water, its use should be prohibited in reinforced concrete, although it may be permitted in unreinforced concrete. Tests made with Mediterranean Sea water indicate that reinforcing steel is vulnerable to corrosion if the concrete is exposed to moist air. If the concrete is permanently and totally immersed, there appears to be little or no danger.[1,2] However, the safest procedure would be to avoid use of sea water for reinforced concrete.

Admixtures and air-entraining agents should be used carefully, in accordance with the manufacturer's recommendations and on the basis of laboratory tests.

Concrete-mix proportioning has as its objective the production of concrete of maximum economy having sufficient workability, strength, durability, and impermeability to meet the conditions of placing, exposure, loading, and other requirements of the structure. Trial mixes, made under laboratory conditions and using the proposed materials, should always be made for large and important works. Trial mixes should also be made in those cases where information about existing materials is inadequate. These mixes are subject to revision in the field as conditions require. Strength, water-cement ratio, maximum size of aggregate, and slump are usually specified, and the proportions of cement, aggregates, entrained air, and admixtures are determined by these trial mixes.

The economy of a mix is affected by the proportions of materials and conditions of placement. Because cement is expensive compared to aggregates, the ratio of cement to aggregates should be as low as reasonably possible. It sometimes happens that the use of a relatively expensive admixture in small amounts is beneficial. For example, pozzolans such as fly ash and burnt shales will improve workability, watertightness, and resistance to aggressive waters, especially of lean mixes. More efficient placing methods permit the use of less workable, more economical concrete.

For maximum economy, cement content must be kept as low as possible, and at the same time, in the interest of durability and strength, the water-cement ratio must be kept low also. Contrary to this is the necessity of providing sufficient water to give mobility and plasticity during placing operations. Thus the designer is confronted with the necessity of providing concrete of low cement content and low water-cement ratio, at the same time permitting sufficient water to make the concrete workable. This is accomplished by using well-graded subangular aggregates of the largest possible size commensurate with clearances within the forms and between reinforcing bars or embedded parts. Sand should be well graded, with a fineness modulus between 2.4 and 3.1, free of flat, elongated particles. Use of an air-entraining agent will compensate for deficiencies in the sand grading and will improve workability as well as reduce bleeding and segregation tendencies. Entrained air reduces the water requirement at any given slump. When it is necessary to use crushed rock or manufactured sand, entrained air is of great value in reducing harshness of the mix. Certain admixtures are of value under some conditions. For example, a water-reducing retarder is especially desirable during hot weather to reduce the amount of water required and to retard cement setting time in order to facilitate finishing operations.

Workmanship in Handling the Materials and Concrete

Workmanship in handling the materials and concrete is the fourth category. It is probable that the greatest portion of concrete distress has been caused by improper methods of handling the ingredients and the concrete itself after the ingredients have been combined in the batcher. Included in such minor failures are the many small discrepancies that appear and which in themselves are unsightly but not necessarily serious. But it must be remembered that serious difficulties frequently have small beginnings, and a small surface defect can develop into a major one. For example, a small crack which may have been caused by drying shrinkage could permit sea water to come in contact with reinforcement, thus giving rise to disruptive forces far more serious than the original cracking. Fortunately, corrective measures can in many cases prevent serious damage.

This category includes preparation of the aggregates, batching, mixing, transporting, placing, and curing. The period of construction offers one of the last opportunities for assuring a well-built structure. Improvements in techniques and equipment during the last 25 or 30 years are making it more and more difficult for poor construction practices to exist, but exist they do, and vigilance on the part of those charged with the responsibility for this phase of construction is necessary.

Good practices in aggregate production and materials handling demand that the ingredients for concrete be handled with a minimum of segregation and contamination. Uniformity of materials (including uniformity of moisture content of the aggregates) is essential to the production of good concrete. Some agencies require that coarse aggregates be finish-screened at the batching plant, thus assuring a minimum of undersize and more uniform material.

Proper construction procedures include preventing segregation, bleeding, and cold joints; working of concrete from corners of the forms, not toward corners and ends; keeping finishing to a minimum; sloping exposed surfaces to provide drainage and avoid formation of puddles of water on the concrete; providing drains for seepage water; providing adequate curing; and assuring protection from extremes of temperature. Construction joints should have a thorough cleanup, such as by a wet sandblast.

The concrete should be permitted to dry thoroughly after curing and before putting the structure into service. A more sound structure will result if temperature is controlled during and immediately after placing, especially of mass concrete. To accomplish this, use a minimum cement content; use low-heat or modified cement; cool the ingredients during warm weather; cool the concrete after it has been placed by means of embedded pipes through which cold water is pumped (a method that is practiced in large dam construction), and by water-curing the surfaces of the structure; use a pozzolan with air entrainment and low slump. Temperature of the concrete when placed should be above 40°F in cold weather and below 90°F during hot weather. During cold weather, water, and perhaps the aggregates, should be heated. However, aggregates should not be heated except as a last resort. Flash set of the cement is apt to result if it comes in contact with hot water or aggregates. Temperature of materials should never exceed 150°F.

The materials comprising concrete should be measured accurately. To this end, aggregates should always be weighed, except for the smallest, least important work. If they are not weighed, then volume batching by measuring the materials in calibrated boxes should be used. Cement should never be batched by volume but should be weighed if fractional sacks are required or if bulk cement is used. Water may be either weighed or measured volumetrically. There are many good meters and other volumetric measuring devices available for metering water. Liquid admixtures may be handled in the same manner as water. Powdered or granular ones may be put into solution and handled as a liquid or weighed. The preferred method is to add them as a solution with the mixing water. This is accomplished with a metering device that measures a predetermined amount of solution into the mixing water as the water is being admitted into the mixer. In weighing aggregates and water, adjustment must be made to the quantities to allow for free water in the sand and gravel.

Good mixers, in good operating condition and operated in accordance with the manufacturer's instructions are a must if one is to have consistently good concrete. Regular maintenance is essential. Worn blades, leaky valves, and accumulations of hardened concrete should be avoided.

During the process of moving the concrete from the mixer to its final location in the forms, much good concrete has been damaged. Segregation, or separation of the rock from the mortar, is probably the most common misfortune that befalls concrete after it leaves the mixer. This can happen in chutes, at points of discharge or transfer, in the forms, and, in fact, at almost any place between the mixer and forms where proper precautions are not taken. These precautions include the use of short chutes instead of long ones, at an angle of less than 30° from the horizontal, down which the concrete slides, not flows; the avoidance of free fall of the concrete, especially if chutes are used; the use of buckets with a capacity of a full batch from the mixer; dry mixes (not over 4-in. slump); consolidation by vibration; tremies, or elephant trunks; and well-proportioned mixes with entrained air. The concrete should be placed as nearly as possible in its final location in the forms, avoiding the use of vibrators to move it about.

The final opportunity for assuring good concrete is during the first few days of its life. During this time it is necessary to see that the concrete is cured properly. It should be assured a sufficient supply of moisture for the proper hydration of the cement, and it must be protected from extremes of temperature, either low or high. Water curing should be continuous for at least 7 days, and longer if possible. Spray nozzles, "soaker" hoses, and flooding are good methods of wetting concrete. Curing by leaving the forms in place should be viewed with suspicion, as drying shrinkage of the concrete or shrinkage of wooden forms may cause loss of moisture through cracks opened up in the formwork, or between the form and the concrete.

Good curing consists of more than merely providing water for hydration of the cement. It requires:

1. Continuously available free moisture at a sustained moderate temperature

2. Freedom from stress that approaches closely the strength developed at the time of its application

3. Avoidance, upon termination of formal curing, of either rapid surface drying or of abrupt change of temperature (thermal shock), which would introduce damaging differential volume changes within the concrete

4. Avoidance of exposure to freezing temperatures until curing has progressed far enough to partially empty the capillaries of their free moisture.[1,3]

Maintenance of the Structure

The fifth and last fundamental is maintenance of the structure throughout its life. This statement merely means what it says: inspect the structure at regular intervals to determine whether unusual deterioration is taking place and to provide adequate protection or repair to minimize the deterioration.

There is a type of deterioration that may be called *normal weathering* (see Sec. 5-7). Such weathering is part of the normal process of aging and is itself harmless. However, inspection of the structure will aid in determining when restorative action is necessary to combat this aging, as well as in disclosing abnormal deterioration.

Should inspection disclose damage, the first step in treatment of the damaged concrete structure is to classify the damage. This classification will assist in diagnosis, as forces that produce each type of damage can be generalized, thus narrowing the field of possible aggressors. After this classification, the cause may then be determined. This process of diagnosis may be quite simple and almost automatic, or it may involve a complicated and intensive job of detective work before the basic causes are found. Sometimes what seems to be the obvious cause is not the cause after all, or it may be one of several contributing to failure. The investigator should consider all facts that might be pertinent. This may involve determining the sources of materials used in construction, loading conditions, construction methods, design factors, conditions of exposure, presence of aggressive substances or forces, evidence of accidental damage such as impact of vehicles, foundation conditions, and others. Once the cause has been isolated, corrective measures may be taken. Such measures may consist in elimination of the cause, changes in the structure to enable it to withstand the destructive action, restoration of the damaged portions of the structure and protection to prevent further injury, or abandonment of the structure and construction of a new one to withstand the action, or a combination of these.

REFERENCES

1.1 Kelly, J. W., and Milos Polivka: Ball Test for Field Control of Concrete Consistency, *J. Am. Concrete Inst.*, May, 1955, pp. 881–888.
1.2 Shalon, R., and M. Raphael: Influence of Sea Water on Corrosion of Reinforcement, *J. Am. Concrete Inst.*, June, 1951, pp. 1251–1268.
1.3 Gilkey, H. J.: Curing Structural Concrete, *J. Am. Concrete Inst.*, May, 1952, pp. 711–715.

2-1. ELEMENTS OF WORKABILITY

The property of fresh concrete called workability eludes exact definition. Blanks et al.[2.1]* define it as "the ease with which a given set of materials can be mixed into concrete and subsequently handled, transported, and placed with minimum loss of homogeneity." Terms such as consistency, plasticity, cohesiveness, mobility, and fluidity all express elements of workability.

The workability of any batch of concrete depends upon the characteristics and relative proportions of the several ingredients comprising the concrete, whereas the degree of workability required for proper placing and consolidation of the concrete is prescribed by the type of structure. Small complicated sections with much reinforcing steel or other embedded parts require concrete of high workability. On the other hand, relatively unworkable mixes can be placed in massive structures of large cross section. In other words, the amount of workability required depends on the type of structure and placing conditions, and the amount of workability available depends on the materials and how they are used.

Workability has a direct bearing on cost, an unworkable mix requiring more time and labor in handling. Unworkable concrete is more apt to suffer from segregation and honeycomb, resulting in costly and unsightly patching and repairs.

Consistency

The measure of the fluidity, softness, or wetness of a batch of concrete is the consistency of the concrete, determined by the method of ASTM Designation: C 143, Test for Slump of Portland Cement Concrete. (The "Kelly ball" test may also be used.[1.1]) The slump, measured in inches,

* Superscript figures refer to chapter and reference number. The references are found at the end of each chapter.

15

is the vertical subsidence of the sample of concrete that occurs when the slump cone is removed from the concrete. A concrete of stiff consistency will slump or subside only a short distance; a concrete of wet consistency will slump more than the stiff (or dry) one. Hence the popular terms "high slump" and "low slump" to denote wet or fluid consistencies on the one hand and dry or stiff consistencies on the other.

The amount of water in the batch is the largest single factor affecting slump. Air entrainment is also significant, as it permits the use of less water for the same slump. Slump is affected by the temperature of the concrete, as shown in Fig. 2-1, a factor that should be considered if trial

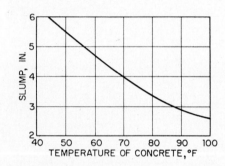

Fig. 2-1. Effect of temperature on slump. Bureau of Reclamation data; constant water-cement ratio; 1½ in. max aggregate.

batches are run in the laboratory at one temperature for concrete that is to be placed at a significantly different temperature. Variations in slump during the progress of a day's operation may result from changes in aggregate gradation, or from uncompensated variations in the moisture content of the aggregate. If dry aggregates are batched into the mix, they will absorb water quite rapidly for a short time, causing slump loss.

There may be a significant loss of consistency or slump in the time that the concrete is in transit between the mixer and the forms. This slump loss is especially severe during hot, dry weather, and results from loss of water from the concrete by evaporation. (This drying of the concrete is sometimes erroneously called *flash set.*)

Cohesiveness

The element of workability that governs the extent of harshness or stickiness is called *cohesiveness.* A mix possessing the proper degree of cohesiveness is neither harsh nor sticky, but is plastic, and does not segregate easily. Cohesiveness is at a maximum in mixes that are neither too wet (high slump) nor too dry (low slump). Usually the finer mixes have a higher degree of cohesiveness than the coarse ones. The addition of cement, fine sand, inert fines, or entrained air increases the cohesiveness, and such addition may be desirable in a harsh, unworkable mix.

Harshness results from rough and angular aggregates, such as crushed stone, or aggregate that contains a high percentage of flat or elongated pieces. A harsh mix lacks plasticity; it is unworkable and noncohesive, tending to segregate easily. Other causes of harshness are coarse sand in the mix, a mix deficient in fines, lean concrete low in cement content, or extremely high slump.

A harsh mix is more apt to segregate than a mix of normal plasticity, and usually requires slightly more vibration for proper consolidation. However, a harsh mix, when the harshness is not due to a high water content, produces a better hardened concrete, a concrete that is less subject to shrinkage cracks.

At the opposite extreme from harshness are mixes that are sticky as a result of too much plasticity. Sticky mixes will not segregate easily, but are apt to require more water per cubic yard than normal ones because of their high percentage of fines, including cement. A sticky mix is subject to shrinkage and cracking upon hardening. Sticky mixes are usually rich mixes with a high cement content, or they may contain an excessive portion of fine sand, rock dust, or similar material.

Measurement of Workability

There is no really accurate means of measuring the workability of concrete. Determination of this property of concrete depends to a large extent on judgment resulting from experience.

Over the years, many devices and methods have been proposed for measuring workability. These have included measurement of the flow of a molded volume of concrete on a jigging table, measurement of the penetration of a calibrated needle or plunger,* and various remolding, compacting, and dropping contrivances. Probably one of the best is the Powers remolding apparatus,[2.2] which measures the effort required to induce a specified and definite change in shape of a certain volume of concrete. However, this apparatus is not practical for field control use and is confined largely to laboratory use.

At the present time, the slump test, augmented by observation of the behavior of the concrete, offers the best means of evaluating workability. Consistency is measured by the slump test; plasticity, harshness, and cohesiveness are determined by noting the appearance of the slump specimen after removal of the slump cone. A harsh, unworkable specimen

---

* Now used to measure the "vibration limit" and time of set of concrete (see Retarders in Sec. 10-8).

will tend to crumble or segregate when tapped lightly with the slump rod. A plastic, workable mix will stick together and subside unbroken. Passing a trowel over the sample in the pan gives an indication of the cohesiveness of the mix as shown by the effort required to smooth the surface.

2-2. FACTORS AFFECTING WORKABILITY

Effect of Aggregates

Characteristics of the aggregates have an important influence on workability, the most desirable aggregate being a natural gravel of subrounded to subangular shape. Aggregates with a high percentage of flat or elongated pieces produce a concrete of poor workability. If it is not possible to change the source of aggregates, use of a richer mix with more cement and/or sand will be of benefit. Sometimes the addition of a small amount of a finely powdered admixture, such as diatomaceous earth or a pozzolan, may be of value, especially in lean mixes. Concrete made with crushed stone aggregate is less workable than that made with natural gravel.

Workability is noticeably sensitive to the grading of the aggregates, especially the sand and finer portion (passing ⅜-in. screen) of the coarse aggregate. Sand should conform to the grading shown in Table 2-1, with the grading falling near the midpoint between the limits. It is

TABLE 2-1. SIEVE ANALYSIS OF SAND

Sieve size	Cumulative per cent passing
⅜ in.	100
No. 4	95–100
No. 8	75–90
No. 16	50–75
No. 30	30–60
No. 50	10–30
No. 100	2–8
Fineness modulus	2.50–3.00

especially desirable to avoid a sand that fluctuates from the high limit on one sieve to the low limit on the adjacent sieve. Sand that is deficient in the fractions passing the No. 50 and No. 100 sieves is particularly undesirable.

Coarse aggregate grading is less critical in affecting workability than the sand grading. Grading of the material larger than ⅜ in. may vary widely with no appreciable effect on workability. However, the amount of pea gravel (material between ⅜ and ³⁄₁₆ in. in size) sometimes has a significant effect, especially if it contains considerable undersize. Undersize from pea gravel consists of rock dust and sand sizes of rock particles, all of them rough in texture, and all of them altering the sand grading, sometimes enough to influence some phase of workability.

Effect of Cement

Differences in the fineness of cement affect the workability of the concrete. Using a cement ground to approach the upper limit of fineness, that is, a finer cement, increases the workability, especially of harsh mixes. The mix is more cohesive, and the tendency of the concrete to segregate and bleed is reduced. Conversely, a coarse-ground cement reduces stickiness of the mix.

The amount of cement also affects workability. A mix low in cement, called a *lean mix*, is apt to be harsh and unworkable.

With one exception, the composition of the cement has no apparent effect on workability. The one exception is the gypsum content.

The presence of unstable gypsum in the cement, resulting from a high temperature in the grinding mill, causes a phenomenon called *false set*. It is also called *premature stiffening, gum set,* or *rubber set*. Stiffening or loss of consistency associated with false set occurs during or shortly after mixing of the concrete, and seriously impairs workability. False set may disappear upon prolonged mixing or remixing of the concrete, permitting normal handling and placing operations to continue. It is an extremely erratic condition, nearly impossible to forecast and difficult to control. No heat is liberated during false set.

Besides reducing workability, false set causes a high water requirement resulting in lower strength, lowered resistance to freezing and thawing, and increased cracking tendencies. It causes excessive bleeding and erratic entrainment of air. It makes control difficult, delays construction, and increases construction costs. It is affected by temperature, mixing time, type of materials in the concrete, and construction methods.

Many varied expedients have been used in attempts to alleviate false set. A change to cement ground at more moderate temperatures invariably results in disappearance of the trouble. Hence, if a certain source is producing cement with a false-set tendency, efforts should be made to lower grinding temperatures.

At the construction site, it may be helpful to lengthen the mixing time, or remix the concrete after a few minutes. One project reported improvement by the addition of 0.2 per cent, by weight of cement, of RDA, a grinding aid, at the mixer; another used 2 per cent of gypsum with good results; still another found that 0.1 per cent of mineral oil was beneficial. However, the only cure that is universally effective is to grind the cement at a reasonably low temperature, usually below 250°F.[2,3]

Related to the use of hot cement is a flash set of the concrete. This should not be confused with false set, as a flash set is actually an accelerated hydration of a small portion of the cement that occurs when the hot cement comes in contact with the mixing water. It usually results in the formation of lumps of cement. If one of these lumps is broken in the hands, it may be found to consist of a center of dry cement covered with a shell of damp, partially hydrated cement; others are composed of a solid mass of partially hydrated cement. In either case they are obnoxious and difficult to break up. There is little that can be done in the field to eliminate them except to try to obtain cooler cement. If a pneumatic cement-conveying system is being used, an aftercooler should be provided to cool the air after it leaves the compressor, or the cement pipes may be cooled by spraying with cold water. Obvious problems present themselves when the latter expedient is used.

A flash set sometimes occurs in the winter, when mixing water is heated, if the hot water comes in contact with the cement in the mixer. Trouble can be obviated if the hot water and aggregates are introduced into the mixer first; then the cement can be added after the cold aggregates have had time to cool the water.

Effect of Admixtures

In all cases in which the aggregate shape or grading causes poor workability, the entrainment of the proper percentage of air has a beneficial effect. Entrained air reduces the tendency of the concrete to segregate, lowers the bleeding rate (speed with which water appears on the surface of the concrete), and expedites finishing. It is also useful in improving the workability of concrete made with well-graded and well-shaped aggregates.

In lean, harsh mixes, the addition of fines enhances workability by increasing the plasticity. Examples of suitable fines are the pozzolans, fly ash, rock dust, and similar materials, or very small additions of such materials as bentonite or diatomaceous earth. The workability of lean mixes is improved by adding 10 to 15 per cent of hydrated lime, by weight of cement. Such additions should not be used in concrete with adequate fines, or in rich mixes, nor should they be used without prior testing to determine their side effects on such properties of the concrete as strength and durability.

There are available a number of admixtures that reduce the water requirement of concrete, delay setting time, or act as cement dispersants. Proper use of these admixtures improves workability. Here again, the user is cautioned to test the proposed admixture in trial batches of concrete before proceeding to use it.

2-3. SEGREGATION

Segregation of concrete means the separation of coarse aggregate from the mortar. Because concrete is not a homogeneous material, but is rather a mixture of materials of different specific gravities and sizes, including microscopic air bubbles, forces are always acting to cause these materials to separate. Many of the blemishes and imperfections of the hardened concrete, such as rock pockets, sand streaks, porous layers, and failure of bond at construction joints, owe their beginnings to segregation.

Mixes that are subject to segregation are the harsh mixes: those that are overly wet, extremely dry, or undersanded. However, even good, workable concrete will segregate if it is mishandled by poorly designed or improperly operated equipment and procedures.

Any of the measures that lend plasticity to a harsh mix reduce the tendency of concrete to segregate, if the concrete is produced at a reasonable slump. A properly proportioned cohesive mix, with a slump between 1 and 4 in., is not apt to segregate easily.

In Chap. 12 handling of concrete is discussed in detail. Types of equipment and procedures conducive to segregation are discussed together with methods of prevention and correction.

REFERENCES

2.1 Blanks, R. F., E. N. Vidal, W. H. Price, and F. M. Russell: The Properties of Concrete, *J. Am. Concrete Inst.*, April, 1940, pp. 433–475.
2.2 Powers, T. C.: Studies of Workability of Concrete, *J. Am. Concrete Inst.*, February, 1932, pp. 419–448.
2.3 Blanks, R. F., and J. F. Gilliland: False Set in Portland Cement, *J. Am. Concrete Inst.*, March, 1951, pp. 517–532.

CHAPTER 3 *Strength*

The strength test is probably the most important test applied to concrete as, justly or unjustly, it is the basis for conclusions relative to quality of the finished product. A high-strength concrete is usually a good concrete in other respects. But high strength, when gained by the use of an excessive amount of cement to keep the water-cement ratio low, is obtained at the hazard of excessive shrinkage and hair cracking of the surface of the structure unless extreme care is taken in placing and curing.

Special cements, admixtures, accelerated curing, and prestressed concrete all directed toward greater speed in construction, have enhanced the importance of strength tests at ages as little as 12 hr. Nevertheless, the standard-cured 28-day cylinder is still considered the medium by which the concrete is evaluated, and, until a better test is devised, it will remain in this position. Some research is being done toward developing tests to evaluate fresh concrete more fully than tests presently being used, and no doubt something will be developed.

3-1. STRENGTH RELATIONSHIPS

All strengths of concrete—compressive, tensile, shearing, and flexural—are related, and the magnitude of one is usually reflected in the others. Tensile strength of concrete averages about 10 per cent of compressive, ranging from 7 per cent at 9,000 psi compressive strength to 11 per cent at 1,000 psi compressive strength. Present knowledge indicates that tensile strength is a function of the square root of compressive. Shearing resistance is about 25 per cent of compressive.

The ratio of deformed reinforcing steel bond to compressive strength ranges from about 18 per cent at 5,000 psi compressive to 25 per cent at 2,000 psi. Bond strength is significantly affected by the quality of the concrete and test method, and to some extent by the type of deformations.

22

Compressive Strength

In the United States, strength of concrete is usually determined by means of cylindrical specimens, 6 in. in diameter by 12 in. long (ASTM Designation: C 31), made of the fresh concrete and tested in compression at various ages. Practice in some other countries is to use cubical compressive specimens. For example, the British standard is an 8-in. cube.

The apparent strength of concrete is significantly affected by the size and shape of the test specimen. For example, if it is assumed that 100 per cent represents the strength of the standard cylindrical specimen with a length-diameter ratio of 2.0, then a specimen with an L/D ratio of 1.0 will have 115 per cent, and one with an L/D ratio of 3.0 will have 94 per cent of the strength of the standard (Table 3-1). Tests by the Bureau

TABLE 3-1. CONVERSION FACTORS TO BE APPLIED TO INDICATED STRENGTHS OF NONSTANDARD-LENGTH COMPRESSIVE-STRENGTH SPECIMENS

$\dfrac{Length}{Diameter}$	Correction factor
3.00	1.06
2.5	1.04
2.0	1.00
1.5	0.96
1.0	0.85
0.5	0.50

EXAMPLE: A 4-in.-diameter core, 6 in. long, broke at 4,000 psi. L/D ratio is $6/4 = 1.5$. Corrected strength is

$$4,000 \times 0.96 = 3,840 \text{ psi}$$

of Reclamation show that the indicated strength of cylinders decreases as the diameter is increased, provided the length-diameter ratio is maintained constant. Cores drilled from the finished structure will usually indicate a higher strength than test cylinders.

A standard American 6 × 12-in. cylinder has about 75 per cent of the strength indicated by the British 8-in. cube, although this may vary appreciably due to quality of the concrete and other factors.

Flexural Strength

Flexural, or bending strength, is important in the design of pavements. The modulus of rupture is a measure of flexural strength, and is determined by testing a beam in bending. Usual practice is to test a simple beam with two concentrated loads applied at the third points, although some agencies test the beams as cantilevers, and some test them as simple beams under center loading. Indicated strength of the latter two methods is higher than that obtained under third-point loading.

Test beams are cast in molds in the field (ASTM Designation: C 31) and tested at specified ages.

3-2. BASIC FACTORS

Materials

In general, one may say that the potential strength of concrete is largely determined by the properties and amounts of materials comprising the concrete. It is influenced by the mineralogical and physical composition of aggregates. For example, the cement paste adheres more tightly to some minerals than to others, and it adheres to a slightly rough aggregate particle better than to a smooth one. At constant cement content compressive strength generally increases with the size of coarse aggregate particles, although there are some exceptions to this. Strength is decreased as the amount of sand increases beyond that required to fill voids in the coarse aggregate. Angular aggregate particles usually give slightly more strength than rounded ones; this effect is especially pronounced in flexural strength. Properly graded and controlled mixtures produce concrete of comparatively higher strength.

Water-Cement Ratio

The ratio of the amounts of cement to water (water-cement ratio) in the mix has long been considered to be one of the basic laws of concrete technology. This law states that the strength of concrete is inversely proportional to the water-cement ratio within the range of practical or usable mixes, all other factors remaining the same. However, because of the great multiplicity of aggregate sizes, shapes, types, and qualities, variations in cements, even though they all meet the same specifications, different mixes, use of admixtures, and great diversity of environmental conditions of mixing and placing, this law should be looked upon more as a guide that as an inflexible rule that applies without question to all concretes under all conditions. For example, at the same water-cement ratio a rich, wet concrete will usually develop less strength than a drier mix with less cement and water. More water is required for the same slump during warm summer weather than in the winter. Keeping these facts in mind, the concrete engineer may apply the water-cement ratio to his own set of conditions with a reasonable degree of confidence. Figure 16-2 is an example of what may be expected.

General Factors

Strength is affected by the age of the concrete and the quality of curing; type and grading of aggregates; quality, fineness, and type of cement; batch proportions; placing and curing temperatures; and presence of alkalies, sulfates, organic materials, clay, or other contaminants in the ingredients; and admixtures. Under certain conditions the presence of carbon dioxide during curing affects the strength. Size and shape of the test specimen, size of aggregate removed to make the specimen, and moisture content of specimen at time of test all influence the indicated strength.

The indicated strength of a compressive specimen is higher if the specimen is permitted to dry out before breaking, but a dry tension or flexural specimen will indicate a lower strength than a moist one. However, this effect is of no important consequence in normal control work. Where, because of size relationships, it is necessary to remove large pieces of coarse aggregate in order to make the specimen, slightly higher strength will be indicated.

Low strength may be caused by excessive entrained air. One case is reported in which low strength was traced to an air meter out of adjustment. While reported air content was about 4 per cent, it was found later to be nearly 10 per cent.

Effect of Substances

Accidental inclusion of organic matter of any kind into the fresh concrete should be scrupulously avoided, as very small amounts of such substances will cause strength seriously lower than normal. They may retard, and may even prevent, setting of the cement. Common sources of organic matter are mixing water from a swamp, mixing water containing sewage or manufacturing plant effluent, roots and other debris in aggregates, and humus or topsoil.

Sugar, fertilizer, stock feeds, and similar materials are sometimes hauled in units later used for handling cement, hence the need for making sure that all equipment that comes in contact with concrete or concrete materials is clean.

Boron is sometimes used in certain concrete for reactor shields. When so used, it should be tested with the proposed materials beforehand, as it is apt to have an unfavorable effect on strength. Sodium benzoate, said to be effective as a corrosion inhibitor to protect reinforcing steel, lowers the strength potential of concrete. Borax delays setting time, as do zinc carbonate, lead carbonate, and calcium hydrate. Magnesium chloride and sodium carbonate accelerate setting time. Almost infinitesimal amounts of some of these substances sometimes have a rather profound effect.

3-3. CAUSES OF LOW STRENGTH

Usually there is no inkling of low strength until test specimens have been broken. By that time it is too late to improve concrete already placed. However, the information is not entirely lost as it at least provides a warning to be on guard for whatever poor practice or materials were permitted in the first place, and assists in determining the course to be followed in subsequent concreting operations. The test hammer (Sec. 3-11) provides a quick, nondestructive test to determine the approximate strength of concrete in place, and indicates whether the concrete strength is actually low, or whether the test specimens gave false indications.

Cement

There are five basic types of portland cement and a number of special cements for specialized usages (Table 10-2). In general, cement available today is made under close control of quality, and it is not usually the cause of low strength. However, there have been instances in which the cement was found to be at fault.

Old cement containing lumps that cannot be broken with reasonable pressure between the fingers will cause low strength. There are reports of cement in storage losing strength at rates from 6 per cent per year to as high as 5 per cent per month. If cement can be completely sealed from moisture and carbon dioxide, it may be kept for several years, but such storage is impossible under normal conditions. Cement should fluff easily and contain no hard lumps.

Premature stiffening, sometimes called false set or rubber set, leads to low strength. This phenomenon is rare and manifests itself by an apparent set or hardening of the concrete which is broken down by continued manipulation of the concrete. The addition of more mixing water also restores workability but such practice is undesirable since it results in a higher water-cement ratio which in turn reduces strength. ASTM Designation: C 359 provides a method of testing for false set. Any suspected cement should be avoided. Fortunately, this difficulty is unusual. It is sometimes caused by using hot cement, that is, cement that is still hot from the manufacturing process. Lower grinding temperatures in the mill sometimes help alleviate the situation.

Appreciable variations in strength of concrete may be due to the use of different brands intermittently, or even may be caused by variations between shipments of cement from the same source. Variations in raw materials, processing, age, fineness, and temperature contribute to these variations. Undetected differences in cement types will affect strength, especially at early ages. If a batching plant has facilities for more than one type of cement, there is always the danger of using the wrong cement, and this sometimes happens. Adequate inspection will minimize these incidents.

State highway departments, branches of the Federal government, and other large users of cement arrange for sampling and testing of cement at the mill and in this way keep informed of the quality. The smaller user should request the manufacturer to furnish a certified mill test report with each shipment. This report identifies the shipment, shows the bin from which shipped, and gives chemical and physical test results.

Aggregates

The effects of aggregates on strength are manifested through the properties of the aggregates themselves, or through the medium of contaminating materials conveyed into the concrete with the aggregates. Although aggregate quality probably affects durability of concrete more than strength, certain qualities, such as mineralogical composition, particle shape, and gradation, do affect strength also. High-strength concrete is more responsive to physical properties of coarse aggregate than low-strength concrete. Surface texture, particle shape, and elasticity are important in affecting both flexural and compressive strength in this case. If an aggregate meets the requirements of ASTM Designation: C 33 it is satisfactory since minor variations in the above properties can usually be overcome by adjusting the mix.

An aggregate containing a relatively large proportion of flat, elongated pieces, or an aggregate that is poorly graded, is capable of making good concrete. However, concrete made with such materials is not as economical as concrete made with normal materials because it requires more cement, water, and sand to overcome harshness and lack of workability.

A frequent source of poor gradation of coarse aggregate is segregation in stockpiles, cars, and trucks and at points of transfer.

The effect of maximum size of aggregate on concrete strength is relatively minor, although it has long been felt that larger sizes of coarse aggregate produced concrete of higher strength than small aggregate. Recent thinking tends to modify this view to some extent, for in some cases it can be shown that higher strength may be obtained with aggregate no larger than ¾ or 1 in.

An aggregate with a specific gravity of less than 2.55 or absorption greater than 1.5 per cent (except lightweight aggregate) should be avoided unless tests and case histories show it to be satisfactory. Soft, friable aggregates should be avoided; each percentage point increase in the Los Angeles abrasion loss requires about 1 per cent more cement for equivalent compressive strength of concrete.

An excessive proportion of mica in the aggregate may be the cause of low strength. There appears to be no evidence of chemical incompatibility between mica and cement, the adverse effect on strength being due to the softness or low strength of the mica. Although the amount of mica present in most aggregates is not harmful, no quantitative data are available to indicate how much can be tolerated. Laboratory tests, including making either mortar or concrete, should be made of any suspected aggregate. In all probability, the mix can be adjusted by using more cement or a water-reducing admixture to produce concrete of adequate strength.

The presence of loam, clay, rock dust, or other adherent coatings should not be permitted since they have an adverse effect on strength. These materials should be removed by intensive scrubbing and washing of the aggregates, an operation that may add appreciably to the cost of processing materials from a naturally dirty deposit.

Loose fines in reasonable amounts are not harmful. Nearly all coarse aggregate, by the time it reaches the batcher, is coated with rock dust and other fine material. If the fines are loose and do not exceed 2 per cent of the coarse aggregate, no harm is done. Finely divided, uniformly distributed clay or silt in the sand, not exceeding 5 per cent of the sand, is not harmful.

The full potential concrete strength will not be developed if the aggregate contains an appreciable amount of organic matter. Humus is present in surface soils, requiring that aggregate deposits be stripped of the surface layer to a depth sufficient to eliminate the offending material.

Crushed stone is frequently screened dry, a process that is satisfactory as long as the stone is actually dry. The presence of varying amounts of moisture results in varying amounts of fines adhering to the stone, causing variations in strength. Gravel usually contains moisture and fines in sufficient amounts to require wet screening. The scrubbing action of high-velocity water jets and movement of the aggregates removes all but the most stubborn coatings.

Certain aggregates of glacial origin may contain organic materials that act as a foaming agent, entraining air in the concrete, thus having a detrimental effect on concrete strength. Such aggregates should be avoided.

Many of the shortcomings of aggregate that affect strength are remedied by adequate and thorough processing as described in Chap. 11.

Good slag aggregates are available that produce concrete of high strength and durability at reasonable cost, but improperly prepared slag aggregate is a potential source of strength irregularities. Very erratic strengths, even retrogression, may result from the use of a slag aggregate containing a high sulfate content. The excess sulfate reacts with calcium aluminate of the cement, producing a substance of greater volume. Such material should be avoided.

Water

If there is any doubt about the quality of water proposed for use in concrete, it should be tested before use. Water from any municipal distribution system is satisfactory. Water from stagnant pools or swamps should be viewed with suspicion, especially if moss and algae are present. As little as 0.5 per cent of organic material in the mixing water causes a serious deficiency in strength. Impure water containing appreciable quantities of sulfates, chlorides, or carbonates (mineral water) should not be used.

Mix Proportioning

The relative proportions of cement, water, and aggregates in the mix are fundamental factors affecting concrete strength. Moreover, air-entraining agents and numerous admixtures all contribute their share of influences on strength. These are discussed fully in Chaps. 10 and 16, and there is no need of repeating the discussion here.

Batching, Mixing, and Placing

Concrete quality is subject to adverse influences at all times unless proper control is exercised. Proper attention to control, as explained in Chap. 12, gives assurance that good concrete will not be damaged by mishandling and carelessness.

Inaccuracies in measuring batch quantities are a source of variations of concrete quality, and therefore of strength variations. Volumetric measurement of solid ingredients should never be permitted since fluctuations in strength may be as much as plus or minus 20 per cent. Sources of batching errors are careless setting of weights on the scales, careless operation, material sticking in weigh hopper so scales do not return to zero between batches, dirty or worn knife-edges and fulcrums on scales, and uncompensated variations in moisture content of aggregates. Other strength variations may be caused by variations in sequence of charging materials into the mixer, delays in mixing batches in which cement is in contact with wet aggregates, and nonuniform or improper mixing time or speed.

Delays in transporting or placing premixed or truck-mixed concrete should be avoided by organizing the job beforehand, routing and timing the batches to conform with the rate of placing. The practice of adding tempering water to ready-mixed concrete is subject to flagrant abuse and should be permitted only under close control. Concrete requiring tempering water to bring it up to its original slump should be wasted if the maximum authorized water-cement ratio is exceeded or if the appearance of the concrete indicates that it will not be possible to vibrate it into place without excessive effort. In any event, waste all concrete not placed within 2 hr after mixing in the wintertime. Less time should be permitted during hot weather.

Segregation of the concrete and lack of thorough consolidation cause variations in quality that are reflected in strength variations, although these variations will not be shown in test results.

Temperature and Curing

A high concrete temperature (80°F or above) during and immediately after placing will result in lower ultimate strength compared with concrete mixed and placed at 40 to 80°F. A low curing temperature causes

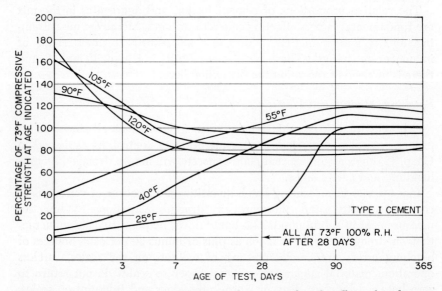

FIG. 3-1. The temperature of mixing and placing significantly affects the ultimate strength of concrete as well as the early strength. (*After Klieger.*[3.1])

concrete to develop strength slowly, thus resulting in low early strength. If curing is continued long enough, the full potential strength will be developed, however, as shown in Fig. 3-1.[3.1*]

The effect of freezing is discussed in Chap. 5. With respect to strength, concrete frozen immediately after mixing will suffer a reduction of 30

* Superscript figures refer to chapter and reference number. The references are found at the end of each chapter.

or 40 per cent in strength; a delay of 8 hr results in considerably less reduction, and a 24-hr delay results in a minor loss of strength.[3.2] McNeese[3.3] found that concrete placed at 75°F must suffer severe freezing within 6 hr to be appreciably damaged, but if it is placed at 40°F, a mild freeze of 25°F may destroy half of the strength. If it is frozen while plastic, then thawed at 75°F, it loses nearly half its strength. If the concrete reaches a strength of 500 psi before freezing, the damage may not be serious.

To develop the full potential strength of the cement requires that there be a continuous supply of moisture at a reasonable temperature. Curing accomplishes this objective either by sealing the concrete against loss of moisture or by supplying moisture on the surface. The effect of inadequate curing is low strength and reduced durability.

3-4. APPARENT LOW STRENGTH

It sometimes happens that low-strength specimens do not truly represent the concrete that was mixed. Proper control requires that specimens be handled in accordance with certain standard methods, such as ASTM Designation: C 31. It is essential that inspectors and technicians receive adequate training in testing and control techniques. Inspectors should have reference manuals and should be given refresher training courses every year or two to keep their techniques in accordance with accepted practices.

There are three steps in making concrete strength specimens: sampling the fresh concrete, making the test specimens, and testing the specimens. Carelessness in any phase of these three steps yields results of dubious accuracy. How to make strength tests properly is described in Sec. 15-6.

3-5. SLOW HARDENING

Sometimes concrete, after being placed, fails to harden properly or fails to gain strength as rapidly as it should. Ultimately, such concrete may reach the normal strength expected for the mix and materials being used, although this is not always the case.

An overdosage of retarder in the concrete delays setting and early-strength gain beyond the anticipated extent, but eventual strength appears to be unaffected, even by gross overages of two or three times the design amount. On one job, two or three batches of concrete containing accidental double doses of retarder went into a bridge deck. After 24 hr the affected concrete was still so soft that it could be dug out with the hands, but after continued curing for a few days, the concrete started to develop strength, and at 1 month the affected areas of the deck were indistinguishable from the rest of the deck, as indicated by numerous readings taken with the impact hammer. Water-reducing admixtures have somewhat the same effect.

Errors and variabilities in formulation of admixtures are a potential cause of variations in concrete using these admixtures. For this reason, products of reliable manufacturers, with a satisfactory record of use, should always be used.

As previously mentioned in this chapter, organic materials adversely affect concrete. The presence of sugar in any of its forms seriously retards or prevents setting. The perverted humor, or even maliciousness, of pouring a soft drink, molasses, or similar material into a batch of concrete (and this has happened) results in costly repairs to and replacement of structural concrete.

If concrete is placed cold and kept at a temperature near freezing (but not frozen) the hydration process will be slowed to such an extent that several hours may elapse before apparent setting starts, and strength gain will be very slow. Even at 28 days, strength will be appreciably below normal. However, under proper sustained curing, especially if the temperature is raised to a minimum of 60°F, strength will increase. The sooner this curing is started, the sooner the concrete will develop adequate strength. No permanent damage is suffered by the concrete.

3-6. ACCELERATED STRENGTH GAIN

There are numerous instances when it is desirable for concrete to develop strength rapidly. In the wintertime, high early strength decreases the length of time for which the concrete requires protection from low temperatures. It expedites removal of shoring and forms, permitting their reuse sooner, and permits putting the structure into use sooner than normally. It is especially desirable in precast and prestressed work, where a shorter operating cycle in the plant effects sizable savings in cost by permitting early form removal and expeditious use of the castings, minimizing the number of forms required and reducing storage area required for curing of units.

Four methods are commonly used, either singly or in combination, to accelerate the early strength of concrete. They are the use of early hardening or high-early-strength cement, addition of an accelerator to the concrete mix, high-temperature curing, and retention of the heat of hydration of the cement.

High-early-strength Cement

Modification of the compound composition of cement by increasing the percentage of tricalcium silicate (decreasing dicalcium silicate) together with finer grinding makes a cement that hydrates more rapidly, resulting in high early strength. Known as Type III, this cement produces concrete with normal 7-day strength in approximately 3 days, and normal 28-day strength at 7 days. Rapid generation of heat of hydration accompanies the early-strength gain.

Admixtures

Certain admixtures work to accelerate the hydration process, the most common being calcium chloride. Because of a possible detrimental effect on strength at later ages, calcium chloride should not be used to accelerate early strength at air temperatures above 60 or 70°F. It is best confined to usage during freezing weather *not as an antifreeze,* but to produce high early strength to shorten the time necessary to protect the concrete from freezing. The effect of calcium chloride depends on the amount used, type and brand of cement, temperature, and curing conditions. It is more effective in rich mixes and usually increases the slump for the same amount of total water. It will precipitate most air-entraining agents unless added to the batch separately. Separate addition may be accomplished by permitting the chloride to flow in with the mixing water, introducing the air-entraining agent into the batch with the sand.

Calcium chloride should not be used in prestressed concrete because of the danger of stress corrosion of the high-strength stressing strand. This has been amply demonstrated in the field and laboratory. A severe case was reported in which a large prestressed concrete pipeline failed because of corrosion of the strand caused by calcium chloride and moisture.[3.4, 3.5]

Retention of Heat of Hydration

It is well known that the cement-hardening process is exothermic, that is, heat is liberated during the reaction between portland cement and water. Elaborate means are devised for the removal of this heat in massive structures such as dams and heavy piers or footings. Properly controlled, this heat can be used to elevate the concrete temperature, thus accelerating strength gain. Use is made of this fact by insulating structure forms in the wintertime, there sometimes being sufficient heat generated to protect the concrete from freezing until the required curing period has elapsed. Reference should be made to "Recommended Practice for Winter Concreting" of the American Concrete Institute[3.6] for tables and charts showing the required insulation for different temperature conditions.

Retained heat of hydration is also useful in curing concrete under high temperature as explained in the following section.

High-temperature Curing

Formerly used only in plants producing such items as pipe and blocks, steam curing has really come of age in the era of prestressed concrete. One of the first (1955) large-scale applications was in the casting yard for the Lake Pontchartrain bridge, where deck units 30 ft wide and 56 ft long were cast and prestressed in groups of eight. Steam curing permitted these units to be removed for transportation to the pier caps 35 hr after casting. Present practice, using 7 or more sacks of Type III cement per cubic yard, a water-reducing admixture, and steam curing, produces concrete with strengths above 4,000 psi in less than 20 hr, as

TABLE 3-2. TYPICAL HIGH-EARLY-STRENGTH CONCRETES

Sacks per cu yd	W/C ratio, gal/sack	% air	Compressive strength, psi				
			14-hr	18-hr	3-day	7-day	28-day
8	3.8	2.6	6,270	6,730			8,180
7¾	4.0	2.7	5,740				7,580
7	4.5	3.1	4,500	4,880		5,680	
8	4.1	3.5			6,530	7,240	8,940

Notes: All concrete made with Type III cement.

Above values represent typical job values.

All specimens steam-cured until broken, if less than 24 hr. Cylinders for later breaks then water-cured at 70°F for balance of time.

Because of possible shrinkage and cracking, cement contents in excess of 7¾ sacks per cu yd are not recommended.

shown in Table 3-2. Even normal Type I cement gives high early strength under these conditions.

Under high-temperature conditions both heat and moisture, which are essential to proper curing, may be lost to the outside through the material used to cover the concrete, hence the importance of providing tight covers, insulated if possible. It should also be kept in mind that more moisture is required to maintain 100 per cent relative humidity at higher temperatures than at low temperatures. At 70°F, 0.016 lb of water is required per pound of air for 100 per cent humidity, but 0.15 lb is required at 140°F and 0.66 lb at 180°F.

Under steam-curing conditions, the heat of hydration serves to raise the concrete temperature in the same way that it does under normal curing. Therefore, there comes a time when the concrete temperature will reach the ambient temperature within the enclosure, then rise above if control measures are not taken, as shown in Fig. 3-2. After the concrete reaches the ambient temperature, the amount of heat should be reduced gradually in order to minimize the temperature differential between the concrete and the atmosphere within the enclosure and to permit a gradual cooling of the concrete.

When the concrete temperature exceeds the enclosure temperature, moisture may be lost from the concrete. If wet steam is used as a source of heat, moisture loss from the concrete presents no problem, but if heat is provided by other means, there must be a source of additional moisture, such as hot-water sprays.

Concrete should undergo a presetting period of approximately 3 hr at normal temperature after casting before being subjected to high tem-

1215522

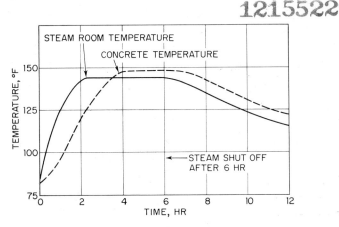

Fig. 3-2. Steam-curing temperatures.

perature. During cold weather, a small amount of heat may be provided within the enclosure to maintain the temperature near 70°F during this presetting period. Temperature should not exceed 160°F during curing. Live steam jets should not play directly on the concrete or forms. Steam is best admitted through many small jets, as would be the case with perforated pipes, rather than through the open end of a hose or pipe.

In summary, optimum conditions for steaming are (1) a delay of about 3 hr after placing concrete before steaming; (2) a temperature between 120 and 160°F; (3) a slow temperature rise, not over 40°F per hr; (4) wet steam; and (5) avoidance of thermal shock upon termination of steaming. Moist curing after steaming improves strength and other properties and should be utilized if possible. The greatest advantage of steaming occurs during the first hours, and it soon reaches a point of diminishing returns (see Fig. 3-3). Temperatures that are too high damage the concrete, and strengths of concrete normally cured for the entire period are usually higher at 28 days and later than those of concrete steam cured during its early age.

Some agencies have experimented with heating of fresh concrete by passing an electric current through it. The reinforcing steel may comprise one electrode, with surface fittings comprising the other.

3-7. MODULUS OF ELASTICITY

When a load is applied to a material, as for example a compressive load on a concrete cylinder, Hooke's law states that, within the elastic limit, the deformation produced is proportional to the stress applied. The modulus of elasticity E is the ratio of increment of unit stress to

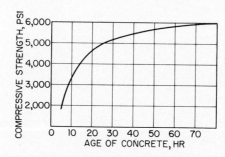

FIG. 3-3. Effect of steam curing. Typical results of steam curing at 140°F to ages shown, starting 4 hr after casting concrete containing 6¾ to 7 sacks per cu yd of Type III cement.

increment of unit deformation, within the elastic limit. Concrete does not follow Hooke's law exactly (Fig. 3-4), the stress-strain curve being slightly curved instead of a straight line. However, within the range of usual working loads, the stress-strain curve for thoroughly hardened concrete is nearly a straight line, if the concrete has been preloaded before testing. The static modulus of elasticity is obtained by loading a specimen, usually a test cylinder, and observing the elastic deformation of the specimen under compression. E is computed by dividing the stress by the strain at any point.

The modulus of elasticity is related to compressive strength, although not directly proportional. However, a high-strength concrete usually has a higher elastic modulus than a weak one. Cause of a low modulus may be a high water-cement ratio, an excessive percentage of entrained air, or any of the causes of low compressive strength.

Present thinking is to the effect that the static modulus is a function of the square root of the compressive strength, and that it is influenced by the density of the concrete. The effect of density is demonstrated by the fact that the modulus for lightweight concrete is significantly lower than that for normal-weight concrete of the same compressive strength. An approximation is given by the formula

$$E = 33W^{3/2} \sqrt{\text{compressive strength}}$$

where E = static modulus of elasticity, psi
W = air-dry weight of concrete at time of test, pcf[3.7]

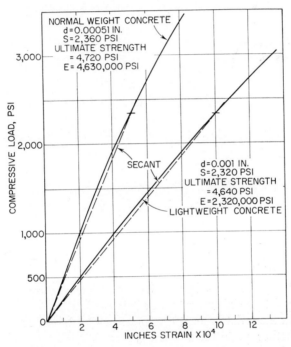

FIG. 3-4. Stress-strain curves. Elastic modulus E measured at ½ ultimate strength.

Secant Modulus of Elasticity

Because of the slight curvature of the stress-strain curve, the stress-strain relationship at any point is a secant to the curve between the origin of the curve and the point at which the modulus is determined. Usual practice is to determine the value at one-half of the ultimate strength of the specimen.

Tangent Modulus of Elasticity

In some cases, the modulus is obtained by determining the slope of a tangent to the curve at the desired stress. This value is limited to certain special usages and is rarely used in practice.

Dynamic Modulus of Elasticity

Electronic equipment is available for determination of the elastic modulus by measuring the velocity of sound waves through the specimen, or measuring the natural frequency of vibration of the specimen. These methods are especially useful in studying the deterioration of concrete, as specimens can be repeatedly tested without damaging them. A decrease in frequency of vibration or velocity of waves indicates a decrease in elastic modulus which in turn reveals deterioration of the concrete.

High-temperature Effects

Of serious importance when considering the effect of a fire on the concrete portions of a building is a significant reduction in the elastic modulus due to heating. Temperature, length of time the concrete is heated, age and quality of the concrete, and other factors affect the actual reduction, but it is significant at 400°F and is more than half at 1000°F.

3-8. FATIGUE OF CONCRETE

Application of repeated loads, each smaller than a single static load that would cause failure, may cause a material to fail in fatigue. Most materials have a fatigue limit—a stress level below which a specimen of the material will withstand an infinite number of cycles of load application without failure.

There appears to have been considerable laboratory work done in investigating fatigue of concrete, but it is hard to draw any general conclusions from these data except that more testing is required. The type of loading, whether plain, reinforced, or prestressed concrete, strength, ambient conditions, and many other factors influence fatigue of concrete. For example, shearing stresses in a beam may be more critical, as far as fatigue is concerned, than compressive stresses. Effect of reinforcing steel bond is varied, and if a beam cracks, subsequent loading usually causes static failure.

Whether concrete has a fatigue limit is subject to debate. However, a limit probably does exist. It depends upon design, method of loading, presence or lack of reinforcing steel, materials, effect of cracks, and many other variables.

3-9. FORM REMOVAL

Concrete may be damaged by too early form removal. Chipping, spalling, and sticking to forms may occur, or dangerous deflections of members may develop. Table 3-3 shows what strength the concrete should have before forms may be removed safely.[3.8] However, it should be pointed out that these are typical values showing relative strengths only, and design values should be considered in any particular case.

When the concrete is not subject to live load and the dead load is negligible, forms can be removed as soon as the concrete will suffer no damage due to this action, for example, side forms on pavement. Prestressed concrete requires special consideration. Forms may be removed

TABLE 3-3. STRENGTH OF CONCRETE FOR SAFE REMOVAL OF FORMS

Structural classification	Minimum strength required, psi
1. Concrete not subject to appreciable bending or direct stress, nor reliant on forms for vertical support, nor liable to injury from form removal operations or other construction activities...............................	500
Examples: Vertical or approximately vertical surfaces of thick sections; outsides of barrels; edges of pavements and slabs; sidewalls of tunnel lining against rock; tops of sloping surfaces	
2. Concrete subject to appreciable bending and/or direct stress and partially reliant on forms for vertical support	
a. Subject to dead load only..	750
Examples: Inside of barrels; arch of tunnel lining against solid rock; underside of sloping surfaces 1:1 or steeper; vertical or approximately vertical surfaces of thin sections	
b. Subject to dead and live loads.................................	1,500
Examples: Inside of galleries and other openings in dams; sidewalls and arch of tunnel lining against unstable material; columns	
3. Concrete subject to high bending stress and wholly or almost wholly reliant on forms for vertical support...............................	2,000
Examples: Roof or floor slabs and beams; undersides of sloping surfaces (flatter than 1:1); walkways and platforms; bridge decks and girders	

Note: For guide purposes only. Consult designer for actual strength requirements in every case.

as for normal concrete, but special values are set for strength of the concrete before stress may be transferred to the concrete. This strength is usually specified at some definite minimum value such as 4,000 psi.

3-10. FIELD-CURED SPECIMENS

At all times, care must be taken to ensure that test specimens truly represent the concrete being mixed, and that they are made and handled under standard conditions. Specimens made and cured under field conditions are more subject to influences of temperature than are most structures, due in part to their area-volume ratio being different from that of the structure, and also because of their smaller size. For this reason, strength results of field-cured specimens should be evaluated carefully, as false indications may be obtained. In a comparison of 91 pairs of cylinders made in early fall in Detroit for 5,000-psi concrete, it was found that field strengths averaged 340 psi below the standard-cured specimens at 28 days, ranging from a maximum of 1,220 psi below to 375 psi above. Seven-day cylinders for the same group showed the field cures to be 255 psi below standard cures. Field-cured specimens are of value in determining time for stripping forms or for similar information, provided the information thus gained is used with caution. The report of ACI Committee 318 states in Section 304 (*c*) that "strength of job-cured cylinders indicates adequacy of curing and protection, and may be used to determine when forms may be stripped, shoring removed or the structure put into service."[3.9]

3-11. TEST HAMMER

A test hammer is available for determining compressive strength of concrete. This instrument operates on the principle that the rebound of

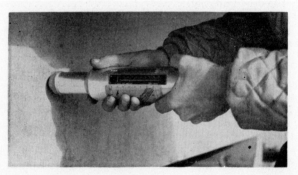

Fig. 3-5. The impact hammer for determining compressive strength of concrete in place.

a steel hammer striking the surface of concrete is proportional to strength. It offers a quick, nondestructive method of determining strength of concrete in place with an accuracy within about 15 per cent. Not as accurate as properly performed compression tests on cylinders or cores and not to be used to replace these tests, it is nevertheless valuable for determining the approximate strength of concrete in place. A more detailed description and discussion appear in reference 3.10.

The instrument should be calibrated on concrete composed of the same materials as the concrete to be tested. To calibrate, place a capped

6 × 12-in. cylinder in a testing machine and apply a compressive load of about 3,000 lb. With the cylinder under this load, take about 15 readings on the cylinder with the test hammer, then test the specimen in compression in accordance with standard procedure. After a number of cylinders of different strengths have been tested in this manner, an average curve can be drawn showing compressive strengths against instrument readings.

Typical usage is one in which the hammer was used to investigate concrete in a bridge column and pier cap that had been placed in one afternoon. The average strength for four 28-day cylinders for the pier cap was 1,930 psi, and for the column, 3,710 psi, leading to the obvious

FIG. 3-6. A group of improperly made test cylinders. Such carelessness is inexcusable in properly trained and supervised inspectors.

conclusion that something was wrong with the concrete or the tests from the cap. All records and operations were first checked; then the impact hammer was used. Sixteen sets of readings were taken at various places on the sides of the cap and 3 sets of readings were taken vertically upward at the lowest indicated strength areas. All sets consisted of 15 readings at each site. A mean of the 15 readings was taken and those that deviated from the mean by more than 3 points were discarded in an attempt to get an average of approximately 10 readings. In this case, the hammer indicated satisfactory strengths throughout the structure.

REFERENCES

3.1 Klieger, Paul: Effect of Mixing and Curing Temperature on Concrete Strength, *J. Am. Concrete Inst.*, June, 1958, pp. 1063–1082.

3.2   Bernhardt, C. J.: Freezing Damage to Fresh Concrete, *Tek. Ukeblad*, Sept. 2, 1954, pp. 681–687.
3.3   McNeese, Donald C.: Early Freezing of Non-air-entrained Concrete, *J. Am. Concrete Inst.*, December, 1952, pp. 293–300.
3.4   *Eng. News-Record*, Feb. 19, 1953.
3.5   Monfore, G. E., and G. J. Verbeck: Corrosion of Prestressed Wire in Concrete, *J. Am. Concrete Inst.*, November, 1960, pp. 491–516.
3.6   Recommended Practice for Winter Concreting, ACI 604–56, Report of ACI Committee 604, June, 1956.
3.7   Pauw, Adrian, Static Modulus of Elasticity of Concrete as Affected by Density, *J. Am. Concrete Inst.*, December, 1960, pp. 679–687.
3.8   Portland Cement Association, Design and Control of Concrete Mixtures, 10th ed., 1952.
3.9   Standard Building Code, Report of ACI Committee 318, *J. Am. Concrete Inst.*, May, 1956.
3.10 Green, Gordon W.: Test Hammer Provides New Method of Evaluating Hardened Concrete, *J. Am. Concrete Inst.*, November, 1954, pp. 249–256.
3.11 Price, Walter H.: Factors Influencing Concrete Strength, *J. Am. Concrete Inst.*, February, 1951, pp. 417–432.

CHAPTER 4 *Volume Change and Shrinkage*

Concrete, like other materials, is subject to changes in volume, either autogenous or induced, depending on the environment and forces acting on it. To the practical man in the field, volume change and thermal properties of concrete are of considerable importance, although the tendency is sometimes to consider them more in the province of the designer. However, they cannot be ignored in the field. Shrinkage and contraction are important to the extent that they affect dimensional stability and the formation of cracks; creep or plastic flow may cause a change in distribution of stresses in the structure which may or may not be desirable; and the thermal properties affect durability to the extent that diffusivity and the coefficient of expansion influence expansion and contraction during temperature changes.

4-1. SHRINKAGE

The term *shrinkage* is used loosely to describe two entirely different actions in concrete: plastic shrinkage of the fresh concrete, and shrinkage of the hardened concrete as it dries out shortly after placing. Symptomatic evidence of either type of shrinkage is *cracking*. In Chap. 7 considerable discussion is given to shrinkage as being the cause of cracking. Woodward[4.1]* says:

Probably the most annoying aspect of concrete construction is that of shrinkage—a change of volume due to set. Cracks are an eyesore; first to the owner, who usually interprets them as a sign of weakness, poor concrete, and imminent collapse; and second, to the engineer, who interprets them as poor concrete quality, oversight in design considerations, or just another contribution to his frustrations. It is a rare, if not mythical, concrete that has no shrinkage cracks. Generally speaking if you have concrete in any large volume you are sure to have some cracks. To keep them to a minimum in size and extent is the goal.

* Superscript figures refer to chapter and reference number. The references are found at the end of each chapter.

43

It is not generally understood, even by engineers, that all the ingredients of the concrete mix have an effect on shrinkage, not only the water and cement content but the aggregates and even the chemical composition of the cement. To get a picture of the practical aspects we should know the relative importance of the various materials and methods.

Shrinkage is caused by all of the following factors, but their order does not necessarily indicate their relative importance.

Chemical composition of cement
Mineral characteristics of the aggregates
Grading of aggregates
Water content or water-cement ratio
Mixing
Proper placing
Quality of curing
Size of pour

This list encompasses practically all factors that should be considered for any high grade concrete.

Proper selection of materials can reduce potential shrinkage by one-half of that which might result from using shrinkage-inducing materials. Well-graded aggregates of the largest practical size should be used, containing an adequate amount of fines (see Sec. 13-1). About 5 to 8 per cent of the sand should pass through the 100-mesh screen, and 15 to 30 per cent pass through the No. 50 screen. The sand should not contain more than 5 per cent clay. Highly absorbent aggregates, such as sandstone and porous chert, should be avoided.

Plastic Shrinkage

Shrinkage of this type manifests itself soon after the concrete has been placed in the forms. It is a shrinkage of the paste surrounding the aggregate particles, occurring either while the concrete is still in a more or less fluid condition, or after the concrete has become rigid but has not developed appreciable strength. Cracks, when they appear, are usually on horizontal surfaces and develop rather suddenly at about the time the water sheen disappears from the surface. Of course, the aggregate particles themselves do not change volume when this shrinkage occurs, shrinkage being confined to the paste. (The aggregate does change volume when contraction is caused by a reduction in temperature.) Hence, to control plastic shrinkage of concrete it is first necessary to control shrinkage of the paste.

As soon as the water comes in contact with cement in a batch of concrete, complex physical and chemical activities commence. There is a reduction in the volume occupied by the water and cement. This autogenous shrinkage, caused by chemical activity between water and cement, is itself not subject to control in the field. Usually a fine-ground cement will produce a gel with greater shrinkage tendencies than a coarser cement, and a cement high in tricalcium aluminate is apt to exhibit more shrinkage, especially if there is not an accompanying increase in gypsum content. A cement with a high ignition loss will probably be high in shrinkage. These and other properties of cement are subject to control only at the mill, and the field man is compelled to govern shrinkage by regulating operations on the job.

An essential requirement for minimizing shrinkage is that the water-cement ratio and total water per cubic yard be kept as low as possible. The use of high-slump mixes, which is probably the most common cause of shrinkage, should be avoided, and concrete should be consolidated by vibration.

It may be desirable to use a cement-retarding and water-reducing admixture. Action of such an admixture is not only to reduce the total amount of water per cubic yard for equal workability, but also to delay hydration of the cement, thus extending the period of plasticity so the concrete will adjust better to early volume changes.

Shrinkage will occur if the concrete is permitted to dry too rapidly. Curing should be started promptly and continued without interruption for the required period.

During hot weather artificial cooling may be of value. On one job heavy concrete members were made by first filling the forms with coarse aggregate (Prepakt) and then applying crushed ice to the aggregate for 24 hr. Water was drained off through holes in the bottom of the forms. These holes were plugged before grout at 60°F was pumped in.[4.2] Other expedients for hot weather concreting are discussed in Sec. 13-1.

Shrinkage may be minimized or prevented by adding a small quantity of superfine, unpolished aluminum powder to the mix, in the amount of 2 or 3 g per sack of cement. Control of shrinkage by this method is desirable only when difficult placement makes a soft consistency necessary, such as filling a cavity by placing concrete through a restricted opening, or placing concrete around a congestion of reinforcing steel and other embedded items, where proper vibration is not possible. The aluminum powder technique is not necessary and should not be used in normal construction because it has variable effects and may possibly lower strength. The painting variety of aluminum should not be used as its action is slower and may not be complete by the time the cement starts to set. Also, the action is slower during cold weather. Tests should be made beforehand to determine the amount of aluminum to use since too much can cause an actual expansion of the concrete.

In preparing a nonshrinking grout for use in such situations as placing under machinery, the aluminum powder technique may be employed. High-silica cement, such as portland-pozzolan, may produce a grout or concrete of low shrinkage. Such a material should be tested first to determine its effectiveness. In some cases, preshrunk grout may be desirable. This is made by mixing a fluid grout and allowing it to stand for an hour or two before using. No tempering water should be used as this will destroy the effectiveness of the shrinkage control and weaken the grout.

An apparent shrinkage may be a loss of volume due to a loss of entrained air. Ordinarily concrete may lose as much as 1 per cent of its fresh volume by reason of normal shrinkage, and another 1 per cent or more may be loss of entrained air occasioned by handling and placing practices.

Bleeding

After concrete has been placed and consolidated, an action known as *bleeding, sedimentation,* or *water gain* occurs, in which the solid particles (cement and aggregates) start to move downward, or settle, and water appears on the surface. Settlement continues until arrested by the beginning of set of the cement, by attainment of maximum consolidation of the solids, or by bridging of the aggregate particles. The rate of bleeding is influenced by the mix proportions, water content of the concrete, temperature, depth of the concrete, cement fineness, and presence of certain admixtures.

Some water on the surface is necessary for finishing, hence total elimination of bleeding is not advisable. Normal bleeding is not detrimental to the concrete; in fact, the settlement that causes bleeding actually results in a slightly stronger paste. Any plastic mix will bleed some.

Finishing is adversely affected by excessive bleeding. Laitance may form on the surface, or the finishing operation may be delayed. Excessive bleeding may result in the settlement of aggregate particles away from the underside of horizontal reinforcing bars, the void thus formed being filled with water, thereby causing a loss of bond.

There are a number of expedients available that are more or less effective in reducing excessive bleeding. Air entrainment greatly reduces the rate, sometimes to the extent that water evaporates as fast as it reaches the surface. Well-graded sand produces concrete with a low bleeding rate. If a coarse sand must be used, it is beneficial to use a fine blending sand, mixing it with the normal sand in the aggregate processing plant, or batching it separately into the concrete. Other expedients that may be of value are:

Reduce the slump by reducing the amount of water in the batch.
Make the mix richer by increasing the amount of cement per batch.
Use a finer cement.
Add a small amount of inert fines or pozzolan.

Shrinkage of Hardened Concrete

Concrete loses moisture as it dries out, and this loss of moisture results in a loss of volume. Concrete will undergo a linear shrinkage of about 0.06 per cent upon changing from a saturated to a dry state. The amounts of cement and water in the mix modify this value, the mixes with high water-cement ratios or rich mixes with high water content having higher shrinkage rates than lean mixes with low water-cement ratios. Hence the desirability of using relatively lean mixes with a minimum of cement and water.

Different cements and aggregates produce concrete with different shrinkage rates. Porosity of the paste increases shrinkage.

4-2. VOLUME CHANGE

The Bureau of Reclamation *Concrete Manual*[4.3] refers to volume change as the expansion and contraction of hardened concrete resulting from wetting and drying or temperature variations.

If the concrete is restrained, cracks are formed as a result of shrinkage or contraction combined with insufficient tensile strength. Expansion under restraint may cause spalling at joints or excessive compressive stress. Under the influence of moisture changes, concrete will withstand the compressive stress induced by wetting expansion but, if restrained, it will crack due to tension resulting from shrinkage as it dries out.

Volume changes caused by temperature fluctuations produce cracking and disintegration similar to that resulting from wetting and drying. The action, however, is somewhat different, as temperature effects involve the aggregate as well as the paste, whereas moisture changes involve only the paste.

Thermal Properties

The most important thermal properties of concrete are conductivity, diffusivity, and coefficient of expansion. *Conductivity* is the rate at which concrete conducts heat. *Diffusivity* is a measure of the capability of concrete to undergo temperature changes. *Coefficient of expansion* is the rate at which concrete changes volume with changes in temperature.

The most important factors affecting the thermal properties of concrete are the mineralogical type of coarse aggregate and the water content of the concrete. Good dense concrete, made of high-quality aggregates, should give no trouble.

If there is reason to believe that the thermal properties are causing trouble, laboratory tests will disclose whether or not this is true. It is known that a high coefficient of expansion causes high stresses in the surface of concrete undergoing temperature changes, and a high-diffusivity gravel, compared with the mortar, causes differential volume changes, both of which adversely affect durability of the concrete. Over a given temperature range, a fast rate of temperature change is more damaging to the concrete than a slow change.

The coefficient of linear expansion for concrete is about 5.5×10^{-6}, or 0.0000055, in./(in.)(°F). The conductivity of normal concrete weighing 150 pcf is about 12 Btu in./(sq ft)(hr)(°F) in the oven-dry state, ranging up to 18 if the concrete is wet. Lightweight concrete of 100 pcf in the oven-dry state has a value of about 4. Conductivity is affected principally by the type of aggregate, density of the concrete, and moisture content of the concrete.

4-3. YIELD

The yield of concrete is defined as the volume of concrete per sack of cement (ASTM Designation: C 138). Under good to excellent control conditions, the actual volume of the hardened concrete in place will be about 2 per cent less than the fresh volume for air-entrained concrete, and 1 to 1.5 per cent less for non-air-entrained concrete. This normal loss of volume is caused by loss of part of the entrained air during handling and placing, decrease in the combined volume of water and cement during hydration, settlement, bleeding, drying shrinkage, and compression of entrained air in the bottom of a lift. The apparent loss can be much higher if the forms bulge or spread. Small irregularities or inaccuracies of the magnitude of ⅛ or ¼ in. in the construction of forms may cause discrepancies as high as 5 or 6 per cent between the computed yardage and that measured in the forms. The error may be higher due to overrun on an irregular subgrade or failure to allow for wasted concrete. Errors in specific gravity of ingredients and in batching will cause errors in yield computations.

Discrepancies between computed yield at the batching plant and the volume of concrete measured in the forms are sometimes a source of disagreement between the ready-mix concrete producer and the contractor. A 4 per cent error in 100 cu yd of $15 ready-mixed concrete means $60 that someone will have to absorb. Therefore, it behooves all persons concerned to see that the many sources of error are minimized.

A further discussion of yield may be found in Sec. 15-4.

4-4. CREEP OR PLASTIC FLOW

Creep may be defined as the deformation of concrete under sustained load, in contrast to elastic deformation that occurs immediately upon application of a load to the concrete and which disappears upon removal of the load. The terms "creep" and "plastic flow" describe the same phenomenon, with "creep" the preferred usage.

Tests by many investigators indicate that creep continues over many years, as long as the concrete is subject to stress. The rate of creep decreases rapidly at first and continues to decrease with time. One-fourth of the total expected creep occurs within about 2 weeks of loading, and fully half of the creep develops within 3 months.

With the increased use of prestressed concrete in modern construction, attention has been focused on creep as an important property of concrete, resulting in intensive study by many institutions and agencies. As results of these investigations become known, light will be shed on the practical measures that can be effected in the field to control the characteristics of concrete that affect creep.

Within the range of normal concrete mixes, creep is proportional to the water-cement ratio and the amount of hardened cement paste. Hence in those situations in which it is necessary to keep creep at a minimum, such as in prestressed concrete, it is desirable to use the minimum cement content and minimum water-cement ratio that will produce concrete possessing other desired properties, including adequate strength. Aggregates should be well graded and of the largest practical size and should consist of types possessing high density and low absorption, with a high modulus of elasticity. Cement should be low in total alkalies, with the percentage of tricalcium silicate near the upper limit of the specifications.

The effect of entrained air on creep is negligible. Therefore, an air-entraining agent may be used in low-creep concrete with confidence, because of its other beneficial effects. The use of a water-reducing admixture may also be of value.

In laboratory tests, Washa and Fluck[4.4] found that inclusion of compressive steel in positive moment areas of two-span continuous beams, equal in amount to the tensile steel, reduced plastic flow deflection by about one-third.

REFERENCES

4.1 Woodward, H. S.: Practical Aspects of Concrete Volume Shrinkage, *Consulting Engineer*, March, 1956, pp. 42–45.
4.2 Concrete Aggregates Get an Icy Bath, *Eng. News-Record*, Sept. 15, 1959.
4.3 *Concrete Manual*, 6th ed., U.S. Bureau of Reclamation, Denver, 1956.
4.4 Washa, G. W., and P. G. Fluck: Plastic Flow (Creep) of Reinforced Concrete Continuous Beams, *J. Am. Concrete Inst.*, Proc. vol. 52, pp. 549–562, January, 1956.

PART TWO

Durability and Appearance

CHAPTER 5 *Durability*

5-1. GENERAL

A discussion of concrete durability can hardly be made without a discussion of all the properties of concrete. Durability is intimately related to all other attributes of concrete: to structural design, to materials and workmanship, and to exposure conditions. In general, we may say that there are six factors that affect durability:

1. Characteristics of materials comprising the concrete
2. Physical properties of the hardened concrete
3. Exposure conditions
4. Loads imposed on the structure
5. Practices used during construction
6. Structural design

Durability is inversely related to the water-cement ratio, being lower when the water-cement ratio is high. Durable concrete requires dense, impermeable concrete of low absorption and low shrinkage, without cracks; adequate entrained air; adequate structural design, including sufficient foundation capacity; prohibition of extreme and abrupt changes in section; sufficient and proper placement of reinforcing steel especially around openings and corners; prudent design and location of joints; avoidance of overloading; correct location and spacing of embedded items; and sufficient drainage. Durability also requires suitable materials; those which have a poor history or which are shown to be unsuitable by laboratory tests should be avoided. It requires quality workmanship, avoiding such things as poorly graded aggregates caused either by wrong classifying setup or segregation during handling. Other practices to be avoided are poor mix proportioning including high water content; careless batching, mixing, and handling; careless placing and consolidation; and insufficient curing.

53

Measures recommended by the Bureau of Reclamation conducive to durability are:[4.3]*

1. Use five to six per cent entrained air.†
2. Use the minimum slump that will permit entraining the proper amount of air. About 1½ inches is the minimum practicable slump. More air-entraining agent may be required at this slump.
3. Reduce the water-cement ratio to about 0.45 by weight (5 gal per sack). The unit water content should not be changed and the additional cement required should be substituted for sand in the mix.
4. In placing concrete in walls, curbs, and slabs, work from corners and ends of the forms towards the center.
5. Exposed unformed surfaces should be sloped to provide quick, positive drainage and to avoid puddles on low spots.
6. Outdoor unformed surfaces should be finished only with a minimum of wood floating.
7. The concrete should receive thorough curing, being kept continuously wet for 14 days or covered with an approved membrane.
8. If seepage will come in contact with or flow over the concrete, permanent drainage should be provided, preferably by a gravel backfill over suitable drains.

5-2. LACK OF DURABILITY

Faulty Materials

Deleterious materials usually find their way into concrete through the normal constituents of the concrete. In the case of aggregates, careful testing, including a petrographic examination, will reveal their presence. Natural aggregates of inferior or borderline quality can be improved by various beneficiation processes, such as heavy media separation, impact disintegration, jigging, or elastic fractionation.

Some feldspars disintegrate to form kaolin, causing soft spots on the surface of the concrete. Rarely, thermal incompatibility exists between the cement paste and aggregates, in which large differences in coefficient of expansion of coarse aggregate and the paste may produce expansive forces sufficient to disrupt the concrete. [The average coefficient for concrete is 0.0000055 in./(in.)(°F). Some limestones may yield a slightly lower value.] Freezing and thawing tests of concrete made with the suspected materials will reveal deficiencies in durability that may be due to this cause.

Many of the effects of materials in the aggregates show up as cracking and other surface blemishes (see Chaps. 7 and 8).

* Superscript figures refer to chapter and reference number. The references are found at the end of each chapter.
† See Sec. 16-2 for actual percentages recommended.

Stutterheim[5.1] reports the case of a building in which large deflections developed in beams and floors, together with map cracking, cracking over reinforcing steel, and corrosion of the steel. The cause was attributed to the use of a fine-grained sandstone for coarse aggregate and a fine aggregate consisting of particles of shale and sandstone. Excessive shrinkage of these materials is said to have caused the deterioration.

The writer knows of a case in which reinforced concrete columns in a dry basement started swelling and exhibiting pattern cracking, resulting in serious deterioration of concrete scarcely 2 years old. Inspection disclosed that the reinforcing steel was badly corroded. Tests of samples of the concrete indicated a large amount of chlorides in the concrete which had reacted with the reinforcing steel to cause expansion. A microscopic examination revealed a very thin blue discoloration on the coarse aggregate particles which was found to be prussian blue. Further detective work finally disclosed that prussian blue was used in small quantities to "whiten" salt, which led to the discovery that barges used for transporting the aggregates had previously been used for transporting bulk salt. It was finally concluded that the source of moisture was water that had accumulated in pores of the concrete and had been sealed in by a surface waterproofing treatment.

Another case was reported from France in which chlorides present in poorly washed aggregates corroded the reinforcing steel. In this case, also, a waterproofing treatment had been applied to the concrete, effectively sealing in sufficient water to promote the reaction.

The aggregates themselves may contain material that is not satisfactory. Certain highly absorptive particles such as chalk expand when they absorb moisture. Porous chert absorbs moisture which, upon freezing, exerts sufficient force to disrupt the concrete. These cherts exist in gravel deposits and as lenses in limestone quarries in the North Central states, especially northern Illinois and Indiana. Other contaminating substances that might exist in the aggregates are silt, clay, mica, coal, shale, slate, humus and other organic matter, chemical salts, soft fragments, surface coatings, cemented particles, and encrustations. On the Kings River in California a black, sootlike coating was found on some of the gravel particles. Analysis showed it to be manganese and iron oxides, probably chemically harmless in concrete, but a possible source of inferior concrete because of its deleterious effect on bond between the paste and aggregate unless it was removed. Opaline coatings on aggregate are deleteriously reactive with cement of normal alkali content. Effects of these various materials are unsound concrete, reduced durability and strength, unsightly surface blemishes, and premature weathering.

Harmful materials may enter the concrete by means of the mixing

water. Normally, tap water is satisfactory, but streams may contain
effluents from sewage plants or manufacturing plants containing harmful
amounts of tannic acid, sugar, carbonic acid, sulfates, or organic material.

Shrinkage of Paste

Tests by the National Bureau of Standards indicate that cements with
high shrinkage rates immediately after hardening tend to crack and
craze sooner than cements with low shrinkage rates. The cement with
the higher cracking resistance will be more durable.[5.2] Tricalcium aluminate content of cement is best kept below 8 per cent. However, finer
grinding, with optimum gypsum content, will tend to counteract this.

Improper Construction Practices

Included in the category of improper construction practice is segregation during placing of the concrete, especially if the concrete is too wet.

Fig. 5-1. Honeycomb in a 48-in. prestressed girder resulting from improper consolidation.

Mortar and concrete of low rock content accumulate in pockets, leaving honeycomb and sand streaks. Porous concrete, or honeycomb, may
also result from insufficient vibration. Rain or other water may enter the
concrete and either damage the concrete (with dissolved materials in
the water) or attack reinforcing steel. Improper cleanup of construction
joints may result in weak layers. To prevent, use a slump as low as
placing conditions will permit. Four inches should be a maximum for
any reasonable placement. Do not cause concrete to flow laterally in the

forms, but deposit it as nearly as possible in its final location, then consolidate by thorough, systematic vibration. Good, dense concrete is essential, properly proportioned and mixed, with the reinforcing steel well embedded (see Figs. 5-1 to 5-3).

FIG. 5-2. Honeycomb in a small concrete step. A rock pocket such as this, in this location, is of relatively minor importance, although it is a potential source of deterioration, especially in a severe climate.

FIG. 5-3. Deterioration of a concrete railing exposed in a mild, humid climate. Penetration of moisture through cracks and porosity caused rusting of reinforcing steel and resulting failure of the concrete.

Attack by Substances

Many substances attack concrete to a greater or lesser extent. Table 5-1, which is abstracted in part from the *Joint Committee Report*,[5.3] lists some of the more common ones. In order to determine the effect of a suspected aggressive substance, tests should be made in accordance with ASTM Designation: C 267, Chemical Resistance of Hydraulic Ce-

TABLE 5-1. EFFECT OF SUBSTANCES ON HARDENED CONCRETE

Group	Substance	Effect on unprotected concrete	Suggested protection
A	Petroleum oils: heavy, light, or volatile	None, except some loss of oil from penetration of lighter oils	1, 2, 3, 4, 5, 6, or 7 (see list at end of table)
B	Coal tar distillates: Phenol, cresol, lysol, creosote	Slow attack	Same as above except 3 and 6
	Benzol, toluol, xylol, cumol	None except some loss of oil from penetration	Same as A, except 6, 7 for intermittent exposure
	Pitch, anthracene, carbonzol, paraffin	None	None required
C	Inorganic acids: Sulfurous	Disintegration	8, 9, or 10
	Sulfuric, nitric		8, 9, or 10 for concentration of 50% or less, below 150°F
	Hydrochloric, hydrofluoric		9 or 10 for concentration of 50% or less, below 150°F
D	Organic acids:		
	Acetic	Slow disintegration	2, 4, 10, or 11
	Carbonic in water	Slow attack	1, 2, 4, 7, 11, or 14
	Lactic, tannic, citric	Slow attack	1, 2, 3, 4, 7, 11, 12, or 14
	Oxalic, dry carbonic	None	None
E	Organic oils: Vegetable, fish, glycerine	Very slight to slight attack	1, 2, 3, 7, or 13
F	Inorganic salts: Sulfates of aluminum, ammonia, calcium, cobalt, copper, iron, magnesium, manganese, nickel, potassium, sodium, zinc	Active attack	1, 3, 7, 8, 10, 11, or 14
	Acid sulfate	Strong attack	Same
	Ammonium sulfate and nitrate	Strong attack	Same
	Chlorides of aluminum, copper, iron, magnesium, mercury	Slight attack	Same

TABLE 5-1. EFFECT OF SUBSTANCES ON HARDENED CONCRETE (*Continued*)

Group	Substance	Effect on unprotected concrete	Suggested protection
G	Chlorides of calcium, potassium, sodium, strontium Nitrates of calcium, potassium, sodium Soluble sulfides (except ammonia) Carbonates Fluorides Silicates	No attack	None
H (miscellaneous)	Bromine Carbon bisulfide Coke Hydrogen sulfide Brine	Active attack Impure vapor attacks In presence of water forms H_2SO_4 If continuously wet Otherwise	8 8 See group C 7 None 3, 7

Protective Treatments:
1. Fluosilicate, sodium silicate
2. Spar varnish
3. Linseed oil
4. Phenol formaldehyde varnish
5. Thiokol, Amercoat
6. Prestressed concrete
7. Epoxy resin surface sealer
8. Glass, vitrified brick, or tile laid in litharge
9. Lead
10. Rubber
11. Bituminous paint or enamel
12. Paraffin
13. Bakelite varnish
14. Neoprene solution in solvent and resin

ment Mortars. The test is made with the materials proposed for use in the concrete exposed to the same concentration of the questionable substance that exists in the field.

Various acids may attack hardened concrete by dissolving the cement, thereby causing either disintegration of the concrete surfaces or internal damage if they can penetrate the concrete through cracks or other openings. Certain ores, coal, or cinders stored near concrete are a source of mineral acids that will be leached out by rain or other water, or manufacturing plant wastes may contain destructive chemicals.

The process known as "ocrating" or "ocration," which has gained some favor in Europe, improves the resistance of concrete to acid attack and wear. Inasmuch as it requires a special sealed gas chamber, it is applicable only to concrete products such as blocks and pipe. In this process, the concrete is placed in the gas chamber, where it is exposed to an atmosphere of silicon tetrafluoride gas which reacts with constituents of the cement, creating a relatively inert and impervious surface on the concrete.

Sulfates may be present in soil or water and react chemically with hydrated constituents of the cement paste, causing expansion and disruption of the paste. In certain areas of the West, the so-called "white alkali," consisting of sulfates of sodium, magnesium, and calcium, ac-

TABLE 5-2. ATTACK ON CONCRETE BY SOILS AND WATERS CONTAINING VARIOUS
SULFATE CONCENTRATIONS

Relative degree of sulfate attack	Per cent water-soluble sulfate (as SO_4) in soil samples	Ppm sulfate (as SO_4) in water samples
Negligible..........	0–0.10	0–150
Positive*...........	0.10–0.20	150–1,000
Considerable†.......	0.20–0.50	1,000–2,000
Severe†.............	Over 0.50	Over 2,000

* Use Type II cement.
† Use Type V cement.
SOURCE: USBR *Concrete Manual*.[4.3]

tively attacks concrete (see Table 5-2). When sulfate exposure exists, a cement low in tricalcium aluminate, such as Type V, should be used. Entrained air is beneficial, and good workmanship in placing, finishing, and curing, producing smooth, dense surfaces free of honeycomb and cracks, is essential. Calcium chloride should not be used. A tested pozzolan is of value, especially if the cement contains more than 5 per cent tricalcium aluminate.

Except under unusual circumstances, petroleum oils do not attack concrete. One exception was in a steel-rolling mill where hot lubricating oil mixed with hot emulsifying water came in contact with concrete machine bases, causing eventual disintegration. Proper design or maintenance would prevent such an exposure.

Where oil is stored in concrete tanks it is necessary to have good, sound concrete, free of cracks. Circumferential prestressing is of value in this case. This is accomplished by wrapping high-strength wire around the tank with a special machine that stresses the wire nearly to its elastic limit. The tank is then coated with pneumatically applied mortar to protect the wire from weathering.

There are a number of proprietary coatings available for coating concrete oil tanks. A Thiokol compound is said to be invulnerable to gasoline. Amercoat compounds are also available.

Heat, blast, and fuel spillage from jet aircraft cause scaling, cracking, and crazing, especially of inferior concrete. Good, dense concrete is usually resistant, and a properly constructed pavement should give no trouble.

Calcium chloride is commonly used as a de-icing agent for pavements, walks, and similar areas. Ice and snow are melted when this salt is sprinkled on them. This usage is becoming much more common, with greater concentrations of salt and more frequent applications. The effect of salt on pavements and walks is similar to the effect of freezing and thawing, which is scaling, spalling, and eventual failure. This effect is minimized when the concrete contains the optimum percentage of entrained air. Nevertheless, there is evidence that air entrainment is not the final answer. Sometimes a surface application of light oil applied to the dry concrete affords some protection for two or three seasons.

Pure carbon bisulfide (CS_2) has no effect on good concrete, but the impure vapor may attack concrete. Lining of tanks with an impermeable nonreactive liner, such as lead sheets, affords protection. If lead sheets are used, the concrete should be permitted to season and dry out first.

Cases of severe corrosion have been reported in which free carbon dioxide in water to which the concrete was exposed leached lime out of the concrete. Concrete exposed to carbon dioxide in water should have smooth, dense surfaces, made with cement low in lime. Design should provide for adequate drainage. Waterproof coatings will provide some protection if it is impossible to keep the water away from the concrete. Dissolved bicarbonates are harmless and will not attack concrete. However, nearly all soft waters will leach the lime out of concrete.

Some metals are corroded when in contact with concrete. On exposure to fresh concrete, aluminum is attacked by caustic alkalies as long as moisture is present. Even though the concrete may dry out and the action cease, there is a possibility of further action if the concrete again becomes wet.

Lead will corrode in contact with fresh concrete but is not affected by hardened and dry concrete. If it is necessary to place lead in contact with fresh concrete, a sufficient extra thickness of lead should be provided to allow for initial attack. Lead may be corroded by calcium hydroxide leached out of concrete.

Copper is immune to attack even when wet, except in the presence of chlorides. For this reason, calcium chloride should not be used in concrete to be placed in contact with copper.

Some corrosion of zinc will occur upon contact with green concrete. This reaction forms a dense film on the surface of the metal which protects the underlying metal from further attack. There is no reaction with dry concrete.

There is some evidence that cadmium is attacked by green concrete, but the evidence is sparse.

Iron and steel are subject to rusting and corrosion in the presence of air and moisture. This reaction is stimulated in the presence of chlorides, and is worsened by electrolytic action if dissimilar metallic couples are present. An example of electrolysis is corrosion of aluminum conduit in concrete of a building in which calcium chloride had been used during cold weather placing. Later galvanic action occurred between the aluminum of the conduit and the reinforcing steel. Stray direct currents may set up an electrolytic action which will cause corrosion if the steel is anodic. Alternating current is harmless, and electricity has no effect on plain concrete.

Corrosion of reinforcing steel is evidenced by cracking and spalling of the concrete. Water enters the concrete through cracks, honeycomb, or other porosity. Prevention is accomplished by proper design and construction. Reinforcing steel should be covered by 2 in. of concrete (3 in. in sea water). Concrete should be dense, without honeycomb, sand streaks, or similar blemishes in order to prevent access of moisture to the steel. Cracks, if they occur, should be patched and filled. If danger of electrolytic action or stray currents is expected, reinforcing steel and other embedded metal parts should be grounded at the time of their installation.

Cavitation and Erosion

Cavitation is apt to occur in conduits carrying water at high velocity where there is an abrupt divergence between the natural path of the water and the surface of the conduit, resulting in turbulence that creates localized areas of vacuum that cause particles of concrete to be removed. Such turbulence might exist at a sharp bend in the conduit or a sudden change in cross section. Projections or depressions in the surface of the conduit will also cause cavitation, for example, fins of mortar that originated in cracks in the forms when the concrete was placed. Clear water will cause cavitation if it is moving in excess of about 50 fps. A surface eroded by cavitation is rough, presenting a pockmarked or honeycombed appearance, in contrast to concrete that has been subjected to abrasion, which is usually quite smooth.

Proper design is important in preventing cavitation, providing stream-lined flow of water. Concrete surfaces should be dense and smooth without surface imperfections of any kind. Absorptive form lining or vacuum concrete will be of value, and unformed surfaces should be hard-troweled. However, excessive troweling or working of the surface should be avoided. Properly proportioned mixes with high strength, low water-cement ratio (obtained by good practices, not merely more cement) and the optimum percentage of entrained air, should be used. Even the best concrete, when exposed to cavitation, will eventually show distress, hence the importance of correct structural design and good construction practices. A heavy coating of resilient rubber is effective in controlling cavitation in an existing structure.

Erosion of concrete occurs when water carrying solid matter flows over concrete. Abrasion of the solids wears the concrete away. As in the case of cavitation, the best protection is proper design, maintenance, and operation. Dense concrete of high strength offers some protection, but it too will be eroded under this exposure.

There have been rare instances of attack of concrete by rock borers in tropical waters. It is doubtful if good concrete has ever suffered any damage from exposure of this nature.

5-3. ALKALI-AGGREGATE REACTION

The alkali-aggregate reaction is a type of deterioration that takes place between certain aggregate constituents and alkalies in the cement. It can cause serious disintegration of concrete, sometimes aggravated by freezing of water in the cracks. This is discussed in Sec. 7-5.

5-4. ORGANIC COMPOUNDS

Food-processing plants impose special problems in the durability of concrete, presenting many types of corrosive organic compounds, as do tanning and fermentation plants. Exposure to organic acids and other compounds should be made only after experience or tests show that no ill effects will follow. Examples of destructive compounds are fatty acids and blood in meat processing plants, fruit acids in packing houses and canneries, and lactic acid in dairies (see detailed list in Table 5-1). Sometimes the attacking compounds may be entrained in the atmosphere, or in steam or other vapors, attacking ceilings or other apparently safe concrete.

Concrete subject to such exposures should have a smooth, dense surface, made with cement containing a minimum of lime and iron. Acid-proof coatings such as tile and certain proprietary compounds may be necessary.

Coolers and freezers have brine solutions that are apt to be harmful. Where the concrete is constantly wet, as in the bottom of a tank containing brine, there would be little effect on good dense air-entrained concrete containing about 6 sacks of cement per cubic yard at a water-cement ratio of 5½ gal per sack or less. The fresh concrete should be permitted to dry out thoroughly after curing and before exposure. Two coats of raw linseed oil, brushed on hot, effectively seal the surface against penetration of brine. Other coatings may consist of epoxy resin or silicone solution.

A wash coat of cement and water of the consistency of heavy cream brushed on the interior of farm silos has been found to improve resistance of the concrete to attack by silage juices. Curing of the coating is important.[5.4]

Organic acids result from the decay of vegetable or animal matter and may be present in swamps. Drainage should be provided, if possible, to prevent contact of the water with the concrete.

Most organic materials, if they become incorporated in the fresh concrete, prevent the cement from setting. Sugar solutions attack hardened concrete, and as little as 0.2 per cent of sugar will seriously damage fresh concrete. Tannic acid also will prevent or delay hardening. These materials usually reach concrete through the medium of the raw materials. Containers, trucks, cars, and all other equipment that comes in contact with cement, aggregates, other concrete materials, or with the concrete itself, must be clean of all contaminating substances. Such equipment should be inspected before use. Adequate inspection must be provided of aggregate production and handling to prevent contamination by pieces of wood or bark, pieces of old fertilizer sacks or sugar sacks used for chinking leaky cars or trucks, and similar sources of organic compounds.

Formaldehyde solutions attack concrete and require an inert coating on the concrete. Certain varnishes are suitable, but should be tested first.

5-5. SEA WATER

Damage to concrete exposed to salt water in the ocean may be caused either mechanically or chemically, or may be the result of a combination of both.

Chemical Attack

Chlorides, sulfates, alkalies, or other substances may be contained in the water and attack the concrete. A cement that is high in tricalcium aluminate is less resistant to such attack than one low in C_3A (not over 5 per cent C_3A). In rare instances, cases have been reported in which certain feldspathic sands were found to be slightly soluble in sea water to an extent sufficient to promote disintegration. Use of calcium chloride as an admixture for acceleration of setting time and early strength should be avoided in concrete to be exposed to salt water.

Physical Attack

Most damage to concrete in sea water exposure is caused by physical attack, which, in turn, sometimes aids chemical attack. In many cases, disintegration results from the water reaching reinforcing through cracks, honeycomb, or other openings, causing the steel to rust. Because the iron rust is of a greater volume than the original steel bar, a strong disruptive force is created which spalls and cracks the concrete. Usually such damage is cumulative, and it may ultimately lead to complete failure.

Mechanical action of waves, tides, and moving objects will damage the concrete, as will cycles of wetting and drying in areas between high and low tides or resulting from windblown spray. In a severe climate, freezing and thawing of water in pores, cracks, and honeycomb are significantly active.

Prevention

The first requirement is to select well-graded, first-class nonreactive aggregates conforming to ASTM Designation: C 33. Cement should be low in C_3A, either Type II or IV. Consideration should be given to the use of an approved pozzolan with a record of satisfactory use in a similar exposure. Under carefully controlled conditions a slag pozzolan cement could be used. Concrete should contain an adequate amount of entrained air, with mixes proportioned in accordance with the procedures described in Chap. 16. The concrete should be workable, with slump and water-cement ratio as low as possible, containing at least 6 sacks of cement per cubic yard. (An excessively high cement content is apt to cause small surface cracks or checking.) Use of a water-reducing admixture will benefit the concrete by permitting the use of less mixing water for the same workability, also enhancing strength and durability.

Chamfers and fillets should be installed in the forms, thus obviating sharp corners on the finished structure. Reinforcing steel should be located at least 3 in. away from the forms so as to provide adequate coverage with concrete. If horizontal construction joints are necessary, they should be located below low water or above high water.

Good workmanship during construction is essential. Concrete should be handled and placed in accordance with good practices. Special care is necessary during placing to avoid segregation, and the concrete should be thoroughly consolidated by means of vibration to preclude honeycomb and sand streaks. Construction joints should be cleaned up by means of a wet sand blast or equally effective means. Concrete should be cured for at least 7 days, then permitted to dry out for as long as possible before exposure.

5-6. COLD WEATHER

Cold weather may damage concrete in either of two ways: first, by freezing of the fresh concrete before the cement has achieved final set, and second, by repeated cycles of freezing and thawing over a period of months or years.

Freezing of Fresh Concrete

Only one freezing of the concrete while still in the plastic state or during the initial hardening period may reduce durability, weathering resistance, and strength by as much as one-half. The length of the period during which the concrete is frozen is not important once it has frozen, and the amount the temperature drops below freezing appears to have no effect. Once frozen, concrete will never attain its full potential strength and durability, even after prolonged curing at reasonable temperatures.

Frost Action

Frost, or cycles of freezing and thawing, damages concrete by the freezing and consequent expansion of water in pores and openings in the concrete. Thus it may be seen that dry concrete is little affected by such action. However, most concrete that is exposed to cold temperatures is also exposed to moisture or water and is therefore subject to attack.

Causes of poor frost resistance include poor design of construction joints; segregation of concrete while placing; leaky formwork and poor workmanship resulting in honeycomb and sand streaks; faulty cleanup of a joint surface before placing concrete against it; flat surfaces that allow puddles of water to collect on the concrete; insufficient or totally absent drainage, permitting water to accumulate against the concrete; and cracks. The fineness and composition of the cement, within the limits normally specified, appear to have little or no effect.

To provide resistance against frost requires that good design principles be followed, taking care that proper and adequate drainage is provided. Horizontal joints should be avoided if possible. However, if such a joint is necessary, it should not be located near the water or ground line, but should be 2 or 3 ft above the ground line or high-water line, or the same distance below the ground or low-water line. Thorough cleanup of the old concrete is essential. Concrete should contain a maximum of 7 per cent air for $\frac{1}{2}$- or $\frac{3}{4}$-in. maximum aggregate, ranging down to 3 or 4 per cent for cobble mixes, and should be made of first-class materials, carefully mixed and handled, with a water-cement ratio as low as possible. Good construction practices should be followed throughout, under proper supervision and inspection. Segregation, sand streaks, and honeycomb must be avoided by careful placement of the concrete as near as possible in its final resting place, followed by thorough consolidation by means of internal vibrators. The objective is to produce good concrete with smooth, dense and impermeable surfaces.

5-7. WEATHERING

General deterioration or decay of a concrete structure may occur gradually over a period of many years. Such weathering may not seriously affect usefulness of a structure but, due to natural weathering action, will result in a rounding of edges and slight roughening or erosion of surfaces, giving a patina of age to the structure. The concrete is sound; a piece broken off will be dense and crystalline, breaking through the aggregates in a clean fracture.

On the other hand, accelerated weathering is usually manifested by the appearance of cracks roughly parallel to the edges of the concrete member, frequently filled with calcium carbonate and dirt, and known as D-line cracks (see Fig. 5-4). Fragments of the concrete present a chalky, dull appearance, and tend to crumble because the aggregate separates from the paste. When the concrete is struck with a hammer, the resultant sound is a dead thump instead of a ringing.

Accelerated weathering may be due to several causes. Frost action causes expansion and cracking. Such weathering is cumulative, the rate of destruction increasing with every season. Attack by outside agencies, such as sulfates and acids, will hasten destruction (see Figs. 5-5 to 5-7).

Abnormal expansion and contraction of concrete cause stresses that are harmful. Such volume changes may be caused by changes in temperature or moisture; unsound aggregates such as shales and cherts; unsound cement (rarely); thermal differences in the materials; or reaction between aggregates and cement.

The study of weathering of concrete is not an exact science, in that there are anomalies that sometimes are difficult to explain. However, if all the facts were known, the reason for some particular case of abnormal weathering would probably be evident. Uhl[5.5] mentioned disparities between weathering of bridge members in severe exposure at high altitudes and suggested several reasons for the differences between weathering of curbs and handrails as compared with other portions of the bridge: (1) The larger surface area per unit volume, compared with other bridge members. The elements have a greater and freer opportunity to attack them. (2) The richer mixes usually specified for such members to promote workability and permit higher slumps. Such rich concrete

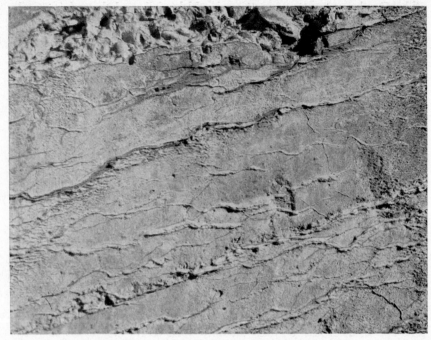

FIG. 5-4. Typical D-line cracking caused by weathering.

FIG. 5-5. Failure of inferior non-air-entrained concrete in a 20-year-old bridge. Note pattern cracking on right, probably caused by freezing and thawing of concrete containing porous aggregate.

suffers from more shrinkage and checking. (3) Working of the concrete surface to provide the desired finish. This leads to pattern checking and crazing as a result of differential volume changes due to nonuniformity of the concrete. Curing for railings and curbs is usually inferior to that given other parts of the structure. (4) Smaller size of maximum aggregate

FIG. 5-6. Deterioration of non-air-entrained sidewalk on a bridge caused by inferior concrete and excess use of calcium chloride for ice removal.

FIG. 5-7. Scaling of sidewalk attributable to overworking wet, non-air-entrained concrete.

in handrail concrete requiring more sand and water. (5) Freezing of the green concrete.*

Uhl then proposes what can be done to provide greater durability for this concrete: (1) Provide better uniformity by avoiding overworking and special finishes. (2) Provide better curing, such as membranes. (3) Use largest possible size of coarse aggregate. (4) Keep adequate spacing between reinforcing steel and the forms. (5) Use low-alkali cement where reaction is possible. (6) Use entrained air. (7) Place concrete at such a season as to avoid freezing weather.

Hydraulic Structures

Being partly wet and partly dry simultaneously, or subject to cycles of wetting and drying, hydraulic structures are subject to especially severe exposure conditions. The water may carry destructive quantities of acid, sulfides, sulfates, or organic material. Hydraulic structures require good, dense concrete with smooth surfaces; ample drainage; well-made joints with water stops where movement is expected; good design, materials, and workmanship; and entrained air. (Entrained air is not incompatible with dense concrete, as the latter implies well-consolidated concrete, without honeycomb or entrapped air.)

Movement of paving slabs or blocks on the face of embankments or reservoirs, sea walls, dams, etc., may be caused by hydraulic back pressure upon sudden lowering of the water level. Abrupt lowering of the water level might occur in the trough of a large wave. Prevention, in the case of continuous slab construction, consists of providing adequate porous drains on the backside of the slab, and placement of weep holes through the concrete slabs. If the slope is paved with individual blocks or slabs, a space should be provided between individual blocks whereby the water can drain out between them.

Surfaces of hydraulic structures in cold climates may suffer damage near the water line by abrasion or adhesion of ice. Coatings seem to be of little value for protection, and the best defense is good, dense concrete with smooth and well-finished surfaces.

5-8. PROTECTIVE COATINGS

Various coating materials are available for application to concrete surfaces for protection against aggressive and disintegrating agencies. While the best protection under normal conditions is good, sound

---

* Because of the greater exposure of small members to the weather, compared with more massive portions of the structure.

concrete presenting a smooth surface to the elements, there are, however, occasions when protection is necessary.

In virtually all cases of attack, water is a contributing factor—either water per se or water acting as the vehicle for aggressive materials. In the first instance, expansion and contraction of concrete caused by alternate wetting and drying contribute to weathering or failure, as do freezing and thawing of water within the concrete. Organic acids and other deteriorating substances may be carried into the concrete by water. Hence there are instances when protective coatings are necessary, although few coatings may be considered permanent.

Bituminous membranes are commonly used, especially for waterproofing, also silicones, paints of various kinds such as portland cement paint or neoprene latex, sodium silicate, and plaster coatings (see Chap. 6).

Mitchell[5.6] reported results of tests in which concrete beams were coated with neoprene latex, the coated beams used in the experiments showing significantly greater durability and abrasion resistance than the uncoated ones. Although further research is indicated, this study demonstrated that permanently durable concrete could be achieved by preventing the ingress of water into the hardened concrete. However, ingress of water could not be entirely prevented by improvement of the concrete, per se.

5-9. AIR ENTRAINMENT

Any discussion of durability is not complete without mentioning the role of purposefully entrained air in concrete. Prior to 1940, use of air-entraining agents was virtually unheard of, but since the mid-forties practically all exposed concrete, especially in severe climates where there are cycles of freezing and thawing, contains entrained air. Air entrainment is probably the most significant single factor contributing to durability of concrete as affected by freezing and thawing.

Addition of an air-entraining agent to the mix results in the formation of countless microscopic spherical voids with an average spacing of about $\frac{1}{100}$ in. between them. These microscopic voids protect the hardened cement paste from the destructive action of freezing and thawing by absorbing or buffering the expansive force of freezing water in the water-saturated paste. Inasmuch as the air voids protect the paste only, air-entrained concrete made with porous, unsound aggregates manifests poor resistance to freezing and thawing.

Air entrainment is not a cure-all for whatever distress concrete may suffer. Entrained air does improve the durability and other characteristics of concrete, and its use should not be undervalued. But it cannot take the place of good materials and competent workmanship. These comprise the foundation of sound concrete construction.

With respect to the durability imparted to concrete by entrained air, two important points should be kept in mind:

1. Prolonged moist curing of the concrete, without an intervening drying-out period before exposure, tends to fill the voids with water and may actually reduce the potential durability originally imparted by the entrained air.

2. Concrete pavements placed in the late fall (October, November) should not be subjected to de-icing salts during their first winter of exposure since scaling may result.

5-10. PAVEMENTS

Street, highway, and airport pavements present many special problems in design, construction, and maintenance. Chapter 14 covers the inspection of pavement construction which, if performed, will do much to prevent the failures described below.

Poor workmanship and inferior materials are the principal causes of pavement failures. These can be generalized as insufficient foundation support, inferior concrete, unstable joint assemblies, inadequate load transfer devices at joints, improper or incomplete joint sealing, insufficient lubrication of dowels, and soft concrete surface.

The best aggregate available should be used for pavements with a high-grade cement conforming to standard specifications. The mix should have between 4 and 6 per cent entrained air, at a slump of 2 in. or less. Water-cement ratios should be as low as reasonably possible: not over 6 gal per bag of cement in a mild climate, and not over 5½ gal per bag in a severe climate subject to cycles of freezing and thawing.

Scaling

Prior to the use of air-entrainment, scaling was a serious problem in areas subject to freezing and thawing, especially when de-icing salts were used to melt snow and ice. Air-entrainment largely eliminated this problem, but there is now some evidence that even this cannot entirely prevent scaling under the extremely heavy salting practiced in some areas. In spite of good construction practices, scaling remains a problem.

Small packages of de-icing agents containing ammonium nitrate and ammonium sulfate have recently appeared on the market for sale to motorists and householders. Because even weak solutions of these materials actively attack concrete, including air-entrained concrete, they should never be used on pavements, walks, or other concrete structures.

The user should use only those de-icing agents known to contain only calcium chloride or sodium chloride.

Spalling at Joints

Poor timing in sawing joints may cause spalling. Other causes are carelessness in making construction joints such as nonvertical ones, or the presence of old concrete or pebbles in the joint which prevent free movement of the joint when the concrete expands. Crushing of the concrete at joints is a similar phenomenon.

Subsidence

Failure of the foundation will permit the slab to subside or drop. This is especially prevalent at bridges, where inadequate compaction of the embankment within and adjacent to the abutments, resulting from manual compaction, does not provide the required support. Subsidence or depression of the approach slab at a transverse joint may be caused by loads exceeding the capacity of the subgrade or of the load transfer devices. The pavement will break in an irregular pattern over a localized subgrade failure, such as might occur in poorly compacted material over a culvert. Reinforcing steel will not prevent such failures, but it will hold the concrete together.

Pumping

An action known as pumping may take place in the presence of moisture when a pavement has been laid directly on a fine-grained, plastic, impervious soil. Poor drainage, even of a permeable subbase, is a contributory cause. A slight vertical movement of the slab under traffic forces water and fine soil to the surface through cracks and joints. Evidence of pumping is especially noticeable immediately after a rainstorm and is characterized by the presence of fine soil and water adjacent to cracks and joints. When vehicles pass over the affected slabs, liquid may be observed spurting out of the crack. Continued pumping results in loss of foundation material and ultimate failure of the pavement. Pumping can be prevented by placing the slab on a permeable, granular subbase and providing drainage away from the shoulders.

When a pavement is failing because of subsidence or pumping, mud jacking may save it. In mud jacking, a slurry of fine soil, cement, and water is pumped under pressure through holes drilled through the slab. Under careful control of pressure and volume of slurry, voids beneath the slab can be filled and the slab brought back to grade. This work requires careful supervision and workmanship, as carelessness can result in cracked slabs or slabs raised too high. Only experienced workmen should be permitted to do it.

Blowups

If a number of transverse joints become filled with solid material during cold weather, expansion of the concrete when the weather turns warm may cause the slab to buckle and crack. Contributory causes are inferior concrete and nonvertical joint surfaces. Joints should be kept free of pebbles, sticks, and other foreign material and should be properly sealed with an approved sealing or filling compound.

Buckling or blowup of a pavement may occur if the concrete is subjected to a temperature appreciably above that existing at the time it hardened. Control is effected by relieving the compressive stresses thus introduced by means of expansion joints. Some authorities claim that the need for expansion joints is eliminated when the pavement is divided into short panels by contraction joints. Others claim that a slab, such as a pavement, is as long as it ever will be while the concrete is still plastic, unless it was placed during abnormally cold weather, hence there is no need of expansion joints. Modern practice is to avoid expansion joints except at structures.

Warping or Curling

If a pavement is laid on soil that undergoes large volume changes upon wetting or drying, curling is apt to occur. Surface water, entering the subgrade through joints and cracks in the pavement, will cause expansion of the subgrade. Any unreinforced slab is apt to warp if there is a large difference in temperature or moisture between the two faces of the slab. This rarely occurs in modern reinforced pavement laid on proper subbase material.

5-11. FOUNDATIONS

Foundation failures are disclosed by cracking of the concrete, which indicates differential movement of parts of the structure; by settlement of part or all of the structure; by tilting of the structure; or by heaving (see Figs. 5-8 to 5-10). Such failures may be caused by:

Exceeding of the safe bearing capacity of the soil.
Foundation that is not deep enough. Footings should be carried below the frost line, or below the depth of influence of volume changes of the soil caused by wetting and drying.
Lowering of the water table.
Excavation near the structure subsequent to its construction.
Vibration of machinery.
Scour in stream beds during floods.

FIG. 5-8. Foundation failure of a small highway bridge brought about by scour during a period of high water in the river.

FIG. 5-9. An unreinforced canal lining, 3½ in. thick, placed on a highly expansive clay fill.

FIG. 5-10. A masonry wall placed on an inadequately prepared foundation.

5-12. CONCRETE PILES

Concrete piles in waterfront structures require first-class materials and workmanship in every respect, as their exposure conditions, consisting as they do of cycles of freezing and thawing, wetting and drying, and the presence of sea water, are the most severe possible. However, this is not meant to imply that care is not required in the manufacture of piles for dry-land installation also. All piles are important structural members and are entitled to careful fabrication. Concrete piles may be either cast-in-place or precast.

Cast-in-place Piles

These members are constructed either by drilling a shaft in the earth and filling the shaft with concrete, or by driving a hollow sheet-metal shell by means of a mandrel. After driving, the mandrel is withdrawn and the shell filled with concrete. Another type consists of a heavy shell (7 gauge or heavier) driven without a mandrel. A special type of cast-in-place pile is the caisson footing in which a shaft is drilled and the bottom belled to a larger diameter to provide an extended bearing area for the concrete.

While these piles may come in the class of "rough" concrete, they are vitally important to the safety and success of the structure they support, and there is no reason to abuse usual good construction practices. They are not subject to weathering exposure such as may be the case with precast piles, but they may be subject to attack by aggressive waters in the soil.

Shell piles may be either reinforced or unreinforced. If reinforcement is used, it is usually assembled into a "cage" that is lowered into the shell after the shell has been inspected. Inspection is accomplished by lowering a light into the shell. A shell which is not watertight, or which shows kinks, bends, or other deformation resulting from driving that would impair the quality of the pile, should be repaired or removed. The reinforcing cage should be provided with chairs or other devices to assure clearance from the sides of the shell. It is usual to place a foot or two of mortar in the bottom of the shell just before filling with concrete. The concrete should be vibrated. If practicable, all the piles in one construction unit, such as a pier, bent, or abutment, should be driven before concrete is placed in any of them. This provides better uniformity in construction, avoids damaging completed piles, and permits removal of a shell if it becomes displaced or damaged because of subsequent driving operations.

Precast Piles

Either reinforced concrete or prestressed concrete may be used for precast piles, fabrication (except for stressing) and usages being similar for both. They are frequently manufactured at a central casting yard at some distance from the construction site, especially if they are prestressed.

Reinforcing in precast piles should consist of longitudinal bars in combination with spiral winding as detailed on the plans. Concrete should normally have a compressive strength of not less than 4,000 psi when the piles are driven, but the plans should be checked to determine what is actually specified for any certain job. Straightness of the piles is important, and specifications require that the maximum allowable deviation of the longitudinal axis from a straight line drawn from the center of the tip to the center of the butt shall not exceed a certain amount, usually ¼ in. per 35 ft of length of pile.

Sheet piling is a special form of precast piles. These are made in the shape of planks, perhaps 8 in. thick and 15 or 18 in. wide, of such a shape that they fit together when driven.

Deterioration

Many cases of deterioration of piles may be traced to rusting of the reinforcing steel. Precautions to be taken include rich mixes of 6 or 7 sacks of cement per cubic yard, of low slump and low water-cement ratio, containing entrained air, made of sound, nonreactive materials and modified, low-heat, or sulfate-resistance cement. Reinforcing steel should be covered at least 2 in. (3 in. in sea-water exposure). Piles should be thoroughly cured by keeping continuously wet for at least 10 days, and preferably 14 days, or by careful application of a high-grade sealing compound. Handling imposes high stresses in a pile and should be done carefully, picking up the pile at the proper points to minimize bending stresses and avoiding shocks and jolts.

Protective Coatings

Painting or coating piles for protection is of doubtful value, although a coating of sodium silicate, applied as a dip, may provide some protection. The Los Angeles Harbor Department impregnates concrete piles with asphalt. This method is described as follows:[5.7]

The Los Angeles Harbor Department pioneered in the practice of waterproofing precast concrete piling (beginning in 1923) by impregnating the outer shell of the concrete to a depth of from ¾ in. to 2½ in. with asphalt. This was accomplished by vacuum-pressure methods similar to the treatment of creosoted wood. After pre-drying at temperatures up to 250°F the concrete is placed in a closed retort in a bath of molten asphalt admitted under a high vacuum, then subjected to air pressure up to 150 psi, with temperature gradients being carefully controlled throughout the entire treatment. Concrete is held several hours at 100 psi pressure after asphalt is removed, then is moved to an enclosed cooling chamber. This process is applicable to precast concrete units of all kinds which fit into suitable pressure chambers (6 to 8 ft. in diameter by 70 to 100 ft. long).

Thousands of bearing piles of this type have been in successful use in Los Angeles Harbor and elsewhere, since their inception in 1925, with no indication of deterioration to date. Asphalt impregnated beams and cylinders, which have been stored in the ocean at an elevation of −35 ft. have been found to be bone dry when tested 30 years later.

It is possible to produce concrete for marine structures which will endure without failure at least 50 years with no sign of deterioration in that interval. The following precautions should be observed for concrete units which are to be exposed to the action of sea water:

1. Proper mix proportions using the optimum cement content and competent workmanship are necessary to provide a dense, impervious, relatively non-absorbent concrete.

2. Embed all reinforcing steel so that it has a minimum cover of three inches of good concrete.

3. Use a minimum cement content of 6½ sacks per cu. yd. with a maximum of 7½ sacks.

4. Use nonreactive aggregates, graded to obtain maximum density. If reactive aggregates must be employed use a low-alkali cement and/or compensate with pozzolans.

5. Use sufficient water in the concrete to produce a plastic, workable mix, having low water-cement ratio, usually not to exceed a total of six gallons per sack of cement.

6. Use Type V cement, having five per cent maximum C_3A. If this type is not economically feasible, a Type II cement may be substituted.

7. In the case of marine concrete which is to be exposed to freezing and thawing action, it is important to use some type of air-entraining agent.

8. Thoroughly cure the concrete by the best means possible.

9. Particular care should be taken not to damage precast units such as long piling by improper handling. They should be lifted with equalized, multiple point suspension slings, or similar devices, wherever necessary. Prestressed piles are less susceptible to handling and tensile stresses than are ordinary reinforced piles.

5-13. CHIMNEYS

Concrete chimneys require special attention. This concrete is subject to attack by acids resulting from the burning of high-sulfur fuels. Such acid-producing constituents are present to some extent in nearly all fuels.

Condensation of moisture inside chimneys is dangerous, and may come from rain water or condensation out of the flue gas. High temperatures also contribute to the vulnerability of chimneys.

The top of the chimney should be sloped to the outside so rain water will drain outward instead of running down the inside surface. Linings should be installed in chimneys built of concrete. Such linings should be acid resistant and may require special properties for highly corrosive gases. For temperatures below 800°F unperforated hard-burned shale or clay brick are satisfactory. Firebrick is necessary if the temperature exceeds 800°F. The American Concrete Institute provides standards for the construction of chimneys. These standards should be followed.[5.8]

5-14. LIGHTWEIGHT CONCRETE

During recent years the use of lightweight structural concrete has become more widespread, even to the extent of its being used in exposed locations. This has led to concern in some quarters as to the durability of such concrete when exposed to freezing and thawing. There should be no cause for concern, however, if the concrete is properly designed, prepared, and protected in accordance with good construction practices. Adequate resistance to freezing and thawing will be provided by entraining the same percentage of air volumetrically as for comparable normal-weight concrete. Batching the aggregates in a dry condition has no significant effect in improving durability of air-entrained lightweight concrete, but improves durability of non-air-entrained lightweight concrete. Materials of recognized good quality should be used of course.

REFERENCES

5.1 Stutterheim, N.: Excessive Shrinkage of Aggregate as a Cause of Deterioration of Concrete Structures in S. Africa, *Trans. S. African Inst. Civil Engrs.*, vol. 4, no. 12, December, 1954.

5.2 *Eng. News-Record*, Sept. 15, 1955, p. 54.

5.3 Recommended Practice and Standard Specifications for Concrete and Reinforced Concrete, *Joint Committee Report*, Am. Concrete Inst. Special publication, June, 1940.

5.4 ACI Committee 714: Eleven-year Study of Concrete Stave Silo Durability, *J. Am. Concrete Inst.*, January, 1961, pp. 797–812.

5.5 Uhl, O. M.: Bridge Maintenance Practice on California Highway System, *California Highways and Public Works*, March–April, 1946, pp. 20–31.

5.6 Mitchell, Warrington G.: Effect of a Waterproof Coating on Concrete Durability, *J. Am. Concrete Inst.*, July, 1957, pp. 51–57.

5.7 Wakeman, C. W., E. V. Dockweiler, H. E. Stover, and L. L. Whiteneck: Use of Concrete in Marine Environment, *J. Am. Concrete Inst.*, April, 1958, pp. 841–856.

5.8 ACI Standard Specifications for the Design and Construction of Reinforced Concrete Chimneys, ACI 505–54, September, 1954.

CHAPTER 6 *Watertightness*

6-1. DEFINITIONS

Flow of water through concrete may occur in either of two ways: (1) by the passage of water through channels in the concrete, the water being under a hydrostatic head and in contact with one surface of the concrete; flow of this type may be of considerable magnitude; (2) by capillarity. No head is necessary for capillary flow, the flow resulting from a constant supply of water in contact with one surface of the concrete, and evaporation from the other side. Flow of the first type, called *permeability*, is controlled by waterproofing, and flow of the second type is controlled by dampproofing.

6-2. CONSTRUCTION PRACTICES

The best way to obtain watertight, impermeable concrete is to incorporate these properties into the structure when it is being built. This is accomplished by building the structure of good high-grade concrete. The following principles and precautions should be observed.

Places where water may be against or on the concrete should be avoided by providing adequate drains and weeps to carry water away from the concrete. Design may include a waterproofing membrane over the surface of the concrete, and water stops in the joints. Movement and crack-producing stresses must be minimized.

The use of sound, well-graded aggregates of low porosity is necessary. Sand especially should consist of rounded particles instead of flat or angular ones in order to produce workable, dense concrete with the minimum water-cement ratio.

Concrete should be plastic and workable, thoroughly mixed, with a water-cement ratio of less than 6 gal per sack in thin sections, or slightly higher in more massive sections. Overwet mixes should be avoided.

80

Entrained air is beneficial in decreasing bleeding and interrupting the water channel structure within the concrete. The use of fine cement is sometimes recommended, but such usage may adversely affect durability.

Handling and placing operations should be such as to avoid segregation and cold joints. Concrete should be consolidated by means of vibration.

Form ties in wall forms should be of the type that can be broken or removed below the concrete surface. Ordinary wire ties should not be used.

Finally, the concrete must be thoroughly cured. This should consist of at least 7 days of continuous wet curing, or the application of a reliable curing compound.

FIG. 6-1. Poorly consolidated concrete on a cold joint. This wall is bound to develop leaks.

The most important consideration is the application of sound construction practices, including good design, good materials, proper handling, and adequate curing. The requirements for workable, durable, strong and crackless concrete are prerequisites for watertight concrete.

In nearly all cases, permeability may be traced to poor construction practices. For this reason tests of permeability on laboratory specimens are of little value. Construction joints are especially vulnerable, particularly the horizontal planes between lifts. Anything that weakens the bond on this surface will cause a leaky joint. Among the causes are weak concrete on the top of a lift resulting from wet or overvibrated concrete, incomplete or totally lacking cleanup of the joint surface before placing the succeeding lift, laitance, rock pockets or honeycomb, and succeeding lift not consolidated sufficiently. Cracks are also a source of leakage. Concrete that has suffered a cycle of freezing and thawing while still plastic is more apt to be porous or permeable than concrete that has not suffered such damage.

6-3. BASEMENTS

Walls and floors in basements, pits, and similar structures should have surface water drained by sloping the ground away from the structure about ½ in. in 10 ft and by the use of splash blocks and gutters under

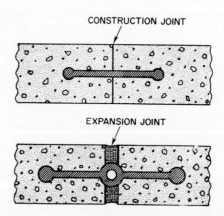

FIG. 6-2. Rubber waterstops. Top: 6-in. flat dumbbell type. Bottom: 9-in. hollow bulb type. These waterstops are used in concrete subject to hydrostatic pressure. The hollow bulb type is used in joints subject to appreciable movement.

downspouts. Subsurface drainage can be provided by means of open-joint tile drains covered with a permeable fill surrounding the structure. Frequently this is all that is necessary. If drainage is impossible, then the structure should be waterproofed. In any event, for those structures that must be completely dry on the interior, the concrete should be protected on the outside. For floors, a vapor barrier consisting of a layer of 35-lb asphalt roll roofing, placed over a porous base, with the joints cemented with tar or asphalt, should be adequate to stop leakage and vapor in a drained location. Metal foil and plastic sheeting are also suitable. Walls should have a bituminous, mortar, or grout coating. In saturated soil, bituminous membranes, or two coats of mortar with hot pitch on the outside, may be necessary. In placing any of these materials care must be exercised to prevent tears, holes, or cracks through which moisture can move.

Condensation in a basement can be prevented by raising the wall and floor temperatures by means of heat or by insulation. Where the insulation is placed on the interior side, a vapor barrier should be provided. Dehumidification of the air is also of value.

Any kind of waterproofing or dampproofing work should be done by persons expert in such work, using the best materials in accordance with the manufacturer's recommendations. The first requirement is good, dense concrete, followed by adequate knowledge of the proposed protective compounds or processes, gained preferably by a satisfactory service record, or by laboratory tests. The latter, however, are apt to be misleading and field experience should be depended on.

Good materials and workmanship are the first consideration in any structure and are essential for watertight concrete. The use of waterproofers or dampproofers, either integral or surface applied, should not be considered as being compensation for poor workmanship, lean mixes, or deficient materials.

6-4. INTEGRAL WATERPROOFERS

Certain materials, when added to the concrete as admixtures, have the effect of reducing flow or capillarity of water through concrete. These materials are known as dampproofers or waterproofers, depending upon their effect.

Powdered admixtures, either inert or pozzolanic, may be of value as a waterproofer in lean mixes or normal mixes lacking fines. They are of no value in rich mixes or normal mixes with adequate fines. In fact, they may be detrimental in the latter.

Calcium chloride is sometimes used for improving watertightness, but its value for this purpose is questionable at the least. Some proprietary compounds sold as waterproofers consist of little more than a calcium chloride solution.

Stearates reduce absorption and retard capillary action but are of little or no value if the water is under pressure. Butyl stearate is recommended in an amount not exceeding 1 per cent by weight of the cement. It should be added to the batch as an emulsion for proper distribution throughout the concrete. Butyl stearate, in the recommended amount, has no serious effect on strength.

Related materials are the soaps, salts of fatty acids such as ammonium or calcium oleate or stearate, that act primarily as water repellents. These are foaming agents and may cause an increase in permeability if the water is under pressure. If used, they should not exceed 0.2 per cent by weight of the cement. In water-curing any concrete containing a water repellent, the concrete should not be permitted to dry out until curing has been completed, as the concrete cannot readily be wetted once it has dried.

Heavy mineral oil in an amount not exceeding 5 per cent by weight of the cement reduces permeability by acting as a water repellent. Oil should have a viscosity of about SAE 60. It should contain no petroleum residuals that emulsify with alkali nor should it contain saponifiable vegetable or fatty oils as these will adversely affect strength. Mineral oil will cause a slight reduction in strength.

Workability agents, by improving the ease of placing and consolidation of concrete, tend to promote watertightness. Examples are water-reducing agents and air-entraining agents.

There is a wide variety of miscellaneous materials available, with varied effects on waterproofing, dampproofing, and strength. Among such products are sodium silicate with organic nitrogenous compounds; silica, lime, and alum; coal tar cut with benzine; barium sulfate, calcium or magnesium silicate with a fatty acid; finely ground or colloidal silica and naphthalene, or a fluosilicate; petroleum jelly and lime; and cellulose materials and wax in an ammoniacal copper solution. Use of any of these compounds is not recommended unless a very careful investigation of their effects on all properties of the concrete is made and their use is entrusted to skilled and experienced persons. In any event, any integral compound is of little or no value in reducing transmission of moisture through a slab on the ground.

Numerous proprietary compounds are on the market, some of which are of practically no value. The user should be sure he knows what is in a compound or admixture before using it in concrete, as some materials may have detrimental effect on strength, durability, or other properties of the concrete.

6-5. SURFACE TREATMENTS

It must be kept in mind that structural movements that produce cracks in the concrete will also crack surface coatings, hence the forces that caused the cracks must be neutralized before corrective measures are taken. The following comments apply to concrete masonry construction as well as to cast-in-place concrete.

Surface treatments consist of two classes: coatings applied as paints, and bituminous membranes. The latter consist of layers of cotton fabric or felt, saturated with asphalt or tar, alternated with layers of the bituminous material mopped on to the surface, usually while hot. Some of these membranes may possess a slight degree of flexibility. They should be protected from damage during backfilling operations.

There are numerous types of coatings. Bituminous coatings may be applied to the surface by painting or mopping, either hot or cold. Linseed oil by itself or in combination with resinous varnishes may be used. Oil paints with a linseed oil or other weather-resistant base are also effective.

Portland cement paints, if properly cured, have considerable value in resisting the penetration of water into concrete surfaces under conditions of moderate pressure. Such paints may be either a mixture of cement and water or specially prepared combinations.

Effective protection of porous concrete against the penetration of water under pressure may be achieved by means of a plaster coat of portland cement mortar applied to the side of the wall exposed to water pressure. Any cracks in the concrete should be chipped out and filled with dry-pack mortar before applying the plaster coat.

Cracks and defective spots on the inside of the wall, on the side away from the water pressure, may be effectively sealed against appreciable hydrostatic head. In the hands of a skillful operator, this method can be used to stop actual flowing leaks. Mortar for flowing leaks should consist of 1 part cement to 2 parts sand. It should be of barely plastic consistency and should contain an accelerating admixture that will reduce setting time to a matter of a few minutes. Lumnite cement, or a mixture of Lumnite and standard cement, sets very rapidly. Type III cement with a liberal amount of calcium chloride, as much as 10 per cent of the cement, will set hard in a very short time. A 1:2 mortar of Type I cement and sand with water containing as much as 50 per cent calcium chloride will set in a few minutes. Use of washing soda (sodium carbonate) in the amount of 5 per cent by weight of cement with Type I cement makes a quick-setting mortar. The proper technique with any of these quick-setting mortars is to work toward the lowest crack or leak.

Cement plaster may be used on the interior as well as the exterior of a wall. However, this affords no protection against weathering or attack by substances in the water, even though the interior is dry. It should not be done in locations where the exterior surface is exposed to freezing and thawing.

In applying any plaster coat, good plastering procedures must be followed. Mortar should be applied in two coats each about ⅜ in. thick. Mortar should be of plastic consistency, consisting of 1 part portland cement to 2 parts plastering sand. The concrete must be clean and barely moist but not wet. Curing should be done as for concrete.

Any movement of the structure subsequent to application of the plaster, resulting from settlement, shrinkage, load, or any other cause that will crack the structure, will also crack the plaster and result in failure of the waterproofing.

Solutions of methyl and ethyl silicone resins dissolved in toluene make effective water repellents when applied to the surface of concrete. Epoxy resins may also be used. These materials should be applied to cured and dry concrete.

Phenolic resin varnish, microcrystalline wax, neoprene, and coal-tar cutback are also effective.

Powdered iron preparations, consisting of mixtures of powdered iron and cement, usually with an oxidizer such as ammonium chloride, are effective. These preparations range from thin coatings to a stiff consistency and are applied with a brush, as paint. Caution should be exercised in their use if they are to be exposed to the weather, as they may cause rust stains.

There are numerous proprietary materials on the market, many of them based on the foregoing materials. The user should make sure that any proposed material has a satisfactory service record and should use it strictly in accordance with the manufacturer's instructions.

CHAPTER 7 *Cracking*

It has been said that cracks in concrete cannot be completely prevented, but they can be controlled. Normally, concrete contracts from the time of placement to final set. This contraction stresses the concrete before it is strong enough to resist, causing incipient cracks. Whether these cracks ever develop depends mainly on the care given the concrete, especially during its early life. If concrete is permitted to dry out in the very early stages after placing and before curing, crazing and cracking will surely occur. If this drying is carried to an extreme, hydration of the cement will stop, but it may be continued again should curing be resumed. However, the cracks may never heal.

Early shrinkage is not the only cause of cracks. Sometimes shrinkage is blamed for cracks that may be due to other causes, such as temperature stresses. Cracking may result from numerous causes, some of them obscure and difficult or impossible to identify. A perversity of concrete is that it sometimes cracks where cracks are not expected, and fails to crack where cracks are expected.

7-1. CONTROL

Generally speaking, cracks can be minimized:

1. If the structure is designed properly, avoiding designs that are conducive to cracking, such as abrupt changes in section. This is especially apt to be serious in architectural concrete, and requires cooperation between the architect and engineer. Provision should be made, by dummy joints, rustication strips, or otherwise, to control the cracking.

2. If use is made of materials that are known to have a satisfactory service record—the longer the better. If such material is not available, then tests should be made, carrying them to destruction in order to determine the suitability of available materials.

3. If the mixes are properly proportioned to make best use of the materials, suiting them to the requirements of the structure.

4. If the workmanship in handling the concrete is of high quality. Equipment and personnel must be used in accordance with the best construction practices.

The reader is referred to the five fundamentals of good concrete construction in Chap. 1. Careful attention to these principles will enable the engineer to obtain the best possible structure.

7-2. CRACKS IN FRESH CONCRETE

Plastic Cracks

Cracks in the fresh concrete, called *preset, green,* or *plastic cracks,* occur while the concrete is still in a plastic state, before the cement has set. They are very erratic in their appearance and occurrence and frequently are independent of weather conditions, developing within 1 or 2 hr after the concrete has been placed, starting suddenly about the time the water sheen disappears from the surface.

Plastic cracks (Fig. 7-1) may vary in width from fine hairlines to as wide as $\frac{1}{8}$ in., and from an inch to several feet in length. Depth is seldom more than 2 in., although the cracks may extend through a thin slab. They may or may not be connected, and ordinarily do not extend to the edges of the affected member. Usually they have no definite pattern, although they may be oriented generally perpendicular to the long axis of a slab. They are entirely different in appearance from cracks that occur in hardened concrete. The latter are sharp-edged and clearly defined, sometimes breaking through aggregate particles, whereas plastic cracks follow around the aggregate particles and do not have the appearance of a clean break as do the posthardened cracks. They will frequently follow reinforcing bars or other embedded materials such as large aggregate particles. They are especially apt to occur in slabs, in the tops of walls and beams, and in footings on sandy soil. They are not progressive; that is, once the crack has formed, the stress in the concrete is relieved and no further cracking develops from this cause. These cracks themselves are usually not harmful, although they are unsightly and are a possible foothold for later trouble. Sometimes delaying the finishing as long as possible permits the finisher to close the cracks. Plastic cracks should not be confused with the common drying shrinkage cracks, which are finer and shallower.

Cracking of the concrete before hardening may result from movement of the forms, subgrade, reinforcing steel, or embedded items; settlement of aggregate particles or reinforcing; premature stiffening; rapid loss of water from the concrete; sagging or slippage of the concrete, especially on slopes; or drying shrinkage. Cracks have been reported to occur even when the concrete surface is under water. Different sands and cements will affect their formation.

Concrete of wet consistency, high-slump concrete, which may be considered necessary because of inefficient consolidating methods or poor mix proportions, is more apt to develop plastic cracks than reasonably stiff concrete. Admixtures containing calcium chloride, such as some integral dampproofers, may contribute to cracking, and should not be used during warm weather.

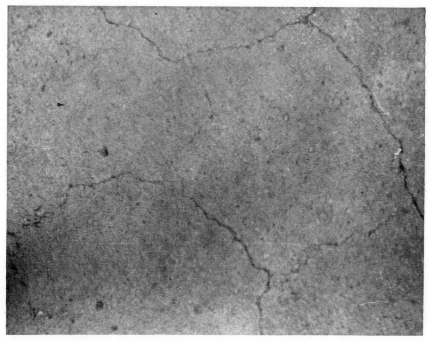

Fig. 7-1. Plastic shrinkage cracks in the surface of a slab.

Settlement cracks may occur at or near the soffit of a beam when the beam and slab are placed monolithically, especially if overly wet or soft concrete is used, or they may develop at the top of a column or wall at the junction with a slab. The remedy in this case is to wait about 2 hr after placing the beam, wall, or column before placing concrete in the slab, using concrete with the minimum slump possible.

Shrinkage may result from segregation and bleeding, causing settlement cracks in the tops of slabs, walls, and beams. Well-graded aggregates, proper mix proportions including entrained air, with careful handling and placing, will minimize these cracks. High mixing, placing, and curing temperatures are conducive to cracking.

The following case illustrates one instance of plastic cracking. Pile sections 54 in. in outside diameter, 16 ft long with a wall thickness of 4½ in., were being made by the centrifugal spinning process. Twelve 1⅛-in.-diameter longitudinal ducts for stressing wires were formed by means of steel rods inside of rubber tubes attached to the end rings of the form. When the sections were removed from the spinning machine, it was observed that plastic cracks had developed on the interior of the sections, following along the ducts, owing in part to slight movement of the rubber tubing during and immediately after spinning. Adjustment of the mix to provide a better grading served to lessen the frequency of the cracks.

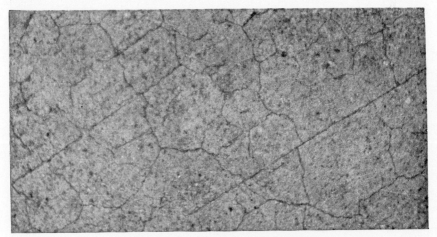

Fig. 7-2. Surface crazing in a sidewalk slab.

In another plant producing the same type of piles, it was found that too early removal of the rods and tubes caused longitudinal cracks inside the pile sections. Delaying removal of the rods for about 45 min eliminated most of the cracks.

Crazing or Hair Cracks

A pattern of fine cracks is due to shrinkage of the surface of the concrete relative to the interior of the mass. This cracking consists of many shallow, random cracks in every direction, usually following a roughly hexagonal pattern, usually several inches apart but sometimes closer together (see Fig. 7-2). Close examination will reveal such cracking in a minor degree on nearly all concrete surfaces, especially troweled surfaces. Cracking of this nature is especially noticeable after the concrete surface has been moistened with water, then starts to dry out. The water being retained in the cracks after the rest of the concrete has become dry makes the cracks clearly visible.

Minor cracking of this nature is not serious in itself, although it can lead to trouble in an especially severe exposure, as, for example, an ocean-front structure exposed to freezing and thawing. Serious pattern cracking is caused by other activities and is discussed later in this chapter.

There are three general causes of crazing: improper and excessive finishing, rapid loss of moisture from the fresh concrete, and temperature stresses. Irrespective of the basic cause, formation of cracks is predestined if overly fluid or rich mixes are permitted.

Finishing faults include such practices as hastening finishing time by spreading dry cement on concrete that is too wet to trowel, or sprinkling water on concrete that has become too dry for proper finishing. These practices are the mark of an incompetent or lazy finisher and should never be permitted. Overmanipulation during finishing, or troweling too soon after placing, causes a concentration of water and fines on the surface that creates a weak, soupy coating which will crack. The amount of finishing necessary to produce the required surface should be kept to a minimum. Screeding, belting, and floating may be done soon after placing, but troweling should be delayed until the surface moisture disappears.

Rapid loss of moisture is the result of absorption of water by a dry subgrade or dry aggregates, or is the result of a high rate of evaporation from the concrete surface. Loss of moisture to absorptive aggregates can be minimized if the aggregates, when batched, are in a moist condition. When placing flatwork on the ground, the subgrade should be well moistened, but not muddy, ahead of concrete placement. When a high rate of evaporation is the cause of a rapid loss of water, prevention of cracking is accomplished by minimizing evaporation after the concrete has been placed and before curing is started. While evaporation is most rapid during hot, dry, windy weather, it also occurs during cool and damp weather, especially if the concrete temperature is higher than the air temperature.

The following steps will serve to decrease harmful evaporation:

1. Protect the concrete and working area with sun shades and windbreaks.

2. Organize the work so as to prevent unnecessary delays. Have adequate and sufficient labor and tools on hand.

3. Start curing as early as possible. Apply paper or plastic sheeting, wet burlap, wet curing blankets, damp sand, membrane curing compound (white pigmented preferred), or other approved curing method as soon as the surface will not be marred by such application.

4. If formal curing is delayed, or if concrete is placed during very hot and dry weather, use a fine fog (not spray) immediately after final finishing. Care is necessary to avoid excess water which will wash the surface and application after the cracks have already started to form.

5. If at all possible, avoid placing concrete in the hot sun, especially in desert areas.

6. When heaters are used inside enclosures during cold weather, protect the concrete near the heaters from excessive heat.

Temperature stresses should be avoided. Applying cool curing water to hot concrete surfaces produces a fine pattern cracking. This is especially prevalent on concrete in arid regions when the concrete is permitted to become dry during intermittent applications of curing water. A similar condition exists when cold water is applied to freshly stripped warm concrete, particularly during cold weather. For best results, the temperature differential between the concrete and curing water should not exceed 25°F. If artificially heated concrete is suddenly exposed to very cold air by removal of the forms, crazing may result even without the application of water.

A case is reported in which vertical cracks, about 8 ft apart, appeared in a wall when the forms were removed. Cause of the cracks was traced to the use of excessively thick insulation on the forms. While the insulation was sufficient to protect the concrete to a temperature of 25° below zero, actual air temperatures never got below 25° above. Temperature of the concrete, which at the time of placing was 75°F, was over 100° when the forms were removed, and air temperature was 35 to 40°.

7-3. CRACKS IN HARDENED CONCRETE

General

After concrete has hardened, it is subject to many forces that stress the concrete and cause cracking. Some of the forces, as discussed in the previous section, are due to temperature changes, such as might occur in winter when concrete that has been kept warm is suddenly cooled, perhaps by the application of cold curing water. Changes may occur within the concrete itself: chemically, by such activities as reaction between aggregates and high-alkali cement, or chemical decomposition of deleterious aggregate particles; or mechanically, as by expansion of aggregate particles caused by moisture absorption or by freezing of water in pores of the aggregate. Some cements are apt to show high shrinkage rates immediately after hardening. Concrete made with such cement is more apt to crack than concrete made with a cement of low shrinkage tendency. Loading may exceed design values, or the design may have been erroneous. Expansion or contraction joints may have been omitted or wrongly placed, as in the case of a low parapet wall which developed transverse cracks about a foot apart as a result of failure to provide weakened plane or dummy joints. Stress concentrations may occur at corners, changes in section, or around openings. Impact may occur through accident.

Movement of part of a concrete building or other structure due to settlement will cause cracks in walls and slabs, or at external columns at the floor level. Sometimes a wall may crack because of settlement of the slab on which it is placed, the slab being relatively flexible compared to the wall. Moisture and temperature variations or too much reinforcement congested in a small area may cause cracks.

If settlement is unavoidable, heavy bases and columns should be constructed first, then after settlement takes place, the remaining concrete in the comparatively thin walls may be placed. Adequacy of foundation material should be investigated beforehand to forestall such difficulties.

Diagonal cracks at corners of door and window openings can be controlled by the use of sufficient reinforcement. It is advantageous to place concrete to the top of such openings, then wait about 2 hr before going on up with the placement, permitting the concrete in the lower portion of the wall to shrink and settle. Concrete should be placed with the minimum slump practicable. A horizontal construction joint located at the level of the top of the openings will aid in preventing cracks.

There have been cases in which anchor bolt holes, left exposed through the winter, filled with water. Freezing of the water exerted sufficient force to crack the concrete. This happened on the pier cap of an unfinished bridge.

When applying shotcrete or pneumatically applied mortar to an area containing reinforcement, the operator should adjust the mix and nozzle operation to minimize rebound. Rebound sand collecting behind the steel will cause the mortar to crack along the lines of the reinforcing steel.

Mass Concrete

In large massive structures, cracks may be caused by heat generation in the concrete as hydration takes place. The surface, being cooler, will be subject to tensile stress as the interior gets warmer. A steep temperature gradient near the surface of a dam or a sudden cooling of the surface will cause cracks to appear, or improper curing practices may cause small cracks to form. If the interior temperature of the structure is still rising as a result of cement hydration, these surface cracks may enlarge and penetrate deeper into the structure. These are entering wedges for many physical and chemical activities such as seepage water and frost action.

Modified or low-heat cement should be used in concrete for dams, massive bridge piers, large footings, and similar structures, keeping the cement content as low as possible. By using pozzolans as a replacement for part of the cement, concrete for the interior of large dams may contain as little as ½ bbl (188 lb) of cement per cubic yard. Entrained air is beneficial. The concrete should be as cool as possible at the time of placement (below 50°F at all seasons), use being made of such expedients as cooling the ingredients by sprinkling the coarse aggregate with cool water (taking care to permit the aggregate to drain before use), placing concrete during cool weather, using ice in the mixing water, early form removal, and limiting the rate of placement whereby the top of a lift is left exposed for as long as possible. In very large structures such as dams, pipe coils through which cool water is circulated may be placed in each lift. Water circulation should be started as soon as concrete placing is started and continued until a satisfactory temperature is attained.

At Hiwassee Dam,[7.1]* a unit of the Tennessee Valley Authority in North Carolina, crack control was attained by use of low-heat cement; low cement content of 0.8 bbl per cu yd, or less; thin casting lift, each placement of concrete being kept to a minimum height compatible with good construction practices; long exposure periods for each lift at the rate of 1 day of exposure for each foot of height of placement; refrigeration of mixing water during the summer; heating of mixing water during the winter; washing of the aggregates, and keeping them cool by means of cool water; use of diagonal keys in vertical contraction joints in the lower third of the dam to provide shear resistance; careful cleanup of construction joints, consisting of two applications of the air-water jet; three weeks' water curing; and artificial cooling of concrete in place.

According to the Bureau of Reclamation,[4.3] the following methods or combination of methods have been used for reducing the temperature rise in mass concrete: use of low-heat cement; minimum cement content; use of pozzolanic material; limitation on the rate of placement so that a greater part of heat of hydration is lost from the top surface of the lift during construction; placement of concrete during cold weather so that heat of hydration will raise the temperature to, or only slightly above, the ultimate temperature; the precooling of concrete ingredients to reduce placing temperature of the concrete; introduction of fine ice into the mix; early removal of forms; use of steel forms to facilitate loss of excess heat from the surfaces; and artificial cooling, begun at the time or soon after the concrete is placed, which not only reduces maximum temperature rise, but also cools concrete to any desired temperature within a

---

* Superscript figures refer to chapter and reference number. The references are found at the end of each chapter.

short time and permits grouting of contraction joints within a reasonable time after concrete placement.

Frost Action

The action of frost, or cycles of freezing and thawing, is *weathering*, which is manifested in its early stages by cracking. Weathering cracks develop in pavements, curbs, walls, railings, and similar exposed concrete as many fine, closely spaced cracks more or less parallel to the edges of the affected members. As they develop, they become filled with a dark deposit of calcium carbonate and dirt and are called "D-line cracks" (see Sec. 5-7). They show up in inferior concrete at any time, up to several years after construction, the period of time depending upon the quality of the concrete and the exposure. This type of cracking is progressive and, unless checked, will result in disintegration of the member. The concrete is low in strength, the matrix being dull and chalky. D-line cracks result basically from failure to provide quality concrete when the structure was built.

7-4. RUSTING OF STEEL

Moisture may enter the concrete through small cracks, honeycomb, or unsound construction joints and cause rusting of the reinforcing steel. This is especially serious in the presence of salt water or certain contaminated atmospheres. Rusting is accompanied by an increase in volume with consequent disruption of the concrete. Prevention is accomplished by proper design to preclude formation of structural cracks. Structures should be built of good dense concrete with at least 2 in. (3 in. in sea water) of cover over the reinforcing steel. Rock pockets and honeycomb should be prevented by good mix proportions and thorough consolidation by means of vibration. Construction joints must be properly cleaned up. If rock pockets, honeycomb, or sand streaks occur, they should be carefully patched. In some cases, waterproofing of the surface may be necessary.

Heavy concrete containing iron or steel aggregate is subject to serious internal expansion and cracking if water can enter the concrete and come in contact with the metallic aggregate. Sound and dense concrete, with smooth surfaces, adequately covering the aggregate, is necessary. In a very moist exposure, the concrete should be waterproofed.

7-5. ALKALI-AGGREGATE REACTION

Certain minerals and rocks react with the alkalies in cement to produce an internal expansion in concrete which leads to cracking and deterioration. The minerals usually associated with this reaction are opal, chalcedony, tridymite, cristobalite, and certain zeolites; the rocks are glassy or cryptocrystalline rhyolites, dacites, and andesites (including volcanic tuffs composed of these rocks) and cherts, both chalcedonic and opaline. Any aggregate containing a significant proportion of any of these materials may be considered to be a reactive aggregate. A petrographic examination of the aggregate will reveal the presence of reactive materials.

Symptomatic evidence of alkali-aggregate reaction consists of random or "map" cracking on a fairly large scale, the cracks opening up, in

Fig. 7-3. A 20-year-old bridge pier showing cracks resulting from alkali-aggregate reaction.

severe cases, over ½ in. wide, but seldom as deep as 18 in., resulting from abnormal expansion of the concrete, especially internal. The cracks and voids are filled with a gelatinous or amorphous deposit which also appears in cracks on the surface. (The observer is cautioned not to confuse this exudation with the D-line deposit found in weathering cracks because of the similarity in appearance on cursory examination.) The concrete, when broken, is lifeless and chalky, and individual aggregate particles, upon close examination, will be found to have peripheral zones of alteration or reactivity. Deterioration is progressive, especially in the presence of moisture (see Fig. 7-3).

It has been found that the use of low-alkali cement (0.6 per cent or less of total alkali) is effective in controlling or preventing this activity, and its use should be specified whenever conclusive evidence exists that a proposed aggregate is reactive. Conclusive evidence may include a petrographic examination of the aggregate, ASTM Designation: C 295; test for potential alkali reactivity of cement-aggregate combinations, ASTM Designation: C 227; and an examination of structures known to have been built with the proposed cement-aggregate combination.

Pozzolans, especially the highly opaline ones, are also effective in controlling alkali-aggregate reactions. The pozzolans are opaline chert, diatomaceous earth, and some of the volcanic glasses and calcined or burnt clays. Portland-slag cement may aid in controlling the reaction, and air entrainment is said to be of some benefit. Calcium chloride should not be used, especially with the pozzolans. An extensive testing program is suggested in those areas where this reaction is expected. The best insurance is to avoid reactive aggregates or use low-alkali cement.

Certain limestones in Ontario, which do not respond to the usual test for reactivity, are said to react with cement alkali, producing map cracking or crazing of concrete in contact with moisture.[7.2]

Internal expansion that leads to pattern cracking may be caused by aggregate particles such as iron sulfides that show an expansive action in concrete, or clay minerals that expand on wetting.

Map cracking may also be caused by delayed hydration of magnesium oxide in concrete containing cement with a high content of this compound.

7-6. FLATWORK AND PAVEMENTS

Thin slabs of large extent, such as pavements and canal linings, are especially susceptible to cracking, being placed rapidly in the open where they are prey to all the adverse forces of the weather. Good materials, properly prepared and mixed, are necessary. The subgrade should be smooth and firm, of soil capable of supporting the expected loads, and damp at the time concrete is placed. Concrete should have a minimum of cement and water consistent with the requirements of the usage. Manipulation of the surface during finishing should be kept to a minimum. Shading of the finished surface is desirable on hot days until curing can be started. A white pigmented curing compound may be used on exposed pavements.

Cracking During Construction

See the previous discussion in this chapter on cracking of fresh concrete. As applied to pavements, cracking during construction may consist of surface checking, hair cracks or crazing, and cracks through the slab.

Surface checking is caused by drying of the upper part of the slab and may be an inch or more in depth. The cracks are usually short and more or less parallel to the center line, although they may run in any direction.

Principal cause is an excessive and rapid loss of moisture from the new concrete which may result from absorption by a dry subgrade or dry aggregates, or by evaporation caused by hot, dry winds. Other causes are an excess of fines or water in the mix or failure to start curing as soon as possible. Checking can be prevented by eliminating the causes: that is, adjust the mix to reduce the quantity of fine material and water, and moisten the subgrade and aggregates. Curing should be started at the earliest possible moment.

Hair cracking or *crazing* consists of very small and shallow connected cracks in a roughly hexagonal pattern. This is a surface condition caused by shrinkage of cement paste brought to the surface by over-finishing, especially by steel troweling. It is especially prevalent when water, sprinkled on a dry surface to facilitate troweling, or excessive dust in the aggregates, causes laitance. Hot, dry winds also may cause crazing. Crazing can be prevented by eliminating the causes, and in unhardened concrete pavement can sometimes be corrected by belting after the cracking takes place. (Belting is described in Sec. 14-5.)

Cracks through the slab are due to a number of causes which may be summarized as disturbance to the concrete before it has hardened. Disturbance of the concrete may result from soft subgrade, movement of side forms, or movement of reinforcement and dowel assemblies. A very absorbent aggregate will sometimes cause sufficient shrinkage to cause cracks. Overly wet or fluid concrete is a contributing cause. Certain soils swell when they absorb moisture, and a slab laid on such a subgrade is apt to crack as the soil absorbs water from the concrete.

Cracking Subsequent to Construction

Cracks that develop in slabs and pavements usually owe their existence to careless construction practices or insufficient maintenance.

Transverse cracking and spalling near joints will occur if joint dowel assemblies are carelessly placed. Dowels must be set parallel to the subgrade and centerline. Devices for holding dowels prior to concrete placement must hold the dowels accurately in place yet be so designed as to permit subsequent slippage of the dowel in the hardened concrete. Dowels should be coated with a bituminous compound to act as a lubricant. Cracking at joints may also be caused by shifting of the slabs.

Random transverse cracking may be caused by subgrade failure, or frictional resistance of the subgrade to movement of the concrete resulting from volume change of the pavement.

Longitudinal cracks will occur if an excessively wide pavement is placed in one operation. Slab width should not exceed about 16 ft without a longitudinal hinged joint or construction joint. Poorly aligned load transfer devices or insufficient depth of a weakened plane joint will also cause a longitudinal crack.

Longitudinal cracks result from differential settlement of the slab. This may occur as a result of softening of the subgrade by infiltration of water under the edge of the slab; the basic cause of this is poor drainage. Solid material entering a joint from the shoulder or ice filling the joint may also be the cause of a crack, especially if it begins at a transverse joint. If the filler in a preformed transverse joint does not reach the pavement edge, leaving a concrete plug at the end of the joint, a crack will result. The same situation exists if a sawed joint does not extend all the way to the pavement edge.

A corner crack is a short diagonal crack extending from a transverse joint to a longitudinal joint or to the pavement edge. It is caused by solid material in the transverse joint, subgrade failure, or weak concrete.

There was a case reported by Elgar[7.3] in which cracks, developing parallel to the edge of the pavement, were found to be caused by shrinkage of the subgrade. This happened during a drought, and it was surmised that the drawing out of moisture from the subgrade by vegetation contributed to the failure.

Laying of unreinforced canal lining on a clay subgrade resulted in serious heaving and cracking of the lining. The clay was highly expansive on wetting. Slight leakage through joints in the lining, plus rain water entering between the lining and subgrade, produced a cumulative effect of more cracking and more expansion until portions of the lining were entirely destroyed.

7-7. PRECAST CONCRETE

Cracking of precast concrete of any type can be minimized if units are designed properly, avoiding unbalanced sections and providing adequate reinforcing. Molds should present a smooth, uncluttered surface to the concrete, with the necessary draft or taper to facilitate stripping of intricate details. Molds should be thoroughly cleaned and oiled after each use, using a form oil that is especially compounded for this use. Waste molds should be painted with shellac or other sealer.

Precast concrete is usually relatively rich concrete, and care should be exercised in order to avoid shrinkage cracks. Water content of the mix should be as low as possible, and the units protected from drying out before curing has been completed. Castings should be removed from the molds as soon as possible. In the case of steam curing, this may be as soon as 8 hr after making. For castings cured at normal atmospheric temperatures a period of 16 to 24 hr is usually adequate. This is affected by the temperature, richness of mix, and type of casting being made. Items such as packerhead pipe, tamped pipe, and blocks, which use an earth-moist mix, may be placed in the curing area and stripped immediately after casting. A fine fog should be used to prevent loss of moisture from the concrete until such time as the concrete is strong enough to withstand normal curing procedures. In certain cases calcium chloride may be used in the concrete to hasten the stripping time.

Sudden changes in temperature, such as might occur by sprinkling cold water on castings recently removed from the steam chamber, must be avoided. Where additional curing is desired after the initial steaming, the castings may be returned to the steam room, or may be allowed to cool, after which water curing can be commenced. If the coating is not detrimental to subsequent processes, such as bonding to other concrete, painting, or other treatment, membrane curing may be used. Castings should have a minimum of 12 hr of curing in wet steam between 130 and 150°F, commencing 2 to 4 hr after the concrete has been placed. They should be handled carefully at all times, especially during the period before final curing has been completed.

All cracking of precast units is not necessarily serious. Small surface cracks and hair cracks are not cause for rejection of units. They will frequently heal, especially in the presence of moisture. More serious cracking has to be evaluated in the light of the type of unit and exposure conditions. In many cases, a crack 0.01 in. in width would be acceptable provided corrosion of the reinforcement is prevented by sealing the crack with slurry or epoxy resin, and provided further that the unit is not weakened structurally by the crack.

More serious cracking would probably call for rejection of the unit. Seriousness may be judged either by the number of cracks in the unit, or by the width and extent of one crack.

Reinforced concrete pipe may crack if the reinforcing steel is too close to the surface. The amount of cover must be determined by the manufacturing process, type and size of pipe, type of reinforcing cage, and experience. As little as ¾ in. of cover is adequate in some cases. (Note that this cover is considerably less than the 2 to 3 in. recommended for structural concrete.) However, careless placement of the cage may result in exposure of the steel either on the outside or the inside of the pipe.

Pipe sections, when steam cured, should have both the exterior and interior exposed to the elevated temperature. Admitting steam to the interior only, especially if the ambient air temperature is relatively low, will cause fine longitudinal cracks on the wall of the pipe.

Horizontal tension cracks may appear in long prestressed piles during driving, especially in the upper portion of the pile. These cracks result from "hard" driving, and the correction is to use less force in driving.

Masonry

The principal causes of cracking in masonry construction are shrinkage of the units, settlement of the structure caused by poor design or workmanship in foundations, and stresses in the structure due to temperature variables or loading.

Shrinkage can be avoided by using blocks that have been dried until they contain less than 40 per cent of the total possible absorption, a condition that is usually met by air-dried blocks 1 month old or older. Blocks must not be exposed to rain while stored on the jobsite. High-pressure steam curing is said to produce blocks that shrink less than those cured by other methods. Other advantages claimed for high-pressure autoclave curing are high strength, light color, resistance to volume change, minimum crazing and cracking, control of porosity, good nailability, and economy of cement. Opposed to these advantages is the cost of equipment and operation, and some restriction of aggregates used.[7.4] Thorvaldson[7.5] reports regressions of mortar tensile strength if specimens are autoclaved too long. This is a rather complicated reaction of certain minerals.

Structural cracks in masonry construction can be prevented by proper design and construction. One-quarter-inch "pencil rod" reinforcing steel placed in horizontal joints, especially at sills and lintels, aids in controlling cracking. Location and length of these bars should be shown on the plans. Bars should be placed in the horizontal mortar joints as the wall is built up. Expansion and control joints should be provided in walls over 25 or 30 ft long. Good workmanship is essential, including the use of appropriate mortar mixes.

Mortar and stucco coatings will crack and peel unless care is taken to see that they are applied properly and cured adequately. At the time of applying stucco to a brick or block wall, the wall must be clean and slightly damp. Curing should commence immediately with a gentle fog, followed after the cement has set by spraying or sprinkling.

7-8. AUTOGENOUS HEALING

Sometimes, under favorable conditions, cracks in concrete may heal themselves. This process is called autogenous healing. In this process there is further reaction of moist, unhydrated surfaces that were exposed in the fracture, or continuation of the gel crystallization mechanism. Favorable conditions for this action are: the original break occurring at an early age while the concrete is still relatively weak; a relatively small crack; a long period of healing under warm and moist conditions; and no subsequent movement of the cracked surfaces. This action is of considerable practical value in healing small cracks in precast units such as piles, or the sealing of water tanks.

Sometimes cracks may be sealed (but not healed) by their filling with efflorescence or other foreign material. There have been cases in which small leaks in concrete tanks or similar structures have sealed in this manner.

7-9. REPAIR OF CRACKS

Cracks in concrete are symptomatic of some condition or conditions adversely affecting the concrete. For this reason, repair and patching of cracks are a waste of time unless the condition of which the cracks are a symptom is first corrected.

Before attempting to fill or repair any crack, the crack should be cleaned out. A high-pressure air jet may suffice for a fine crack. Larger cracks should be cleaned by the removal of spalled and loose concrete and all foreign material. Concrete should be fairly dry when mortar is used as a filling material, and should be thoroughly dry for epoxy repairs. Concrete should be dry if a bonding agent is used.

If appearance is important, care should be taken in the choice of materials and methods, otherwise the repair may be an unsightly eyesore, serving to draw attention to the crack rather than to obscure it. A condition of this nature may exist in architectural concrete, such as a terrazzo floor where color matching is important.

Cracks Due to Weathering

Probably there is little to be gained by patching D-line cracks or other cracking associated with weathering. Repair in this case consists of removing *all* the affected concrete down to sound concrete. Any concrete of doubtful soundness should be removed and the area patched in the best possible manner, as described in Sec. 13-15.

Plastic Crack Sealer

If continued movement of the concrete is expected, cracks may be filled with a plastic sealer. A material of this type retains its plasticity and permits slight movement of the concrete without breaking the seal, this being especially desirable to prevent passage of moisture through the crack. Resilient joint fillers may be either hot-applied or cold-applied. Materials for hot application consist of a mixture of asphalt, rubber, and a filler, or similar materials, and are usually black in color. There are also asphaltic fillers for cold application, but the hot-applied filler is preferred.

Recently, the epoxies have been used successfully for resilient crack fillers. Epoxy has superior bonding properties, if the crack surfaces are properly primed.

Mortar Filling

Large cracks can be filled with dry-tamped mortar. Mortar for this application consists of 1 part portland cement to 2½ parts mortar sand passing the 16-mesh screen, mixed to a damp consistency such that a ball molded in the hands will stick together and hold its shape. In order that the repair match the original concrete as closely as possible, white cement should be substituted for part of the normal gray cement. The mortar is tamped into the crack with sticks, bars, or similar blunt instruments, and the surface is struck off with a wood float. A steel trowel should not be used, as this will darken the patch. Upon completion of the repair the mortar should be cured, either by the application of water or a liquid membrane-forming compound.

Bond of the mortar to the concrete is improved by the use of a bonding agent. There are several proprietary compounds available, including epoxy which is applied to the concrete surfaces to be repaired, and a latex compound which may be added to the patching mortar. Either of these compounds may be used as a curing compound by application to the finished patch surface.

Epoxy Resins

Small cracks can be filled with epoxy resin, using a pressure process. For this method, holes are drilled about 2 ft apart in the concrete along the crack to a depth of about 1 in. Zerk-type pressure fittings are sealed into these holes either by cementing them in place with epoxy or by inserting them in a soft metal sleeve which is anchored by tapping the fitting with a hammer. The surface of the crack is then sealed with the epoxy adhesive, leaving small vent holes every 6 in. After the adhesive on the surface has cured, the crack is filled by using a high-pressure hand-operated grease gun to force the epoxy adhesive into the crack through the fittings. Adhesive for this application should contain no filler.

Large cracks may be filled with an epoxy mortar consisting of the epoxy adhesive mixed with mortar sand in the proportions of 1 part adhesive to 3 parts sand by volume. After first cleaning the crack of all loose concrete, dirt, and other foreign material, the mortar is troweled into the crack. Complete filling is assured by working the mortar into the crack with a knife blade or similar instrument.

Toluene is sometimes used for thinning epoxy, but its use is not recommended because of the tendency to use too much. Epoxies have a relatively short pot life; that is, they become hard and unworkable in a matter of a few minutes to a half-hour or so. For this reason, small amounts should be mixed at a time. Manufacturers' instructions should be followed in mixing and application. Tools and mixing equipment should be cleaned by scrubbing with toluene before the material starts to harden. Because of their toxic nature, epoxies should be used in a well-ventilated place, and contact with the skin should be avoided.

REFERENCES

7.1 Crackless Concrete for Hiwassee Dam, *Eng. News-Record,* Sept. 14, 1939, pp. 69–72.
7.2 Damaging Reactions in Concrete, *Engineering,* London, vol. 187, no. 4846, Jan. 23, 1959.
7.3 Elgar, W. H.: Soil Movements as Affecting Paved Surfaces, *Surveyor,* 1944, pp. 427–428.
7.4 Easterley, Harry W., Jr.: Correlation of Shrinkage and Curing in Concrete Masonry Units, *J. Am. Concrete Inst.,* January, 1952, Proc. vol. 48, pp. 393–402.
7.5 Thorvaldson, T.: Effect of Chemical Nature of Aggregate on Strength of Steam Cured Portland Cement Mortar, *J. Am. Concrete Inst.,* March, 1956, Proc. vol. 52, pp. 771–780.

CHAPTER 8 *Concrete Surfaces*

8-1. CAUSES OF BLEMISHES

Any consideration of concrete surfaces must first recognize that there is more than one condition influencing the diagnosis and treatment of blemishes appearing on the surface of concrete. It is not always easy to determine the exact cause of imperfections and blemishes, as any one flaw may have several possible causes, and there may be even more possible methods of relief or repair.

Generally, defects may be classified into three groups, based on their causes:

1. Blemishes that appear as a consequence of the use of inferior materials which cause abnormal activity within the mass of the hardened concrete. Examples are popouts and certain cracking.

2. Injury that appears as a result of outside forces attacking the concrete. Examples are cavitation and scaling due to de-icing salt.

3. Flaws resulting from poor construction practices. Examples are honeycomb and unsatisfactory alignment of the concrete caused by inferior formwork.

This chapter deals principally with surface conditions resulting from improper construction practices and unsuitable materials. Sound structural design and high-quality materials are of no avail if the project is constructed under indifferent supervision and inspection. Good, dense concrete, made of high-quality materials under conditions of competent control and inspection, is necessary for the production of the type of concrete surfaces required for satisfactory quality and appearance. A dense, smooth surface is important: first, because imperfections may be the weakness by which weathering damage or other deterioration gets started; and second, for aesthetic reasons, because the quality of a structure is frequently judged by its appearance.

8-2. SURFACE SOFTNESS

One expects the surface of concrete, whether formed or finished, to be hard and firm upon completion of curing. Anything less is unacceptable.

Softness may take the form of a uniform condition over the entire area, or may consist of localized spots of concrete that have failed to harden properly.

Dusting is a common symptom, in which the surface becomes powdery under foot or wheeled traffic, and the wearing surface is eroded away. While dusting is more noticeable in a floor, it may occur anywhere. There have been cases where concrete walls could not be painted because of excessive dusting. Some types of pressed board, when new, contain a constituent that may cause a soft, dusty concrete surface, if used for lining forms, unless the board is effectively sealed with shellac or plastic.

Soft areas owe their origins to several causes. The possible inadvertent inclusion of organic material should be investigated whenever soft spots are discovered in concrete, either formed or unformed. One of the most unusual that has come to the author's attention was a sidewalk in which small spots in the surface failed to set. Examination of the spots and analysis of the operation disclosed that truck mixers, in approaching the site, passed through an almond orchard where green almonds dropped into the open mixer spouts as the tree branches brushed against them. These became incorporated in the mix and the tannic acid caused failure of set of the cement around the almonds.

Tannin, or tannic acid, from any source prevents setting of the cement. New form lumber may contain an excess of tannin, especially if the lumber has not dried thoroughly. Sappy areas may be especially troublesome, even on dry lumber that has been oiled. These sappy areas should be painted with shellac or whitewash, or one of the new plastic types of form coating.

Flash set of the cement may cause soft or weak spots in the concrete. This is especially apt to occur in the winter when the mixing water is being heated. Water should never be heated to a temperature above 160°F, and, when charging the mixer, the hot water and cold aggregates should enter first, then the cement. If a batch of concrete shows evidence of flash set, it should not be retempered by the addition of more water, but should either be used as is, or wasted.

When using a curing (sealing) compound, particular care should be taken to make sure that it is applied at the right time. If the concrete surface has become too dry before application of the compound, a soft surface is liable to result.

The effect of carbon dioxide on green concrete is a soft surface. Carbon dioxide may come from unvented salamanders or heaters used for heating an enclosure during cold weather. An immediate and complete sealing of the concrete by the application of a liquid curing compound effectively protects the concrete if it is impossible to vent the heaters outside the enclosure or use a source of heat that does not generate carbon dioxide. After about 24 hr the effect of carbon dioxide is negligible, or it may actually result in a harder surface. (This does not mean that subsequent exposure to carbon dioxide of already softened concrete results in a satisfactorily hard surface.)

Occasionally, a soft surface may be traced to the form oil. One type of liquid form coating is specifically designed to retard or prevent hydration of the cement, and is used for special architectural treatment, or for construction joints. When this coating is used, the concrete surface is washed with a water jet as soon as the forms are removed. The result is a rough textured surface, with individual aggregate particles exposed.

8-3. POPOUTS

Popouts are unsightly blemishes that may occur any time after the concrete has hardened, even a year or more after the concrete has been

Fig. 8-1. Popouts on a concrete canal lining. (*U.S. Bureau of Reclamation photo.*)

placed. They are especially apt to develop in horizontal, or nearly horizontal, surfaces. A popout is caused by a particle of material beneath the surface of the concrete which, under certain conditions, expands with such force as to break out a conical piece of concrete with the apex of the cone at the expansive particle and the base on the surface of the concrete (Fig. 8-1). Usually it is the presence of moisture that sets off a reaction with an end product of larger volume than the original particle. Common offenders are particles of soft and unsound chert, lignite, shale, and soft, fine-grained limestone. In a warm, humid climate, expansion of certain iron sulfides sometimes causes popouts. Freezing of water in highly absorptive pebbles develops sufficient force to cause popouts. Porous cherts are especially troublesome in this respect.

In one case popouts were traced to delayed hydration and consequent expansion of particles of periclase and artinite. It was discovered that these materials, resulting from the burning of dolomite, had become incorporated into the concrete by way of the cement which had been hauled in hopper-bottom cars without adequate cleaning, after having been used for hauling the magnesium compounds. More care in inspecting the cars before loading cement would have prevented this unfortunate incident. Cars, barges, trucks, and other cement-handling equipment should be inspected and cleaned regularly. This is especially important if they have been used for handling other materials.

Another case of popouts was traced to pieces of glass in the coarse aggregate. Broken bottles had been thrown into the stockpiles from an adjoining soft-drink bottling plant, and the resulting reaction between the glass and the cement resulted in expansion of the glass fragments.

Cinder concrete may suffer from stains and popouts if the cinders are not aged sufficiently, and if hard-burned free lime, free magnesia, or calcium sulfate is present. The danger may be averted if the crushed cinders are stored in a continuously wet stockpile for several weeks. Magnetic separation is desirable to remove tramp iron.[8.1]*

Rarely, slag concrete will suffer from popouts if particles of unburned flux from the smelting process find their way into the concrete. These particles are high in silica and magnesia.

The only cure for popouts is to prevent them in the first place, and the surest way to prevent them is to use aggregates free of deleterious particles. Some of the deleterious materials are difficult to identify, and some may enter the concrete by devious routes. Nevertheless, a petrographic examination, performed by an expert in this field, is the only way that one may be reasonably sure of identifying the constituents of the proposed aggregates, and of knowing whether or not there are deleterious particles. Aggregates containing porous chert and other particles of low specific gravity can be beneficiated by heavy media separation which removes the light particles by flotation (see Sec. 11-3).

In a structure where appearance is especially important, popout cavities can be filled with an epoxy mortar consisting of epoxy resin and aggregate with enough cement to provide a satisfactory color match with the existing surface.

8-4. EFFLORESCENCE AND LAITANCE

Efflorescence

Laitance and efflorescence are frequently confused, as each is a deposit or coating that appears on the surface. Efflorescence may be defined as a

---

* Superscript figures refer to chapter and reference number. The references are found at the end of each chapter.

deposit of crystalline salts on the surface of hardened concrete, brought from the interior of the mass by water, and deposited on the surface by evaporation of the water. Nearly all concrete and concrete products are more or less subject to efflorescence. When water moves through cracks and porosity in the concrete, it brings to the surface the soluble calcium hydroxide that results from the reaction between cement and water. After evaporation of the water, the calcium hydroxide remaining on the surface reacts with carbon dioxide in the air, forming calcium carbonate, the familiar white, crystalline deposit. Other less common forms are caused by sodium chloride or similar salts in the mixing water; organic matter in the mixing water or aggregates, high lime or gypsum in the cement; zeolites, or similar aggregates that are capable of base exchange; leaching of any water-soluble constituents; and materials that may be carried into and through the concrete by ground water.

If efflorescence must be removed, it is suggested that attempts be made to wash it off with water. If this is not effective, it can be dissolved by dilute hydrochloric (muriatic) acid. The dilute acid is prepared by adding 1 part of acid to 8 or 10 parts of water. The surface to be treated is first moistened with water, then the dilute acid is brushed on, after which the surface is thoroughly washed with copious quantities of clear water. Because of its corrosive nature, the acid should be handled with great care. Workmen should be provided with rubber protective clothing and goggles. The acid should not be permitted to come in contact with anything that might be damaged by it. A small inconspicuous area should be treated first to determine what effect the acid will have on the surface.

Obviously, the best preventive is to keep moisture away from the concrete where this is possible. Well-proportioned mixes, thoroughly consolidated and cured, will produce watertight concrete and help prevent cracks through which water can pass. Construction joints should be avoided when possible, but if a joint is necessary, it should be properly made (see Sec. 12-6). Drains and weeps should be provided to carry water away from the back side of retaining walls and similar structures.

Laitance

Laitance occurs as a light gray or nearly white substance consisting of cement particles, water, and the fine particles of silt and clay from the aggregates, appearing on the top surface of concrete during and immediately after consolidation. This layer of laitance has practically no strength and is especially undesirable on construction joints, or fill planes, as its weakness prevents bond between the old, hardened concrete and the fresh concrete placed in the succeeding lift.

The presence of excessive amounts of silt, clay, rock dust, and similar materials in the aggregate increases the likelihood of laitance forming on horizontal surfaces of concrete containing these materials. Overly fluid mixes are apt to segregate under vibration, leaving a layer of laitance on the surface. Excessive or too early floating and troweling, by bringing to the surface large quantities of water and fines, are conducive to the formation of laitance.

8-5. STAINS

Stains on concrete surfaces result from either of two causes: first, a stain-inducing material may have been inadvertently incorporated in the concrete when it was mixed; or second, the material may have been spilled on the hardened concrete.

Stains Resulting from Internal Materials

Certain iron pyrites will oxidize and hydrate when near the surface of concrete, causing a brown stain. If the aggregate contains pieces of pyrites, the suspected particles may be tested by immersing them in lime water. Reactive types of pyrites will produce a brown precipitate in a few minutes, while the nonreactive type remains stable, without the precipitate.[8.2] Ironstones, or ferruginous concretions, will stain the concrete if they become embedded near the surface. In heavy concrete containing iron or steel aggregate, rust stains are apt to develop where metal particles are exposed.

Discoloration of the surface results if nails or other pieces of metal become lodged against the forms and subsequently become incorporated in the concrete. Careless placement of reinforcing steel, permitting it to touch the forms, will result in rusting of the exposed steel and consequent staining.

When using calcium chloride as an accelerator, lumps may settle near the surface of the concrete, causing stains, unless the salt is added in solution to the concrete.

Form oils or coatings, if incorrectly used, sometimes cause stains. Form oils are especially formulated for specific uses, such as steam curing, and each one should be used for the purpose intended, as recommended by the manufacturer.

Spillage on Concrete

Because of its absorptive surface, concrete will absorb most materials that might be spilled on it, making removal of stains difficult. Before any large-scale attempt is made to clean stains from concrete, a trial should be made in an inconspicuous part, if possible, to determine what the effect might be. Attempts to remove a stain from old concrete usually result in the removal of dirt also, leaving an area lighter in color than the rest of the surface.

A series of tests was made by the Hydro-Electric Power Commission of Ontario, using various agents for removing different materials from test panels of concrete.[8.3] These are discussed below.

Copper. A green discoloration results from water coming in contact with copper or bronze, then flowing onto concrete. Removal is accomplished by mixing 1 part dry powdered ammonium chloride and 4 parts by weight of diatomaceous earth with sufficient ammonia water (10 to 30 per cent by volume of 26°Bé ammonium hydroxide) to produce a smooth paste. A layer of paste $\frac{1}{8}$ to $\frac{1}{4}$ in. thick is spread over the area and allowed to dry, then is removed. The treatment is repeated, if necessary, and the area finally washed with water.

Rust. The stain should be soaked for $\frac{1}{2}$ hr with a solution of 1 oz of sodium citrate in 6 oz of water. (Brushing the solution on at short intervals is satisfactory.) Then the surface is sprinkled with crystals of sodium hydrosulfite and covered with a paste of whiting and water. On a vertical surface, the paste is applied with a trowel, with the crystals sprinkled on the paste so they will be in direct contact with the stain. The paste is allowed to dry, then scraped off, and the treatment repeated if necessary.

An alternative method is to use a saturated solution of sodium hydrosulfite mixed with fuller's earth instead of the whiting paste and crystals. However, considerable sulfur dioxide gas is generated, and this method should only be used outdoors.

Linseed Oil. Fresh linseed oil is first soaked up by the application of any absorptive material such as hydrated lime, talc, whiting, or sawdust. For final removal, and removal of dried linseed oil, a paste is made of 1 part trisodium phosphate, 1 part sodium perborate, and 3 parts powdered talc, to which is added liquid green soap or a strong solution of soap in hot water to produce a paste. A $\frac{1}{8}$-in.-thick layer of paste is applied to the stain and allowed to dry, then removed. The application is repeated, if necessary; then the surface is scrubbed with water.

An alternative, although less effective, method is to apply cotton batting saturated with hydrogen peroxide to the stain, over which a second layer of cotton saturated with ammonia is placed.

Petroleum Oils. Liquid oil should be carefully removed first, by absorption with fuller's earth, talc, whiting, hydrated lime, or portland cement, repeating the treatment as necessary to remove all the oil.

Longtime accumulations of oil and dirt should be scraped off, then the area scrubbed with strong soap solution, scouring powders, or trisodium phosphate.

If a stain remains on the dry concrete after the above treatment, a paste of benzol and hydrated lime, whiting, talc, or similar material is applied and allowed to dry thoroughly, repeating as necessary.

An alternative method is to spread warm asbestos fibers, saturated with amyl acetate, over the stain.

Grease. The grease is first scraped off; then the surface is scrubbed with scouring powder, soap, trisodium phosphate, or detergent. Finally, a paste of diatomaceous earth and benzol is applied to the dry surface, and the treatment is repeated until no further improvement is made.

Asphalts. These materials are very difficult to remove and require thorough scouring first. Petroleum asphalt is best removed by cooling with ice and chipping and scraping, then scrubbing with abrasive powder and water. Emulsified asphalt may be removed by scrubbing with abrasive powder and water. The asphalt will penetrate into the concrete if an attempt is made to remove it with a paste of diatomaceous earth and a solvent such as benzene.

Partial removal of a cutback asphalt stain is accomplished by repeated applications of a paste of diatomaceous earth, followed by scrubbing with scouring powder and water.

Smoke. The surface is first scrubbed with scouring powder and water, then bleached with sodium hypochlorite (ordinary laundry bleach) solution applied by means of a saturated cloth.

Creosote. The benzol paste method, followed by scrubbing with scouring powder and water, is effective.

Paint. Fresh paint is first soaked up in cloths, paper towels, or other absorbent material; then the affected area is scrubbed with scouring powder and water. Paint remover or solvent causes the stain to penetrate and should not be used on fresh paint. Dried paint is removed by flooding the area with methylene dichloride paint remover for a few minutes; gentle scrubbing is followed by thorough washing with water. Final scrubbing with scouring powder and water may be necessary.

Ink. Most ordinary writing inks may be bleached with commercial sodium hypochlorite solution, applied by flooding, by saturation of white cloth pressed against the stain, or by application in a paste. If a brown stain remains, it is removed by the methods recommended for iron stains.

If the bleach treatment is not effective, a solution of ammonia water may be used.

8-6. FORMED SURFACES

Formed surfaces are those that are cast against molds or forms, and consist of such items as walls, columns, or the underside of beams and slabs (other than slabs on the ground). Vertical, or nearly vertical, surfaces must be formed.

Formwork

The first consideration in designing formwork is safety. Failures of forms and shoring have resulted in spectacular construction accidents involving injury and death to workmen and extensive property damage. Pressures on formwork can reach substantial values, as discussed in Sec. 12-3.

Secondly, the concrete surface reflects the form surface. It is quite obvious that a smooth surface cannot result from rough formwork. Of course, there are instances when rough form lumber is used to impart a rough texture to the concrete for aesthetic reasons, but these forms require as careful workmanship as any other.

Unsatisfactory alignment of concrete surfaces results from poorly designed forms and slipshod construction. Frequently misalignment of the concrete is caused by movement of the form while the concrete is being placed and vibrated. Movement of forms during concrete placement can be prevented by attention to important details. Proper spacing of studs and walers prevents bulging; adequate fastening, bracing, and wedging restrain movement of the form under pressure of the concrete while it is being vibrated; and tight joints restrict leakage of grout from the concrete.

Sand Streaks and Honeycomb

One of the most exasperating experiences in construction is to remove the forms and find an otherwise near-perfect surface marred by unsightly streaks and voids. These voids, known variously as *sand streaks, rock pockets,* and *honeycomb,* result from either of two primary causes:

1. Loss of cement grout from the concrete by leakage through the forms. Leakage of this type occurs whenever there are openings and can be minimized by making sure that individual boards and panels of lagging or sheathing fit accurately together. When a form is attached to old concrete, as is the case when constructing a wall in several lifts, the form must conform to the profile of the old concrete, without cracks. Knotholes and other holes should be plugged or covered.

2. Failure to consolidate the concrete thoroughly. Concrete should be consolidated by means of vibration, systematically and thoroughly applied to each increment of concrete placed in the form.

Contributory cause is segregation of the concrete, resulting from efforts to "flow" the concrete into place without adequate vibration, or resulting from the use of overly fluid mixes, mixes that are lean and harsh, or mixes containing sand deficient in fines. Segregation also results from various handling errors as discussed in Chap. 12.

The only remedy for these defects, once they exist, is drastic removal of all affected concrete down to good, sound concrete and replacement with new concrete or mortar in accordance with the discussion in Sec. 13-15.

Sticking to Forms

Almost as maddening as discovering honeycomb on a newly stripped concrete surface is to find that much of the surface concrete has pulled away by sticking to the form. Fortunately, this does not happen very often and its prevention is comparatively simple.

Any form or mold used for containing fresh concrete until it hardens must be coated with a material that prevents bond between the concrete and the form. These "form oils," as they are called, may be specially compounded mineral oils, waxes, or lacquers, or even job-mixed concoctions of fuel oil and lubricating oil. Correct use of any of the compounds commercially available will assure a satisfactory surface.

Sometimes concrete will stick in localized areas to metal forms, even though the form is apparently well coated with oil. Sticking may result if, in placing concrete, the concrete slides over the surface of the form, scraping the oil off the form. In applying oil to any form, the surface must be clean before application of the oil. Spots of rust, dirt, or old mortar are sure to cause trouble later when the form is stripped from the concrete. With respect to steel forms, care should be exercised in cleaning them. While the metal must be clean, too vigorous use of wire brushes, sandblast, or abrasives, to the extent that bright metal is exposed, should be avoided. After cleaning and oiling forms with a non-drying oil, it is sometimes helpful if the forms can be exposed to warm sunshine for 2 or 3 days.

The use of galvanized sheet steel is not recommended for lining forms because of the danger of excessive sticking.

8-7. AIR BUBBLE HOLES

Small pits, bubbles, or voids, sometimes called "bugholes," often appear in formed concrete surfaces. These voids are of the magnitude of $\frac{1}{2}$ in., more or less, in diameter. Occasionally, they are covered with a thin skin of dried paste which breaks away under slight pressure of the fingers, exposing a void that had previously been invisible. These voids may be the result of air voids, or small concentrations of free water. They are nearly impossible to prevent on vertical formed surfaces and are sure to occur on surfaces placed against forms that slope inward over the concrete (see Fig. 8-2).

There has been much controversy about the effect of entrained air on these defects; suffice it to say that they were as numerous in the days before entrained air as since. Concrete placed against tight forms such as steel or plywood is bound to have at least a few of these small voids. They do not impair the structural integrity of the concrete, and in many instances their presence is not unsightly. The only time they may possibly be dangerous is in case the concrete is subject to specially severe exposure conditions. Acting as small reservoirs, they could entrap water which, upon freezing, exerts a disruptive force on the concrete. However, the writer knows of no case in which this has actually happened.

Sometimes bubbles and blisters will appear in fresh concrete during troweling. In one case, this was caused when the partially hardened base

Fig. 8-2. Concrete surface showing air bubble holes.

was sprayed with water, then dusted with dry cement. Apparently, water was trapped in the aggregate voids by the cement topping and was released when the troweling was done. This made small bubbles appear in the surface immediately after the troweling. Sprinkling water or cement on a surface to be finished is no way to prepare it and should never be permitted.

Prevention

Sticky, oversanded mixes should be avoided. Aggregates should be well graded with adequate, but not excessive, fines in the sand. Concrete should be of a plastic, workable consistency, neither too fluid nor too stiff, with a slump of 2 to 3 in., or at most 4 in., for any normal placement.

Observance of the following suggestions will help to minimize formation of these troublesome voids:

1. Do not place concrete rapidly in deep lifts. Place it in shallow layers, from a few inches to a foot in depth depending on the type of structure, and vibrate each layer.

2. When placing against a form sloping inward over the concrete, vibrate each layer only enough for thorough consolidation.

3. When placing against a vertical form, somewhat more vibration than is normally used is desirable.

4. Vibrate the form. This should be done by means of properly designed form vibrators attached to the forms. They should operate only on newly filled forms, not on empty areas or on old concrete.

5. If the area is accessible, spade the concrete next to the form, using a $\frac{3}{8}$-in. rod bent into the shape of a stirrup about 6 in. across. Work this stirrup up and down briefly next to the form while vibration is in progress.

6. Make the forms of tongue-and-groove or shiplap lumber with small cracks through which air and water, but not mortar, can escape.

7. If the additional cost can be justified, use absorptive form lining or the vacuum process. However, these are expensive expedients and should be used only where an unblemished surface is imperative.

Filling of Voids

If, for the sake of appearance, it is considered necessary to fill the voids, the surface may be either sack-rubbed or stoned. These expedients do nothing to improve the concrete structurally, but when properly done, do improve the appearance. Either treatment should be applied as soon as possible after the forms have been stripped. The greener the concrete is when treated, the better chance there is that the treatment will be permanent.

In sack rubbing, the concrete surface should be moist but not wet before mortar, mixed to a barely damp consistency (earth moist), is spread over the concrete surface with a piece of burlap, rubber float, or similar tool. Mortar should consist of 1 part cement to 2 or $2\frac{1}{2}$ parts sand passing the 16-mesh screen (ordinary window screen). Sufficient white cement should be used so the patches, when dry, will match the parent concrete. The concrete surface should be rubbed smooth with the burlap or float, making sure that the voids are filled flush with the surface. The mortar in the void should be neither raised above nor depressed below the concrete surface. Curing should be applied in the usual manner, either water curing or liquid-membrane curing compound.

A stoned, or sand, finish is similar except that the mortar is of a thick, creamy consistency. After the mortar has been spread, the surface is immediately rubbed with a carborundum stone, taking care to cover the entire area thoroughly. A thickness of mortar of about $\frac{1}{32}$ in. should be left to provide a proper finish over the area, as contrasted with sack rubbing, which fills the voids only, leaving the surface unchanged. The final step is prompt and adequate curing.

It may be desirable to use one of the proprietary bonding agents for this application, after tests to determine its suitability. These methods of patching should not be used for honeycomb or rock pockets, as such defects require removal and replacement of the unsound concrete.

8-8. FLOORS AND SIMILAR WEARING SURFACES

Although some unformed surfaces are those on the tops of such structural elements as pier caps and walls, by far the greatest areas of unformed concrete are those comprising floors, pavements, walks, and construction joints. These surfaces may suffer cracking, crazing, peeling, dusting, and other complaints if the concrete is not properly made and handled. Assuming that satisfactory materials were used, that the concrete was of the correct consistency, and that mixing and placing operations were done in an approved manner, then the remaining operations are finishing and curing. It is here that much good concrete is damaged.

Finishing should be the minimum likely to produce the desired surface. If a screeded and floated surface is adequate, no troweling should be permitted or required. Sufficient mortar should be available at the surface for finishing purposes, and no more. Wet and oversanded mixes and excessive working of the concrete result in an excess of water and fines on the surface, inevitably leading to an inferior finish. Such a surface is weak, lacks durability and abrasion resistance, and is liable to spall or peel.

Construction and inspection of floors are discussed in detail in the section on Floors in Sec. 13-5.

8-9. PRECAST CONCRETE

Precast concrete, such as panels and prestressed units, normally presents no problems in surface treatment not encountered in cast-in-place concrete, except that special architectural treatments are apt to be encountered. The same principles of good workmanship should be followed. Being cast in a central plant, they are perhaps more amenable to control. Uniformity of appearance is usually important, which makes patching and repair even less desirable than on normal structural concrete.

Precast panels are apt to present a hodgepodge appearance unless steps are taken to assure a relatively uniform appearance. To minimize shade variations and discoloration of precast panels and to make the precast panel more attractive, the following measures are suggested by Leabu:[8.4]

1. Cement and aggregates should be from the same sources throughout the job. When using gray cement periodic checks should be made at the supplier for variation in shades of gray. No two suppliers have the same shade of gray cement.

2. In erection, some attempt should be made to match panels to minimize shade variations. Variation of color should be kept to a minimum, especially in adjacent panels.

3. The client and architect should be properly educated as to what to expect in the regular concrete panel and be prepared to accept the end results.

4. White cement should be used where shades of gray are not acceptable, keeping in mind that even white cement has a blue or yellow cast, depending on the manufacturer.

5. Textured panels will reduce the monotony of a smooth, troweled surface.

6. Methods of curing and storage of panels before erection should be uniform for all panels.

7. Surface treatments, such as exposed aggregate, mosaic, or marble chips, quartz aggregates with white sand and cement, or other decorative exterior finishes, will overcome the monotony of a plain concrete panel, but at additional cost.

8. A sharp contrast in panel shade by the use of colored cements may be used effectively in some pattern to relieve monotony of natural appearance of regular concrete provided that the colored cements retain their basic color without fading.

9. Avoid the use of exposed steel or iron inserts, edge angles, etc., that will rust and stain finished surfaces.

8-10. ARCHITECTURAL TREATMENTS

Concrete lends itself to many attractive and decorative treatments for exposed surfaces, both interior and exterior. Formation of these special architectural surfaces is discussed in Sec. 13-9. However, it should be pointed out at this point that acceptable surfaces will never be made without uniform, high-quality concrete, made with good materials, properly consolidated in the forms, and adequately cured. Variations in slump, aggregate content, cement content, and amount of consolidation will show up as variations in texture and color.

REFERENCES

8.1   Seaton, S. G.: Study of Causes and Prevention of Staining and Popouts in Cinder Concrete, *J. Am. Concrete Inst.*, January, 1948, pp. 361–380.

8.2   Midgley, H. G.: Staining of Concrete by Pyrite, *Mag. of Concrete Research*, London, August, 1958, pp. 75–78.

8.3   Harrison, D.: The Removal of Stains from Concrete, *Research News*, Hydro-Electric Power Commission of Ontario, Toronto, July–September, 1959, pp. 19–24.

8.4   Leabu, Victor F.: Problems and Performance of Precast Concrete Wall Panels, *J. Am. Concrete Inst.*, October, 1959, pp. 287–298.

PART THREE

Construction and Inspection

CHAPTER 9   *Inspection Fundamentals*

9-1. WHAT IS INSPECTION?

The purpose of construction inspection is to assure that materials and workmanship entering into the project comply with the plans and specifications. As applied to concrete, inspection includes the following:

1. Investigation, testing, and approval of sources of aggregates and other materials for concrete
2. Inspection of the contractor's plant and equipment
3. Proportioning, control, and testing of concrete
4. Examination of subgrade, foundation, forms, and placement of reinforcing steel or other embedded items
5. Inspection of batching, mixing, transporting, placing, curing, and repair of concrete
6. Observation of factors affecting the concrete such as weather, working conditions, and safety
7. Preparation and maintenance of records

On a large job, such as a dam or major highway project, the inspection force may consist of a large number of men, covering every phase of concreting from the batching plant to final acceptance, even including inspectors in the aggregate processing plant. At the other extreme, inspection of construction of a small building may be handled by the resident engineer or clerk of the works, assisted by a part-time inspector from a testing laboratory.

The degree of inspection required for any one project is something that the engineer or architect should decide before specifications are written. The instructions in this and the following chapters have been prepared in sufficient detail to apply to almost any project and might appear to be more detailed than necessary for the small project. However, inspection on the small job is just as important as on the large one and can be

121

handled on a part-time basis through the means of a commercial inspection agency.

The practice of having the contractor employ the testing or inspection service is neither desirable nor advisable and should be avoided. Regardless of who makes direct payments for inspection, the owner pays for it anyhow, and it is far better to have this cost out in the open instead of buried in the contractor's unit costs.

The recommendations of the Concrete Industry Board of New York City[9.1]* are typical of the modern approach to this problem:

1. The owner or architect and not the contractor should employ a qualified testing laboratory to carry out the requirements of the specifications.
2. The scope of the services to be provided by the testing laboratory shall be specifically defined.
3. As a professional service the laboratory should not be engaged on the basis of competitive bidding.
4. A separate and detailed section of the specifications should be prepared to cover the inspection, testing and reporting requirements.
5. The laboratories shall be adequately equipped and shall provide experienced and qualified personnel to carry out such responsibilities as may be delegated to them.

The results of inadequate inspection are not always spectacular failures, as shown in Fig. 9-1. Most of them, instead, are little publicized. However, failures have occurred since time immemorial. Feld[9.2] quotes five basic rules in the code of laws of Hammurabi (about 2200 B.C.) covering structural failures. The Harper translation quoted by Feld reads as follows:

If a builder build a house for a man and do not make its construction firm and the house which he has built collapse and cause the death of the owner of the house—that builder shall be put to death.

If it cause the death of the son of the owner of the house—they shall put to death a son of that builder.

If it cause the death of a slave of the owner of the house—he shall give to the owner of the house a slave of equal value.

If it destroy property, he shall restore whatever it destroyed, and because he did not make the house which he built firm and it collapsed, he shall rebuild the house which collapsed at his own expense.

If a builder build a house for a man and do not make its construction meet the requirements and a wall fall in, that builder shall strengthen the wall at his own expense.

* Superscript figures refer to chapter and reference numbers. The references are found at the end of each chapter.

Feld continues:

In 1918, the American Railway Engineering Association published an editorial article, "Study in Failures of Concrete Structures," with the subheading "A Compilation of Failed Concrete Structures and Lessons to be Drawn Therefrom." The study covers a period of 25 years and classifies the causes under the headings: improper design; poor materials or poor workmanship; premature loading or removal of forms before complete setting; subsidence of foundations, fire, etc. The final conclusion is, "The one thing which these

Fig. 9-1. What was supposed to be a fluted architectural surface was ruined by careless removal of the forms.

failures conclusively point to is that all good concrete construction should be subjected to rigid inspection. It should be insisted upon that the inspector shall force the contractor to follow out the specifications to the most minute details. He must see that the materials used are proper and are properly mixed and deposited, also that the forms are sufficiently strong and that they are not removed until after the concrete has set. It is believed that only by this kind of inspection is it possible to guard against the failure of concrete structures."

9-2. THE INSPECTOR

The inspector's job is not an easy one, nor is it one to be assigned to whatever employee happens to be available. Inspectors should be selected on the basis of their aptitude for this type of work, and should be given adequate supervision and training.

It is the inspector's duty to see that the intent of the plans and specifications is faithfully carried out. Careful attention to each detail is necessary if the proper end results are to be obtained. A competent inspector knows and understands the plans and specifications and keeps himself informed of job conditions at all times. Cooperation should be willingly given; however, the inspector should avoid acceptance of unusual favors, as he should be under no obligations to the contractor or producer. The inspector should always accept only satisfactory work and materials, explaining the necessity of his action whenever a rejection becomes necessary.

Unnecessary requirements and restrictions should be avoided, so as to enable the contractor to perform his work in the most advantageous and profitable manner, at the same time accomplishing the construction in accordance with the plans and specifications.

Suggestions and instructions relative to the acceptance or rejection of workmanship or materials should be given to an authorized representative of the contractor or producer, and not to the workmen. The inspector should carefully refrain from continuously giving instructions, otherwise he may find himself acting as a foreman for the contractor's or producer's workmen and may thus be inviting claims by the contractor.

In the course of their duties, inspectors frequently come into possession of confidential information relative to production or composition of materials under their inspection. This information, of course, should not be divulged to competitors or the general public.

Inspectors, in their dealings with contractors and producers, should refrain from criticism of their supervisors or the agency by which they are employed. In the final analysis the supervisor is responsible for the work, and he may have reasons for making overall decisions that cannot be revealed to the inspector at the time. In case of a difference of opinion between inspectors, or between the inspector and his supervisor, the inspector should collect the facts and present them, together with his opinion, to his supervisor and request advice concerning doubtful procedure or materials.

In addition to the required daily inspection reports, the inspector should keep a diary containing a summary of all instructions issued relative to the work, and a brief record of all important conversations with the contractor or his representatives; he should also keep a record of the weather, temperature, and the day and hour of the beginning and completing of each item or section of work, time lost, and the cause of each delay. Diaries should be turned over to the resident engineer when a job is completed or when an inspector leaves the job before it is completed.

Training

One of the most important aspects of inspection is adequate preparation. Those persons assigned to inspection should have a background of construction experience, should be intellectually capable of understanding the engineering principles being applied, and should be interested enough to assure themselves and their employer that the final product meets the specification requirements. In addition, they must have been thoroughly trained.

Training is essential regardless of the previous career or qualifications. Such training should consist of meetings in which persons familiar with the several features of the job lecture to the inspectors and demonstrate procedures. In some cases, the demonstrations may have to be made at the site in order that certain equipment may be used. Discussion should be encouraged. If questions and comment do not come spontaneously, the lecturer may ask some person to comment on a certain phase of the discussion. This will usually engender participation by others. Many good ideas can be developed in such a discussion, and it gives the participants a feeling that their ideas are being considered by the management (as they should be) and that their ideas can help to formulate inspection procedures.

On-the-job training is important and should form an integral part of the training program. It is especially effective when the new inspector, not familiar with certain phases of the work, can be assigned as an assistant to the experienced man. In this way he learns by doing, and he is given an opportunity to apply the knowledge gained in the formal lectures and demonstrations.

Training is not a one-shot proposition. To make it effective, it is the responsibility of the supervisor to carry on informal training continuously. Such training should be implemented with manuals and letters of instruction issued from time to time as required by the progress of the work. It is a good plan to have a manual of instruction for inspectors which should contain both administrative and technical procedures. Supplemental letters of instruction may be issued as conditions require. However, a word of caution must be introduced at this point. Such letters should be kept to a minimum in quantity and size; the issuance of instruction letters should be infrequent, and when issued they should be brief, simple, and clear: brief, because men do not want to wade through a sea of words to find out what it is all about; simple, so that they can be understood by a beginner as well as by the old hand; and clear, so there

can be no reason for misunderstanding. Many instruction letters are soon
forgotten, even when read, because they are too wordy, too technical,
poorly written, not clear, or not necessary in the first place.

The Pontchartrain Bridge job, the first big prestressed concrete job
in this country and the largest in the world at the time, illustrates the
problem and a solution. The problem was not only a lack of inspectors
who knew prestressed concrete, but a lack of any inspectors at all.

The engineer was confronted with the problem of expanding an inspection force rapidly to meet the contractor's schedule for a $40 million job,
with headquarters in a small town that had never experienced a large
construction job and that was located 70 miles from any large city. The
problem was met by transferring personnel for key positions and hiring
experienced men for chief inspector positions. Subordinate positions were
filled by hiring experienced inspectors whenever available, and inexperienced men when necessary.

On-the-job training was given the new men. This took the form of
pairing inexperienced men with the older hands to give them a general
idea of inspection. In addition, a short course of instruction in concrete
inspection was provided. Besides lectures, demonstrations were made of
such procedures as making test specimens, and the use of testing equipment such as strain gauges. All lectures were mimeographed and passed
out to all participants at the beginning of each session. Subjects covered
were general requirements of inspection, materials, what constitutes good
concrete, significance of tests, prestressed concrete, detail procedures for
inspection of concrete and stressing operations, and demonstrations of
techniques.

On the Northern Illinois Tollway, a series of preliminary meetings was
held for all personnel of the section engineers. Subsequently, at the start-
up of paving operations on each section, another meeting was held for
paving inspectors. The object of these meetings was to acquaint all concerned with the specifications and inspection manual, to discuss good and
bad construction practices, and to point out what was expected in the way
of concrete paving inspection. The consulting engineer had prepared a
Materials and Inspection Manual[9.5] which was found to be of great value
in standardizing inspection operations and providing inspectors with a
reference manual. Additional sources of information and guidance are the
ACI Manual of Concrete Inspection[9.6] and McKaig, *Field Inspection of
Building Construction.*[9.7]

Accident Prevention

Adherence to safe construction practices is the responsibility of the
contractor. However, the inspector should observe the job for unsafe
conditions and point them out to the foreman or superintendent.

9-3. FIELD LABORATORY FACILITIES

The field laboratory may be simple or elaborate, depending on the size of the job and degree of control to be exercised. On a large job, such as a large concrete dam or major highway project, the field laboratory may be a complete unit in itself with curing facilities for a large number of test specimens, sieve shakers, and other testing equipment. On most private jobs, laboratory facilities are usually provided by a commercial testing laboratory, with a minimum of facilities on the site, the specifications usually requiring the contractor to provide space for the field laboratory. A minimum of equipment for the most rudimentary control would include the following items:

Slump cone
$\frac{5}{8}$-in.-diameter steel rod, 24 in. long, bullet-pointed at one end
Platform scale, at least 100 lb capacity, graduated in 0.01 or 0.02 lb
Laboratory scale, 1,000 g capacity, graduated in 0.2 g
Apparatus for measuring air content of concrete ("air meter")
Calibrated unit weight container, $\frac{1}{4}$ or $\frac{1}{2}$ cu ft capacity (the bottom of the air meter may be used for this purpose)
Apparatus for determining moisture content of aggregates (hot plate, oven, or stove for drying specimens; Chapman flask; or other apparatus)
Molds for concrete test specimens
Armored thermometer
Pocket rule
Buckets, scoops, shovel, pans, graphite lumber crayon, etc.
Project specifications
Reference specifications
Sample bags—cloth, plastic, or paper

Where more elaborate control facilities are contemplated, more items of equipment will be required for performance of more comprehensive testing. Appendix A lists the principal standard specifications and test methods appertaining to concrete and concrete materials.

9-4. TESTING LABORATORY

Departments of the Federal government, state highway departments, the large cities, some consultants, and others provide their own laboratory and inspection facilities. Most building construction and some heavy construction inspection is handled through commercial testing agencies. In the latter case, jobsite facilities are usually a minimum with the central

128   *Practical Quality Control for Concrete*

laboratory providing more complete testing equipment for a number of jobs in the area.

Frequently, the testing laboratory is called upon to make off-site inspections at the source, such as mill and shop inspection of cement and reinforcing steel. However, it should be stressed that final inspection and acceptance of any material are to be made at the time it is incorporated in the work. When such off-site inspection is permitted, the representative of the engineer or architect at the site should make sure that the material is properly identified. Individual pieces or units may be marked, stamped, or tagged by the testing laboratory. Bulk materials, such as cement, should be placed in bins, tanks, drums, or other suitable containers that can be sealed and identified. Each carload or truckload of approved materials should be accompanied by a tag or card of identification issued by the testing laboratory showing date, source, material, quantity in shipment, identity of transporting unit, destination, and reference to laboratory test report covering the material. These tags should be collected and retained by the inspector receiving the material at the jobsite.

REFERENCES

9.1 *Manual of Recommended Practice for Inspection and Testing of Concrete Materials and Concrete,* Concrete Industry Board, Inc., New York, 1957.
9.2 Feld, Jacob: Failures of Concrete Structures, *J. Am. Concrete Inst.,* December, 1957, pp. 449–470.
9.3 Harper, R. F.: *Code of Hammurabi,* University of Chicago Press, 1921, pp. 83ff.
9.4 Study of Failures of Concrete Structures, *Bulletin,* American Railway Engineering Association, vol. 20, no. 211, pp. 3–28, November, 1918.
9.5 *Materials and Inspection Manual,* Illinois State Toll Highway Commission, 1956. Prepared by Joseph K. Knoerle and Associates, Consulting Engineer.
9.6 *ACI Manual of Concrete Inspection,* Report of Committee 611, Inspection of Concrete, American Concrete Institute.
9.7 McKaig, Thomas H.: Field Inspection of Building Construction, Dodge Books, McGraw-Hill Book Company, Inc., New York, 1958.

The basic question concerning the use of any material in construction—cement, admixture, form oil, or anything else—is: What is its history? If the material in question has a satisfactory history of usage showing compatibility with other materials with which it will be used, under similar conditions of exposure, it is satisfactory for use, with one important condition: The material supplied to the project must be the same as that represented by the history. Among the factors that affect the characteristics of any product are:

1. Change in source of raw materials
2. Change in method of formulation
3. Change in process system or control
4. Change in management or ownership of the producing company

New sources will, of course, require investigation and testing before approval can be given.

10-1. APPROVAL OF SOURCES

It is frequently desirable or necessary for the engineer or architect representing the owner to approve of a proposed source of materials. Armed with this approval, the contractor can then place his supply orders with firms that are capable of producing materials conforming to the specifications.

Source approval of manufactured materials usually presents no problem. Cement, reinforcing steel, wire and strand for prestressing, and similar items are manufactured to well-established standards and may normally be expected to conform to appropriate ASTM or other standard specifications.

The engineer should instruct the contractor to designate materials sources as early as possible in order that preliminary approval of these sources may be made. This preliminary approval may be based on knowledge that the proposed source has a satisfactory record of producing material to meet project specifications, it may be based on manufacturer's certifications to that effect, or it may be based on results of tests and inspection made under direction of the engineer or architect.

A request for source approval based on manufacturer's certification, together with pertinent supporting data, should be directed by the contractor to the engineer or architect. Supporting data should contain information about the history and service record of the materials as well as typical mill, factory, or shop tests, including tests by an independent testing laboratory.

Any preliminary approval of sources should be considered as tentative approval and the contractor is still responsible for furnishing materials from sources that conform to specification requirements.

Preliminary investigation and inspection should not be made on the basis of requests from materials suppliers, as to do so would involve study of numerous materials that would never be used in the job. Only specific sources and materials, as requested by the contractor and intended for use in the project, should be inspected and tested.

10-2. OFF-SITE TESTING AND INSPECTION

In the case of some projects, especially large ones or jobs that are in progress for a considerable period of time, it is sometimes desirable to perform inspection of materials at the point of manufacture.

Materials that are inspected at the source of supply may be tested, tentatively approved, marked, and either placed in storage, or shipped immediately to the project. Such approval is given as a convenience to the contractor to expedite the work, and any materials so approved must still comply with the specifications at the time they are incorporated in the work.

Adequate identification of approved materials should be provided in every case. Individual pieces or units may be marked, stamped, or tagged. Bulk materials should be placed in bins, tanks, drums, or other suitable containers that can be sealed and identified. Each car- or truckload of approved materials should be accompanied by a tag or card identifying the load. These tags are collected by the inspector receiving the material at the jobsite.

The usual procedure in the control of manufactured raw materials, such as cement and steel, is to perform the inspection off the site at the mill, shop, or warehouse. Off-site inspection of such manufactured items can be handled by a commercial testing agency, this being especially desirable when the engineer or purchaser does not have testing and inspection facilities of his own capable of making inspections in plants located in different parts of the country. Procedures are well standardized and may follow the same general pattern whether done by the engineer's own organization or by a testing agency. To trigger the inspection and authorize the inspector to enter the plant, the engineer should be provided with copies of the contractor's purchase order for the material to be inspected. Upon receipt of a copy of this purchase order from the engineer, the testing agency contacts the supplier named thereon and arranges for inspection. A statement on the purchase order to the effect that the material is subject to inspection by the engineer will facilitate this inspection.

10-3. ACCEPTANCE ON MANUFACTURER'S CERTIFICATION

In many cases, the engineer or architect may accept certain standard materials on manufacturer's certification. A request for such approval is made by the prime contractor, the same as for source approval, and should be accompanied by pertinent data to support the acceptance. The supporting data should contain information about the history and service record of the materials, as well as mill or shop tests, and test results by an independent testing agency. The manufacturer of materials accepted on certification should be required to furnish certified tests for each lot or consignment, showing actual test results, a statement that the materials conform to specification requirements (citing the specifications), a statement certifying that the formulation and manufacturing procedures have not changed from those prevailing at the time the original acceptance was made, and explaining how the certified materials are identified or marked.

The engineer should be circumspect in accepting material under certification; whenever the expense can be justified, inspection and tests should be made. Examples of errors that may be disclosed are substitution of structural or hard-grade reinforcing steel for intermediate grade, or unsuspected variations in an admixture. By making standard mortar tests of cement samples from different shipments, variations in strength have been found that explain in part fluctuations in concrete strength.

10-4. REJECTION OF MATERIALS

Materials not meeting the requirements of the specifications should not be used in the work unless specific approval is obtained from the engineer or architect for the use of such materials.

Rejected materials should be disposed of in such a manner as to ensure that they will not become intermingled with accepted materials and shipped to the site of the work. Permitting rejected materials to become intermingled with acceptable materials may be cause for rejection of the entire lot, including materials that have been accepted.

There will frequently be requests for retests when materials have been rejected because of not meeting the specification requirements. Retests should not be made unless there is some reason to question the accuracy of the original test, and then only with the approval of the engineer or architect. If retests are made, at least two samples should be tested for each sample that originally failed. Both of the retests should pass, and the questionable materials should be closely inspected visually. Reports of retests should clearly indicate that the results were obtained from samples of materials that originally failed to meet specification requirements.

10-5. OBTAINING AND HANDLING SAMPLES

Sampling Methods

The basic requirement of any sampling procedure is to obtain a sample that is truly representative of the material being sampled. Sampling methods are based on the mathematics of probability, and a sampling plan can be developed for any set of conditions. However, it is not necessary for the field man to make a statistical analysis whenever he desires to sample any given material. Instead, standards have been established for this purpose by the American Society for Testing and Materials and other organizations, based on the appropriate statistical background. Reference to the ASTM or other designation for any material will provide information on the sampling method to be adopted. In the pages that follow, special attention is given to methods of handling samples of aggregates, concrete, and related materials.

Sampling Liquids in Barrels

Before a sample is taken, complete mixing of the material is necessary. Some materials, such as liquid curing compound, are shipped in drums equipped with mechanical agitators. The agitator should be operated for several minutes until the material is thoroughly mixed and blended.

If the material is in an open-head drum, the head should be removed and a portion of the liquid poured off into a clean container. The material in the drum is then stirred with a power stirrer, compressed air, or by hand. Hand stirring should be avoided, if possible, as it is slow and inefficient. After the material is thoroughly mixed, the liquid previously poured off should be slowly blended with that in the drum.

If the material comes in a bunghole type of drum, mixing is more difficult. If compressed air is available, good mixing can be done by means of a length of ½-in. pipe long enough to reach the bottom of the drum. The pipe is connected to a source of air, free of moisture and oil, under about 20 psi pressure, and is inserted through the bunghole. The pipe should be moved around through the material in the drum in order to mix all parts thoroughly.

If no compressed air is available, the drum may be turned on its side and rolled back and forth for a total of 200 or 300 ft. Additional rolling may be necessary if the material does not appear to be well mixed.

The sample should be taken immediately after mixing is completed. From an open-top drum, it may be dipped out of the mixed material. From the bunghole drum, the sample is taken after several gallons have been drawn off. A sample should consist of a quart of the mixed material taken in a clean, friction-top can.

Cube-root Method

In sampling from barrels, boxes, or other individual containers or units, the cube-root method should be used. In this method, the number of units sampled is equal to the cube root of the number of units in the lot being inspected. These individual samples are combined into one overall sample for testing. For convenience, Table 10-1 shows the number of

TABLE 10-1. NUMBER OF SAMPLES BY CUBE-ROOT METHOD

Units in shipment	Units sampled	Units in shipment	Units sampled
2–8	2	217–343	7
9–27	3	344–512	8
28–64	4	513–729	9
65–125	5	730–1,000	10
126–216	6	1,001–1,331	11

samples for shipments of various sizes. This method applies especially to bituminous materials, paints, and other materials packaged in cans, barrels, or similar units. The number of samples of masonry units should be in accordance with Table 13-3.

Shipping Samples

When samples are to be shipped to a laboratory, complete information should accompany each sample. A transmittal form containing all pertinent information relative to the sample should be sent to the laboratory, and a copy of the form should be placed in a heavy manila tag envelope and the envelope attached securely to the sample or the container. If the material permits, a copy should be placed inside the container. Information required includes:

1. Construction contract number.

2. Sample number. A log of samples should be kept, using a serial number for each sample sent to the laboratory, by means of which a record may be kept and test results identified.

3. Name of material.

4. Type of material; class, trade name or brand, size, grade, type, or other identification.

5. Reference specifications. Including modification, if any.

6. Manufacturer and source. The name of the manufacturer or producer should be shown, not that of a jobber or dealer.

7. Date material received or made, date sampled, or other dates as applicable.

8. Intended use. This is important in determining tests to be made.

9. Quantity represented. If not known, an approximation can be given.

10. Station, car number, structure number, or other location identification.

11. Tests required.

12. Name, address, and title of sampler and shipper.

The following instructions apply to preparing and shipping samples:

1. Samples should be packed to withstand rough treatment. Liquid materials should be shipped in screw-top cans or friction-top cans with lids soldered in place unless otherwise specified or required. Friction-top cans, with lids not soldered in place, and glass jars, should be surrounded and packed with suitable absorbent material in sufficient quantity to absorb all the liquid if the tops of the cans should come off or the glass jar should be broken. All packages containing liquid samples should be marked "Fragile—Liquid." Mark pipe, tile, and concrete test specimens conspicuously "Handle with Care—Fragile."

2. The method of transporting the samples will depend on the size, weight, or quantity of material being shipped, and the time element. Small and lightweight samples may be sent by parcel post or express. Intercity bus lines usually provide rapid and reliable express service. Large and heavy samples should be sent by rail or motor freight. Air freight or express is desirable when speed is necessary.

3. All containers in which samples are shipped should be clean, free from tears and holes, and tightly woven to prevent loss of fine material. Burlap bags treated with plastic may be used if the plastic is perfectly tight and nearly vaportight. Sacks which have contained sugar or fertilizer should not be used.

10-6. CEMENT

Types

The several types of cement commonly in use are shown in Table 10-2. Some specifications permit the substitution of slag cement (Types IS and

TABLE 10-2. PORTLAND CEMENT TYPES

Type	Description
I	Always available, and supplied to most jobs unless another type is specified to meet special conditions.
II	Modified cement. C_3A content is lower than in Type I (not over 8%), resulting in lower heat generation and moderate sulfate resistance. Concrete made with Type II cement has most of the properties of concrete made with Type I cement, plus smaller volume change, enhanced sulfate resistance, and less tendency to bleeding or water gain.
III	High-early-strength cement. High in C_3S and C_3A. Used when rapid strength gain is required. Concrete made with Type III cement will have at 3 days strength equivalent to normal 7-day strength, and at 7 days the strength will be equivalent to normal 28-day strength.
IV	Low-heat cement. C_3A content is low and C_2S is high. This cement develops strength much more slowly than the others and is used in massive structures, such as dams and large footings, where the low heat of hydration reduces cracking that results from high temperature when using other types of cement. Concrete develops strength slowly and requires curing for 3 weeks. Ultimate strength is equal to that obtained with Type I cement.
V	Sulfate-resistant cement. Very low C_3A content. Used in concrete in a severe sulfate exposure. Heat generation is almost as slow as Type IV.
Slag cement	Type IS portland blast-furnace slag cement contains between 25 and 65% of granulated blast-furnace slag interground with Type I cement clinker.
Pozzolan cement	Type IP portland pozzolan cement consists of between 15 and 50% of siliceous, or siliceous and aluminous, pozzolan blended with Type I cement. Possesses low shrinkage rate.

Notes: Any of the foregoing type designations followed by the letter A indicates air-entraining cement—for example, Type IA.

There are several specialized cements of limited usage not included in this table—for example, masonry cement and aluminous cement.

ISA) respectively for Types I and IA because of their similarity in performance.

In some areas, low-alkali cement is specified as a protection against the reaction of alkalies in the cement with certain siliceous constituents of the aggregate (see Sec. 5-3). Low-alkali cement contains not more than 0.6 per cent total alkalies, computed as the percentage of sodium oxide (Na_2O) plus 0.658 times the percentage of potassium oxide (K_2O).

Approval

Depending on the size and type of project, and the practices of the engineer or architect, cement approval may be handled in several ways. The most simple method is to have the producer furnish a certified mill test report with each shipment (see Sec. 10-3). This practice is sometimes modified by the engineer taking samples, either at the source or jobsite, permitting cement to be used on certification pending results of tests of the samples. As long as test results indicate satisfactory compliance with the specifications, this method is quite satisfactory. However, if a test gives results that fail to comply, there is a delay until further sampling and testing indicate compliance. Some governmental agencies and other users of large quantities of cement sample and test the cement at the time of manufacture. The cement is then stored in reserved silos at the mill, from which shipments are loaded out for the project, under inspection by the engineer (or owner) or a testing agency working for the engineer or owner.

Cement is manufactured under close quality control, and rarely fails to meet specifications. However, wide fluctuations in properties may exist even though the cement meets the specification requirements.

Handling and Inspection

If cement is inspected at the source, each carload or truckload should be accompanied by a tag or card from the inspector, showing the type and brand of cement, source, number of barrels or weight of shipment, date tested, date loaded, name of testing agency, and number or name of vehicle. The inspector should inspect cars and trucks of cement for evidence of contamination or damage, and should pick up the shipping report which accompanies each shipment. He should supervise the removal of seals and record the seal numbers.

Cement delivered in bulk should be stored in weathertight bins which will protect the cement from dampness. Care should be exercised in transferring from carrier to bin to prevent the cement from becoming wet or contaminated with foreign material. Infrequently, pieces of tramp iron or other material have been found in cement, coming from the mill or hauling equipment. Such items should be removed when found, as they can damage cement-handling equipment. Their presence should be reported to the shipper. Exposure of cement to air should be kept at a minimum, as atmospheric moisture causes partial hydration.

Sacked cement should be stored in a weathertight building in such a manner as to permit easy access for inspection, to protect it from dampness, and to permit removal in chronological order of receipt. Occasional sacks should be weighed as a check on the weight furnished.

Different brands or types should never be mixed. Cement salvaged from spillage around bulk cement bins, from broken sacks, or from cleaning sacks should not be used. At the time of use, cement should contain no lumps that cannot be broken by light pressure between the fingers.

Cement is measured in sacks (94 lb each) or barrels (4 sacks or 376 lb). No cement is ever packed in barrels, shipments being made either loose in bulk, or in paper sacks. Formerly, cement was packed in cloth bags, but this method has been largely supplanted by paper sacks.

10-7. WATER

Sources

Water from any source of domestic supply may be used for mixing and curing concrete without testing. Water from a stream or lake may be used, provided it is clean and otherwise conforms to the specification requirements. Stagnant or muddy pools, swamps, and marshes should be avoided. The intake to the pipeline should be installed so as to provide at least 2 ft of water below it and should be provided with screens or other enclosure to exclude grass, roots, mud, or other solid material.

Quality

The Bureau of Reclamation limits turbidity to 2,000 ppm. The Illinois Division of Highways requires that water

. . . shall be clean, clear, free from sugar, and shall not contain acid, alkali, salts, or organic matter in excess of the following amounts when tested in accordance with A.A.S.H.O. Designation: T 26:

(*a*) Acidity and Alkalinity
    (1) Acidity—0.1 Normal NaOH, 2 ml. Max.*
    (2) Alkalinity—0.1 Normal HCl, 10 ml. Max.*
    * To neutralize 200 ml. sample.
(*b*) Total Solids
    (1) Organic .... 0.02% max.
    (2) Inorganic .... 0.30% max.
    (3) Sulphuric anhydride (SO_3)............................ 0.04% max.
    (4) Alkali chloride as sodium choloride (NaCl).............. 0.10% max.

When standard 1:3 mortar briquettes made with cement, sand, and water from the sample are compared with briquettes made with the same cement and sand and distilled water, there shall be no indication of unsoundness, marked change in time of set, or variation of more than 10 per cent in strength.

Usually, the presence of harmful impurities will be known by the color, taste, or odor of the water. If the water is reasonably clear and does not have a brackish or salty taste, it is probably satisfactory.

Sampling

A sample should consist of 1 qt in a glass container. The container should be rinsed with the water being sampled before the sample is taken.

Natural sources are apt to vary quite appreciably between wet and dry seasons, hence it may be necessary to obtain more than one sample during the progress of a job. The most serious danger is that the flow in a stream decreases to the point that the concentration of organic material in the water becomes excessive.

10-8. ADMIXTURES

An *admixture* may be defined as any substance, other than cement, aggregate, and water, that is added to a batch of fresh concrete for the purpose of altering any of the properties of the concrete. A vast number of compounds are available, ranging in value from highly beneficial, through innocuous, to those compounds that are actually harmful.

Some of the early manufacturers of admixtures made such extravagant and fantastic claims for their materials, claims that were not possible to fulfill, that many engineers became prejudiced against all admixtures, looking upon them as improbable patent medicines that were worthless at best, and usually positively damaging. Today we find many reliable concerns manufacturing a variety of admixtures for many purposes. As all prescriptions, these admixtures have their specific uses, and must be used under proper technical supervision. The user is cautioned to use only those materials, known by well-established usage or exhaustive laboratory tests, to perform the desired result without harmful side effects. Reputable manufacturers will furnish information about their products, and will service a job once the product has been sold.

Admixtures can be grouped into several classifications, depending upon their action in the concrete. Some admixtures may affect more than one property of the concrete.

Sampling and Testing

Methods of sampling and acceptance have been discussed earlier in this chapter. It is good practice to use only those admixtures produced by reputable manufacturers with experience in making specification materials.

The U.S. Bureau of Public Roads has made exhaustive studies of air-entraining agents and other admixtures. Results of these investigations are reported in detail in references 10.2 and 10.5. The report of ACI Committee 212[10.1]* is another excellent source of information on these materials.

In studying any proposed admixture, the engineer should know the type of admixture, trade name, manufacturer, local dealer or representative, and the length of time the product has been in use. He should also determine the effect of the admixture on durability, permeability, strength (compressive, flexural, bond), drying shrinkage, time of set, and, for pavement, resistance to salt scaling. Other properties of the concrete that may be affected are the amount of air entrained, workability, mixing water requirement, sulfate resistance, alkali-aggregate resistance, and

* Superscript figures refer to chapter and reference numbers. The references are found at the end of each chapter.

cracking tendency. The user should know whether an accidental over-dose can be tolerated without adverse effect, whether reliable, automatic dispensing equipment is available, and the type of service given by the distributor.

Air-entraining Agents

Admixtures of this type (commonly abbreviated AEA) are now generally accepted for use in nearly all concrete, especially in areas where the concrete is exposed to freezing and thawing. Their use is recommended for all exposed concrete. The types commonly available are organic salts of sulfonated hydrocarbons and salts of sulfonated lignin. Synthetic detergents, petroleum acid salts, fatty and resinous acids and salts of wood resins are also sources of air-entraining agents.

Air-entraining agents should conform to the requirements of ASTM Designation: C 260, and the manufacturer should furnish proper certification to this effect.

Accelerators

The methods of increasing the rate of hydration for early strength development, discussed in Sec. 3-6, include the use of accelerators.

The one accelerator commonly used is calcium chloride in an amount not exceeding 2 per cent of the weight of cement in a batch of concrete. If as much as 4 per cent of chloride is used, there is danger of a flash set, and the full ultimate strength of the concrete is not attained.

Calcium chloride should conform to the requirements of ASTM Designation: D 98. Because of its highly hygroscopic nature, it should be kept in tightly sealed containers at all times. It should not be used if it becomes sticky or caked.

There are a number of other chemicals that accelerate the hydration of cement, but none is used to any extent because of difficulty in handling them, cost, or erratic results. With some of these materials, almost infinitesimal changes in the amount have a pronounced effect. Triethanolamine is an accelerator, sometimes used in formulating a water-reducing admixture to overcome the retarding tendency of the water reducer. Other accelerators are sodium carbonate, calcium oxychloride, soluble silicates and fluosilicates, and mixtures of aluminous and portland cement (see Sec. 13-15).

Retarders

A retarder is an admixture that slows the chemical process of hydration so that the concrete remains plastic and workable for a longer time than concrete without the retarder. However, once the cement starts to set, strength gain should be at the normal rate. Retarders are used to delay the set of cement during difficult placements that require the concrete to be in a plastic condition longer than normally and to overcome the acceleration of set during hot weather. Rarely, a retarder may be effective in dispelling the tendency of a cement to false set.

Many chemicals have a retarding action on portland cement, some of which are extremely erratic and unreliable. Inorganic compounds consist of boron compounds (borax, boric acid, calcium borate), sodium bicarbonate, and certain phosphates. Sugar is a powerful retarder, very small quantities completely preventing hydration. The useful products usually fall into either the starches or cellulose products, such as ligno-sulfonic acid and its salts or dextrins, or acids and salts containing some of the hydroxyl groups. Commonly used retarders are either metallic salts of lignosulfonic acid, such as calcium lignosulfonate, or salts of organic hydroxycarboxylic acid. Many of these products are refined by-

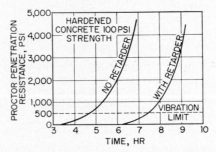

Fig. 10-1. Typical hardening curves for normal and retarded concrete.

products of the paper manufacturing industry. These admixtures, in addition to their retarding action, act as water reducers, as discussed in the next section. Modification of the material during the manufacturing process permits the producer to make an admixture that will feature either the retarding or the water-reducing property.

Evaluation of a retarder is accomplished by the method of ASTM Designation: C 403. This method specifies the use of a calibrated needle (Proctor soil needle) that is pressed into a sample of mortar sieved out of the concrete. When the hardening process has progressed to the point where the penetration resistance is 500 psi, the concrete is said to have reached the vibration limit, and can no longer be made plastic by revibration. Beyond this point, a delayed second layer of concrete would not become monolithic with the layer below and a cold joint will probably result. The vibration limit is the point in the hydration process which it is desirable to postpone by means of the retarder.

As hydration continues, the concrete begins to gain some strength. When the penetration resistance reaches 4,000 psi, the concrete has a compressive strength of about 100 psi. The period of time elapsed between the vibration limit and 100 psi strength should be about the same for retarded concrete as for the unretarded concrete.

Water Reducers

An admixture of this type, as its name implies, is used for the purpose of lowering the mixing water requirement, at the same time providing equal or superior workability. Many of the retarding admixtures also reduce the water requirement (for the same slump or consistency) and some entrain a small amount of air.

Chemicals commonly used for water reduction are the lignosulfonates (calcium, sodium, or ammonium) and salts of hydroxycarboxylic acids.

Dampproofers and Waterproofers

Probably there has been more controversy about these materials than any of the other admixtures. This may be due in part to the patent medicine merchandising that has been done by some of the manufacturers, and because some of the products have been little more than calcium chloride solutions sold at fancy prices. However, this situation is changing, and some materials are now available that perform a useful function. For example, a number of surface-coating materials are obtainable, some of which form a hydrophobic coating in the pores of the concrete but do not plug the pores, thus permitting moisture to escape but resisting the penetration of water from the outside.

The reader is referred to Chap. 6 for a discussion of these materials.

Workability Agents

The use of admixtures for improving workability was discussed in Chap. 2.

The water-reducing agents are usually looked upon as workability agents also. Because many of these also function as retarders, the proprietary compounds may include calcium chloride or triethanolamine as an ingredient to offset the retarding effect.

A small amount of hydrated lime is sometimes useful as a workability agent in a lean mix. An amount not exceeding 15 per cent by weight of the cement may be added. Total water per batch should not be increased because of its effect in decreasing strength. The objection to the use of hydrated lime is its tendency to leach out of the hardened concrete in the presence of water.

Bonding Agents

Polyvinyl acetate (PVA) improves the bond of concrete to old concrete. PVA is usually supplied as an emulsion or dispersion and is used in varying amounts depending on the application. Other advantages besides improvements in bond strength are crack resistance, better strength, elasticity, and wear resistance. Some polyvinyl acetate latices are reemulsifiable when exposed to moisture and are apt to soften, thus damaging the bond and strength of the patch. For this reason, only those PVA bonding agents known to contain an ingredient designed to render the dried film resistant to moisture should be used.

A copolymer latex of butadiene or styrene may be used for a bonding agent, provided it is suitably stabilized to inhibit coagulation in the presence of cement, and contains a moisture protection ingredient.

Formulations of epoxy resin and polysulfide liquid polymer are available as bonding agents.

Other Admixtures

There are several proprietary admixtures claimed to impart various desirable properties to the concrete. None of these materials should be used without an understanding of their composition or without adequate testing with the proposed cement and other ingredients.

Experimental work has been done on various materials supposed to inhibit the alkali-aggregate reaction (see Sec. 16-2). However, much remains to be done before final conclusions can be reached.

Under some circumstances calcite powder will increase strength and durability and decrease permeability. However, results are erratic, and some observers obtain contrary results.

10-9. POZZOLANS

As defined in ASTM Designation: C 219, a pozzolan is "a siliceous or siliceous and aluminous material, which in itself possesses little or no cementitious value but will, in finely divided form and in the presence of moisture, chemically react with calcium hydroxide at ordinary temperatures to form compounds possessing cementitious properties." The word "pozzolan" comes from the name of the town of Pozzuoli, Italy, situated near the source of volcanic ash used by the Romans in construction of many of their structures.

Pozzolans may be either natural or manufactured; some natural pozzolans are unprocessed, while others are processed in some manner.

Natural Pozzolans

Natural pozzolans are volcanic tuff, volcanic ash, pumicite, obsidian; they are of andesitic, dacitic, or rhyolitic composition. Pumicite usually requires no processing to prepare it for use. In Friant Dam the natural pumicite used in the mass concrete was used direct from the deposit with no processing whatever. This pumicite had over 95 per cent passing the 325-mesh sieve. Other natural pozzolans are siliceous sedimentary rocks such as opaline chert and diatomaceous earth, the latter sometimes used without processing. The other natural pozzolans require grinding and size classification to reduce the material to the fine powder suitable for use.

Processed Natural Pozzolans

Calcined or burnt shales and clays are heated in rotary kilns and after cooling are crushed and ground to the required fineness.

Manufactured Pozzolans

Crushed and ground blast-furnace slag and fly ash are manufactured pozzolans. Fly ash, sometimes called "precipitator ash," is the fine combustion product resulting from burning certain types of pulverized coal in industrial furnaces. Principal sources are steam power plants. Fly ash consists of very fine spherical particles which are carried out of the furnace in the flue gas and subsequently collected in precipitators.

10-10. REINFORCING STEEL

Specifications

Steel for reinforcing bars may be new billet-steel or rerolled rails and car axles. Typical restrictions are those expressed in the Illinois State Highway Standard Specifications:

Billet-steel and axle-steel of intermediate grade may be furnished in any size. Hard grade billet-steel, hard grade axle-steel and rail-steel may be furnished in diameters from one-half to one inch. Tie bars between lanes of concrete pavement or concrete base course, which are bent and subsequently straightened during construction, shall be electric-furnace or open hearth billet-steel or axle-steel, structural grade. Tie bars between concrete pavement or concrete base course and concrete gutters or concrete curbs shall be electric-furnace or open hearth billet-steel or axle-steel, structural grade. Bessemer steel shall not be used. Spiral reinforcement for columns and concrete piles shall be either structural or intermediate grade billet-steel or axle-steel, or cold drawn steel wire conforming to A.S.T.M. Designation: A 82.

The following specifications should apply:

Billet-steel bars: ASTM Designation: A 15
Axle-steel bars: ASTM Designation: A 160
Rail-steel bars: ASTM Designation: A 16
Special large size billet-steel bars: ASTM Designation: A 408
Fabricated bar mats: ASTM Designation: A 184
Welded wire fabric: ASTM Designation: A 185

The last two items are fabricated mats or mesh for use in pavements, slabs, pipe, and certain other structural uses.

Except in special cases, such as smooth dowels, deformed bars (bars with various patterns of ridges or ribs on them) are universally specified instead of smooth ones in order to give better bond with the concrete (Table 10-3). ASTM Designation: A 305 defines the general requirements for deformations for bars in sizes No. 3 to 11 inclusive. Requirements for deformations on large size billet-steel bars, sizes 14S and 18S, are included in ASTM Designation: A 408.

TABLE 10-3. DEFORMED REINFORCING BAR SIZES

Bar no.	Size, in.	Nominal diameter, in.	Nominal cross-sectional area, sq in.	Nominal perimeter, in.	Weight, lb per ft
2	¼	0.250	0.05	0.786	0.167
3	⅜	0.375	0.11	1.178	0.376
4	½	0.500	0.20	1.571	0.668
5	⅝	0.625	0.31	1.963	1.043
6	¾	0.750	0.44	2.356	1.502
7	⅞	0.875	0.60	2.749	2.044
8	1	1.000	0.79	3.142	2.670
9	1	1.128	1.00	3.544	3.400
10	1⅛	1.270	1.27	3.990	4.303
11	1¼	1.410	1.56	4.430	5.313
14S	1½	1.693	2.25	5.32	7.65
18S	2	2.257	4.00	7.09	13.60

Notes: All sizes are furnished with deformations except bar No. 2, which is plain. Bar numbers are based on the number of eighth inches included in the nominal diameter. The nominal diameter of a deformed bar is equivalent to the diameter of a plain bar having the same weight per foot as the deformed bar.

Bars Nos. 9, 10, and 11 are round bars equivalent in weight and nominal cross-sectional area to the old 1-in., 1⅛-in., and 1¼-in. square bars.

Bars No. 14S and 18S are outside the scope of the ASTM Specifications. They are special sizes made to order by some manufacturers.

Manufacturers roll a bar size and manufacturer's identification on the bars, most of them using a characteristic pattern of deformations for this purpose. Markings vary slightly from manufacturer to manufacturer. The practice of rolling some sort of identification on the bars to indicate different grades of the same type of steel—high-strength billet-steel, for example—has been under study in an attempt to develop a uniform system of marking which can be used by all manufacturers.

Handling and Storage

When delivered to the jobsite, reinforcing steel should be free of oil, grease, loose mill scale, paint, or other contaminant. The light coating of rust that is usually present is not detrimental; in fact, it may actually improve bond. However, heavy rust, pitting the steel to such an extent as to reduce its cross-sectional area, should be cause for rejection. If a bar appears to have rusted excessively, a sample may be cleaned and weighed to determine compliance with the reference specifications.

Steel should be stored on the jobsite on platforms or other supports off the ground so as to protect it from damage and dirt, and in locations where trucks will not splash mud on it, and where workmen will not walk over it. Storage on the site longer than necessary is apt to result in excessive rusting or contamination.

Steel should be cut and bent (fabricated) in the shop rather than on the job. If bending in the field is necessary, it should be done cold, although in an emergency, and under close control, heating may be permitted provided the temperature does not exceed a dark cherry red, and provided further that the steel is slowly air-cooled. Rapid cooling in a blast of cold air or in water is detrimental and should not be permitted.

Inspection

Because of the many steps in warehousing, fabrication, and other handling, it is sometimes difficult to identify any one shipment of fabricated reinforcing steel with any certain heats of steel from which the material was rolled, although most manufacturers are able to provide this information, especially on large shipments. However, typical mill test reports are available, and check tests for yield, elongation, ultimate strength, and bending can easily be made of samples from the site.

Usually the steel is inspected at the mill or shop, and bundles shipped to the job are identified with tags from the fabricator and the inspection agency. The inspector at the jobsite should examine the steel for excessive rust, oil, or dirt, and shipping damage such as bending or breakage. The hard grades of steel are especially susceptible to breakage, particularly during cold weather.

A sample of steel for physical tests should be about 30 in. long. Samples to be shipped by public carrier should be wrapped in burlap.

10-11. PRESTRESSING STEEL

Specifications

Steel for prestressed concrete consists of stress-relieved high-tensile-strength wire or strand or, less frequently, high-strength rods. The following types are regularly used:

1. Small-diameter strand ($\frac{1}{2}$ in. or less in diameter) made up of six uncoated wires wrapped helically about a center wire. Used mostly for pretensioned concrete. ASTM Designation: A 416

2. Two- or three-wire twisted strand, consisting of two or three wires twisted helically. Used mostly for pretensioned concrete, especially thin slabs and panels

3. Cold-drawn single wire, uncoated and stress-relieved, or hot-dip galvanized, used in groups of two or more essentially parallel wires for posttensioning. ASTM Designation: A 421

4. Cold-stretched alloy steel bars. Used mostly for posttensioning

5. Large diameter strand consisting of 37 or more wires. For post-tensioning

Detail requirements differ for different users, but the reference ASTM specifications provide sufficient detail for the applicable types. The American Railway Engineering Association specifies that bars shall be made from either AISI-5160 or AISI-9260 steel, with a minimum tensile strength of 145,000 psi. Strength of the wire and strand is usually specified as 250,000 psi or more. The elastic modulus is about 28,000,000 psi.

Handling and Inspection

Many of the comments relative to reinforcing steel apply to stressing steel also. For example, a small amount of rust has been found to be beneficial to bond, but severe corrosion should not be permitted. Avoidance of corrosion requires somewhat more care for stressing steel than for reinforcing steel, as high-strength steel is more susceptible to corrosion. Severe corrosion may occur if the steel is exposed to galvanic action while in storage.

In pretensioned concrete, and some types of posttensioned concrete, the prestress forces are maintained exclusively by bond between the steel and the hardened concrete, hence the importance of maintaining the steel free of deleterious coatings and contamination.

10-12. CONCRETE CURING MATERIALS

The oldest and universally accepted curing material is water, clean water that meets the requirements set forth previously for mixing water, used in accordance with the advice in Sec. 12-9. Several materials and methods are used to retain the mixing water still present in the hardened concrete which is adequate for hydration of the cement.

Sheet Material and Mats

Pavements and slabs may be cured by covering with an impermeable sheet material. Materials used for this purpose include kraft paper reinforced with cotton, jute, or glass yarn embedded in a bituminous cement between two layers of paper, the top or exposed surface being white in color to reflect the sun's heat. ASTM Designation: C 171 should govern. White polyethylene sheeting, at least 4 mils (0.004 in.) in thickness, is also used with highly satisfactory results.

Mats, which are kept continuously wet by sprinkling, may consist of several layers of burlap spread on the slab. Burlap reclaimed from other uses or sacks should not be used, and the burlap should be free of substances that might be injurious to fresh concrete. Curing mats may be made from cotton, jute, sisal, or similar material. Some mats have a waterproof covering that aids in keeping the moisture in.

Sealing Compounds

The purpose of a concrete sealing compound is to seal the surface of new concrete against the loss of moisture, thus retaining the water in the concrete for hydration of the cement, or curing. This material, variously known as sealing, curing, or membrane-forming compound, is a paintlike liquid that, when sprayed on the concrete, forms an impervious membrane over the surface.

Compounds can be classified as white pigmented, gray pigmented, and clear, the last containing a fugitive dye to aid in observing the coverage. The dye should render the film distinctly visible for at least 1 hr after application and should fade completely in not more than 1 week. All compounds should be of a consistency suitable for spraying, should be relatively nontoxic, should adhere to a vertical or horizontal damp concrete surface when applied at the specified time and coverage, and should not react harmfully with the concrete. The clear compound should not darken the natural color of the concrete.

Curing compounds are ready-mixed when they arrive on the job, but need vigorous stirring or agitating before they can be used. Under no circumstances should they be thinned or otherwise altered on the job. Usually, the drums in which sealing compound is shipped are equipped with agitators which should be operated before and during the time the compound is being sprayed.

Pigmented compound consists of a finely ground pigment in a vehicle consisting of a solvent and waxes, oils, or resins. The compound made with an all-wax base is sometimes used, but is of heavy consistency that makes it difficult to spray, especially in cold weather. The most commonly used type is made with a wax and resin base, although a straight resin base is sometimes specified, even though it is a little more expensive. In any pigmented compound, the pigment has a tendency to settle, hence the need for constant agitation of the material in the drum during application.

The clear compound is formulated with either a wax and resin base or an all-resin base, some users now specifying the all-resin type. One advantage claimed for the resin type is that it does not tend to segregate as the wax and resin type does, hence there is less need for agitation.

Sealing compounds should conform to the requirements of ASTM Designation: C 309. Sealing compounds are used on many jobs without testing or certification. It is good practice, however, to obtain a certification from the manufacturer if tests are not made.

10-13. JOINT FILLERS

Types

Joints in pavements, slabs, and walls are usually filled or sealed with some material to keep foreign matter out of the joint, at the same time allowing movement at the joint. One type, used by the Bureau of Reclamation for filling contraction joints in canal linings, is a cold applied internal-setup material composed of two components mixed on the job, the components consisting of a fluid flux oil and a dry mixture of powdered asphalt and mineral filler. This material is sometimes used in highway pavement joints also. Most highway departments specify a hot-applied bituminous material, usually an asphalt-rubber mixture which is heated in special kettles on the job.

Fillers for expansion joints are usually preformed strips of the required dimensions to fill the joint space. They may consist of various felts and fibres saturated and bonded with bituminous binder (usually asphalt), self-expanding cork, sponge rubber, or certain synthetic plastic materials. Sometimes strips of selected cypress or redwood are used.

Sampling

In sampling liquid bituminous material, the method of sampling liquids in barrels may be used. If it is necessary to heat the material, care should be exercised not to overheat it. A thermometer should be used.

In sampling semisolid material, the outer 3 in. should be chipped off before cutting the sample, using a hatchet or any sharp-pointed tool for digging into the barrel. Never use a solvent, such as kerosene, at any time. The several portions of the sample should be pressed into a 1-gal friction-top can, filling the can.

Self-expanding joint filler expands when exposed to moisture. Therefore it should be kept dry and wrapped in waterproof wrapping until time for use. In taking samples for shipping, the sampled packages should be closed tightly immediately after sampling, using waxed paper, tape, twine, and whatever is necessary to seal the package tightly. The samples should be immediately wrapped in waxed paper, then in heavy paper, and boxed or crated for shipment to the testing agency. Material should be inspected for dimensional accuracy and adequacy of waterproof covering. Packing should be rigid enough to withstand transportation and handling without damage to the filler. Joint filler should not be used if the waterproof wrapping is torn or damaged.

Special care should be taken to prevent inclusion of water resulting from rain or snow into the sample, or into the sampling equipment or container. A very small amount of water can ruin a sample. The sampler should be sure that all sampling equipment is clean and dry.

If the material is received in drums, packages, or cakes, the cube-root method may be used to determine the number of units to be sampled.

10-14. OTHER MATERIALS

Forms and Appurtenances

Normally, the choice of form materials is entirely in the hands of the contractor, although the specifications may sometimes state a requirement for a certain form surface to produce a certain surface or effect on the concrete. Forms are usually of wood, frequently of steel, and, rarely, of other materials, such as rubber or plastic for special effects. Intricate architectural details are sometimes cast against "waste molds." A waste mold is one made of plaster which, after the concrete has hardened, is removed piecemeal, being wasted or destroyed in the process.

There is almost an infinite variety of form ties, steel supports, and other hardware used in forms, each serving a specific function.

Coatings for forms may consist of various oils, waxes, and lacquers. Development of synthetic resins during recent years has resulted in a number of special coatings for special purposes. A coating that is suitable for one condition will not necessarily be satisfactory for another. For example, an oil for a steel tunnel form would not perform if it were to be used on a steel form for concrete to be steam cured, nor would it be satisfactory on a wood form.

Forms are discussed in considerable detail in Sec. 12-3.

Coloring Materials

There are a number of chemical stains available on the market. These are proprietary compounds and normally present no problem in selection.

Color in concrete is frequently attained by the use of a small amount of mineral pigment. The synthetic varieties are recommended because of their uniformity and intensity. Iron oxides should be used for shades of black, gray, brown, red, and yellow; chromium oxide for greens; and cobalt blue for blues. Combinations may be desirable for special color effects.

Terrazzo

Aggregates for terrazzo floor finish consist of chips of marble or other decorative stone selected for their color effect. Size of chips may be varied depending on the effect desired.

Adhesives

Bonding agents may, in a general sense, be classed as adhesives, as they promote the bond (adhesion) of new concrete to old. In its strict sense, however, the term adhesive means a substance that is used to join hardened concrete or other solid material to hardened concrete. Epoxy resin is extensively used for this purpose.

Epoxy resin is sold under a multitude of trade names. The material consists of two components: the basic resin, and a curing agent, which are packaged so that a full can of one component is mixed, on the site, with a full can of the second component in small batches that can be used up in 2 or 3 hr.

This method of packaging and handling is necessary because of the short pot life of the epoxy-curing agent mixture. *Pot life* is the period of time during which the material can be used after it has been mixed; it is different for different formulations and decreases with rising temperature. Normally it is in the range of 2 to 4 hr.

Toluene is a good solvent or thinner for epoxy before it hardens, but once it hardens, there is virtually no way to soften or remove epoxy. Tools, spillage, and any surface on which the epoxy is not wanted must be cleaned with toluene before the resin becomes hard.

Epoxies and curing agents are formulated by the manufacturers in a number of ways to produce materials for a variety of uses. Epoxy may be used as a bonding agent, for fastening broken pieces of concrete back into place, to join metal hardware to concrete, to grout dowels into holes drilled into concrete, and to bond nonskid materials to floors and pavements.

REFERENCES

10.1 Admixtures for Concrete, Report of ACI Committee 212, *J. Am. Concrete Inst.*, Proc. vol. 51, pp. 113–148, October, 1954.

10.2 *Public Roads*, vol. 27, no. 12, U.S. Bureau of Public Roads, Washington 25, D.C., February, 1954.

10.3 Entrained Air in Concrete, Symposium of 15 papers, *J. Am. Concrete Inst.*, Proc. vol. 42, pp. 601–699, June, 1946.

10.4 Lerch, William: Basic Principles of Air-entrained Concrete, Portland Cement Association, 1953, 36 pp.

10.5 *Public Roads*, vol. 31, no. 6, U.S. Bureau of Public Roads, Washington 25, D.C., February, 1961.

CHAPTER 11 *Aggregate Processing and Inspection*

11-1. AGGREGATE SOURCES

Preliminary Approval

One of the first steps when a job starts is to obtain information about the aggregates. If preliminary aggregate tests are required, the engineer should have the laboratory obtain samples and make tests as soon as the contractor has designated the source. If no preliminary tests are required, the engineer should at least be sure that the proposed source is an established one, with a satisfactory record of use as regards durability, strength, and other desirable qualities of concrete.

Most construction jobs, especially in urban areas, are supplied with concrete from established ready-mixed plants, which in turn have well-established aggregate sources. These established sources have usually been well inspected and tested by various agencies, and trustworthy test results are available. The engineer should make sure that whatever test reports are offered truly represent the material to be used, and that there have been no changes in characteristics of the pit or quarry face being worked.

For the purpose of preliminary approval, the quality of the material is of greatest importance. Grading is of secondary importance as it can be corrected by processing.

If it is considered desirable or necessary to make an evaluation of an unfamiliar plant or source, more elaborate steps become necessary. An inspection of the deposit and plant should be made and a report prepared, covering the following information:

1. Name and address of operator, or owner in case of a new deposit
2. Location of deposit, and plant if any
3. Age and condition of plant, if any
4. Availability of transportation facilities

5. Extent of deposit

6. Capacity of plant and stockpiles

7. Description of plant, including type and condition of equipment for excavating, transporting, crushing, screening, washing, classifying, and loading

8. Approximate percentage of the several sizes produced

9. Availability of truck or car scales

10. Principal users of product

11. Service history, if available, of structures made with aggregate, including name, type, and size of structure, age, data on concrete, and comments relative to the condition of the structure

12. Any other pertinent comments

Samples from undeveloped deposits should consist of sufficient pit-run or ledge material to yield the necessary quantities of each size for testing. Samples from processing plants should consist of a sufficient amount of each specification size for testing. About 100 lb of each size is sufficient. In general, the sampling procedure should conform to ASTM Designation: D 75.

Tests to be performed on these samples for preliminary approval should include: sieve analysis, specific gravity, absorption, unit weight, petrographic examination, clay lumps, organic, minus 200-mesh (material passing a 200-mesh sieve), soundness, mortar-making properties of fine aggregate, Los Angeles abrasion of coarse aggregates, lightweight material, and soft particles.

Results of these tests, together with the report of the source inspection, are the basis for acceptance or rejection of the source, or for making additional studies that may be needed for acceptance or rejection.

Prospecting New Deposits

Large jobs in rural or isolated areas usually require that a new source of aggregates be developed. Prospecting for aggregate sources requires painstaking and thorough exploration of the area, and should be done by persons familiar with the geological processes by which aggregate deposits are formed and the effects of aggregate characteristics on the properties of concrete.

Aerial reconnaissance, geophysical procedures, and electrical and sonic methods are used extensively in making geological studies. Topographic and geological maps, available from state and federal agencies, are of considerable help in locating promising areas. Cut banks and bars along streams frequently provide information, as do excavations, such as railroad and highway cuts. In the final analysis, if the project is large enough, test pits, core drill holes, cased holes, and similar methods may be indicated.

Considerations recommended by the Bureau of Reclamation are set forth in detail in the *Concrete Manual,* pages 85ff. The following is especially pertinent:

When searching for suitable aggregate, it is important to bear in mind that ideal materials are seldom found. Deficiencies or excesses of one or more sizes are very common; objectionable rock types, coated and cemented particles, or particles of flat or slabby shape may occur in excessive amounts; clay, silt, or organic matter may contaminate the deposit; or weathering may have seriously reduced the strength of the particles. Moreover, ground-water conditions or excessive overburden may seriously impede operations at a deposit. Unfortunately, the conditions within the body of the deposit cannot be directly observed at the surface. However, interpretations based on surface observations are greatly aided by an understanding of the geological conditions and processes which have acted on the material. Frequently such an understanding will permit a distinction to be made between conditions which are merely superficial and those which may be expected at some depth. Final conclusions on these matters will usually require thorough exploration, but as much pertinent information as practicable should be obtained during the reconnaissance and preliminary exploration.

Many objectionable features of sand and gravel deposits are remediable by proper processing. Crushing may supply deficiencies in fine gravel or even in sand sizes, or blending sand may be available. Washing may serve to remove deleterious clay, silt, or organic matter. Selective excavation may be a satisfactory means of avoiding the use of objectionable parts of the deposit. Whether these or other methods of processing are justifiable will usually depend on the magnitude of the project and the availability of satisfactory materials from other sources. Such considerations must influence preliminary explorations. Accessibility, proximity to the job, and the workability of a deposit are essential considerations in evaluating its suitability.

The quantity of aggregate which a deposit may yield should be roughly estimated and compared with the probable requirements. Areas may be estimated roughly by pacing. Depth and grading of the material may be judged by examining the banks of channels or other exposures. Except for an estimated deduction for waste, based on the appearance of the material, it may generally be assumed that a cubic yard of material in place will produce aggregate for a cubic yard of concrete.

It is often necessary to sample quarries or undeveloped rock formations. For preliminary aggregate investigations, requirements for sampling operating quarries, or inactive quarries where finished materials are in storage, are similar to those for commercial sand and gravel deposits.

Samples from undeveloped rock formations must be taken very carefully so that the material selected will, to the greatest possible extent, be typical of the deposit and inclusive of any significant variations of rock type. Representative samples may be difficult to obtain. Overburden may restrict the area from which material can be taken, and obscure the true character of a larger part of the deposit. Moreover, surface outcrops will frequently be more weathered than the interior of the deposit. Samples obtained from loose pieces on the ground or collected from the weathered outer surfaces of outcrops are rarely representative. Fresher material may be obtained by breaking away the outer surfaces, or if necessary, by trenching, blasting, or core drilling.

In sampling undeveloped bedrock formations, certain geological considerations are pertinent. In stratified deposits, such as sandstones or limestones, uniformity in a vertical direction must be evaluated because successive strata are often very different in character. The dip of stratified formations must also be considered because inclination of the strata with respect to surface slope will bring different strata to the surface in different parts of the area. Attention must be directed to the possibility of zones or layers of undesirable material. Clay or shale layers or seams may be so large or prevalent as to necessitate selective quarrying, excessive wasting, or special processing.

11-2. SPECIAL TYPES OF AGGREGATES

Slag

In areas near steel mills, blast furnace slag is frequently used for concrete aggregate. A nonmetallic product of blast furnaces, air-cooled slag consists mainly of lime silicates and aluminosilicates.

After cooling, the slag is crushed and sized in much the same manner as conventional aggregates. The resulting product is hard, angular, and somewhat vesicular.

Slag should be permitted to age in the stockpile for several weeks before being used in concrete in order to leach out undesirable sulfur compounds. It should be free from metallic iron and reasonably free from glassy pieces and clay lumps, and should have a unit weight (ASTM Designation: C 29) of not less than 70 pcf. Good concrete can be made with slag, although the slag imparts a somewhat harsh character to the mix, usually requiring more sand and water for satisfactory workability.

Lightweight Aggregate

Aggregates for lightweight concrete may be either natural or artificial. Natural lightweight aggregates consist of volcanic cinders, tuff, and pumice, and are found in the western part of the United States. These materials, although light in weight, are strong and sound, requiring only crushing and screening. Lightweight concrete of good strength and other desirable properties can be made from them. Some deposits of diatomite have been found to produce satisfactory aggregate.

Artificial lightweight aggregates are produced from a number of raw materials. Hot slag, when quenched in water, expands and forms a vesicular material that is satisfactory for lightweight concrete. Quality and unit weight vary widely, depending on the rate of cooling. Expanded shale and clay, prepared by heating the material to its fusion point, are sold under many trade names. Sometimes the raw material is sized before heating. Some types have a coating which glazes the surface and decidedly reduces water absorption, which aids materially in control of the fresh concrete.

Coal or coke, when burned in high-temperature industrial furnaces, produces cinders that are suitable for use in concrete. Cinders have been used for many years, especially in concrete block. They should be permitted to age in the stockpile for several weeks before being used to wash away sulfur compounds.

Concrete of very low unit weight (as low as 15 pcf) can be made from heated and expanded pearlite or biotite mica (vermiculite).

All lightweight aggregates require the same care in handling as normalweight materials. Some of them, being angular and rough, tend to break down during handling, and all of them will segregate.

Heavyweight Aggregate

High-density concrete for radiation shielding and counterweights contains various materials of high specific gravity. These are discussed below.

1. *Barite.* An ore composed chiefly of barium sulfate ($BaSO_4$). It has a specific gravity of about 4.3. It is relatively soft and, compared with normal aggregate, is of poor physical quality.

2. *Limonite,* $2Fe_2O_3 \cdot 3H_2O$. Specific gravity ranges from 3.6 to 4.0. Hardness varies from soft, claylike material to hard stone suitable for concrete aggregate. It is somewhat friable and breaks down in handling.

3. *Magnetite,* Fe_3O_4. Specific gravity from 4.9 to 5.2. Magnetite is harder and heavier than limonite.

4. *Iron and Steel.* Scrap steel punchings and graded cast iron are sometimes used for coarse aggregate. These materials have a specific gravity of 7 or 8. It is recommended that they be permitted to rust before using.

11-3. AGGREGATE PROCESSING

Because of the lack of uniformity in sources of supply and the difficulty in maintaining uniformity in the finished product, adequate control of aggregate production and handling is a problem that requires constant vigilance on the part of the inspector. Deleterious materials are ordinarily removed by washing or heavy liquid flotation; unsatisfactory grading is corrected by crushing, screening, classifying, and recombining; segregation and breakage are controlled by careful handling and finish screening; and moisture content is kept constant by adequate storage prior to use.

Production—General

Trees, shrubs, and other vegetation should be removed from the area to be excavated; then the surface soil is stripped and wasted to a depth sufficient to eliminate all topsoil and organic matter. Roots, sticks, grass,

FIG. 11-1. A triple-deck classifying and washing screen. Raw material fed into the far end of the screen is washed, sized, and discharged into chutes at the near end. Fines passing through the bottom deck fall into a hopper. Screens may be either horizontal or sloping. (*Diamond Iron Works photo.*)

and leaves should not be permitted to enter the processing plant. In severe cases, this may require stationing one or more workmen at the conveyor belt to handpick such objects.

Sand and gravel should be processed wet. That is, screens should be provided with spray nozzles which direct high-velocity water jets onto the aggregate as it passes over the screens as shown in Fig. 11-1. The jigging action of the aggregate on the screen, together with the scrubbing action of the water, removes all but the most stubborn coatings.

The amount of water required for washing aggregates varies widely, depending on the amounts of silt, clay, or other material to be removed, size of plant, and other factors. A rough guide is: each cubic yard of material produced per 10-hr day requires 1 gal of water per minute. For example, a plant, to produce 400 cu yd of aggregate in a 10-hr day, should be supplied with about 400 gal of water per minute.

Disposal of wash water is a problem that is becoming more acute because of the increasing concern with stream and lake pollution. Sometimes the water can be returned to an excavated portion of the pit where it is permitted to remain long enough for the suspended solids to settle. Passing the water through a sand filter usually removes most of the objectionable suspended matter. Reuse of the wash water may be desirable, provided care is taken to avoid a dangerous buildup of suspended or dissolved substances in the water that may do more harm than good.

Dry Processing

Crushed stone, lacking the fines to be processed in a gravel plant, is usually screened in a dry condition. Sometimes, because of a lack of water in arid areas, it becomes necessary to process sand and gravel in a dry plant. Aside from the dust nuisance, the most serious problems in a dry gravel plant are twofold: first, removal of coatings from the coarse aggregate, and second, avoidance of segregation of the sand. Then, too, because the raw material is seldom completely dry, clean separation is difficult.

Some scrubbing of the coarse aggregate may be achieved by passing it through a horizontal revolving cylinder containing horizontal bars that lift the aggregate and cause a tumbling action. This eliminates some of the soft particles also.

Segregation of dry sand is difficult to control. The best method is to add 6 or 7 per cent moisture by spraying water onto the sand as it passes on the conveyor to the stockpile.

Sand

Pit-run sand usually does not conform to the specifications and must be processed. Grading defects may be corrected by adding blending sand, by crushing a portion of the excess of large sizes, by removing a portion of the excess sizes, or by a combination of these procedures.

If correction of sand grading is to be accomplished by using a blending sand, two alternatives are possible: the blending sand may be fed into the aggregate plant feed and processed with the normal pit sand, or it may be handled separately and proportioned separately at the concrete batching plant. Another successful method, when done under close supervision, is to feed both sands simultaneously onto a conveyor belt. Subsequent handling of the sand tends to mix it, as long as the sand is damp.

Sand should be processed wet. There are a number of classifying and dewatering machines available, most of which operate on the principle that large particles settle faster than small ones when suspended in water.

Other modern hydraulic sizers operate on the hindered settlement principle and are capable of classifying several different-sized grains of fairly uniform specific gravity. Hindered settlement is a process in which the material is fed into a vertically rising current of water. Feed and water velocity are so regulated that the large particles settle and are removed from the bottom of the tank, while the small particles are carried by the water over weirs at the top. Classifiers of this type may consist of

Fig. 11-2. In the drag washer, sand and water are flumed to the center of the sand drag. The dirty water flows off and the sand settles in the box where the steel flights drag through the sand bed, carrying the sand up the incline. Excess water drains back into the box, and sand is carried off by means of a chute or conveyor. (*Diamond Iron Works photo.*)

one or more compartments, each compartment regulated to separate particles of different fineness.

Water jets installed in the bottom of a screw classifier can be used to vary the sand grading by varying the amount of water admitted.

After passing through the classifiers, the several sand fractions are recombined in the proper proportions to produce the required gradation.

In washing sand, uniformity should be required. The feed to the classifiers should be maintained at as constant a rate as possible. Water flow and weir elevations should be changed only as indicated by the cleanliness and grading of the sand produced. Figure 11-2 is a view of one type of sand washer.

Sand manufactured by crushing stone or rock usually results in a harsh concrete mix and should be avoided as much as possible for concrete aggregate. If crushed sand is necessary, that produced by a rod mill or hammer mill has the best particle shape. The product of roll crushers has the least desirable particle shape, containing a high percentage of thin and elongated pieces.

Coarse Aggregate

In most processing plants, one of the first steps is screening out the sand, including the fine crusher material, unless specifications prohibit use of crusher fines in the sand. Once the sand has been scalped (that is, removed by screening), the coarse material is then passed through various stages of crushing and screening.

Coarse material is crushed by several types of machines: large jaw crushers or gyratory crushers may be used for initial breaking of oversize material, gyratory or cone crushers for intermediate size, and corrugated rolls for the smaller sizes. Figures 11-3 and 11-4 show two types of crushers. Screens are usually of the vibrating type, either horizontal or sloping, single-deck or multiple-deck, although there are a few instances when revolving cylindrical screens are used, especially for scalping over-size material for crushing. Some plants keep crushed and uncrushed material separate, while others mix them.

The variety of plant arrangements and flow sheets is almost as great as the number of deposits being processed. Each deposit and each usage imposes its own set of requirements on the processing arrangement. A small, portable type of plant is shown in Fig. 11-5.

Aggregate Beneficiation

Many natural gravels include minerals and rock particles that are not suitable for use in concrete, and therefore require special processing to improve, or beneficiate, them. For example, some deposits in Michigan, Indiana, and Illinois contain porous cherts of relatively low specific gravity. These particles are unsound and cause popouts and unsoundness in the concrete.

Four methods of beneficiation are commonly in use, none of them 100 per cent effective. They are:

1. *Heavy Media Separation.* In this process, coarse aggregate is passed through a tank containing a high-density suspension of magnetite and ferrosilicon in water. The suspension is regulated so rock particles below a certain specific gravity, say 2.55, float in the suspension and are wasted. Heavy particles sink and are reclaimed. This process is effective for either hard or soft rocks and is effective in removing hard, porous chert. Sub-

sequent washing of the gravel removes the suspension material, which is salvaged for reuse. Usually the separation is done in two or three stages. The machine shown in Fig. 11-6 is a single-stage cone separator.

2. *Elastic Fractionation.* This process is based on the rule that hard particles, because of their elasticity, will bounce more than soft, friable ones. Separation is effected by dropping the gravel onto a sloping steel

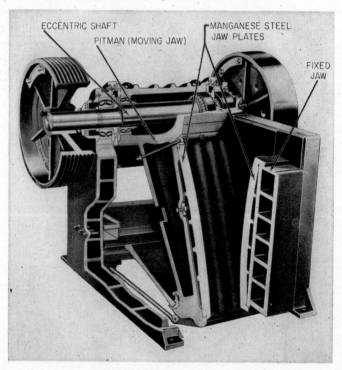

Fig. 11-3. A large jaw crusher for making primary reduction of pit-run material. Crushers of this type frequently have jaw openings as large as 30 by 42 in., and occasionally larger. Stroke, even on large machines, rarely exceeds about 1 in. (*Pioneer Engineering Works, Inc., photo.*)

plate, so arranged that hard rocks rebound into receiving bins, and the soft material is taken off into waste. Usually the bounce material is recirculated, as separation is not thorough.

3. *Jigging.* Based on the hindered settling principle, jigging is accomplished by passing the gravel through a tank in which water is subjected to vertical pulsations, either by means of compressed air jets or vibrating diaphragms. The pulsations tend to float the light material if its specific gravity is appreciably lower than that of the heavier gravel (see Fig. 11-7).

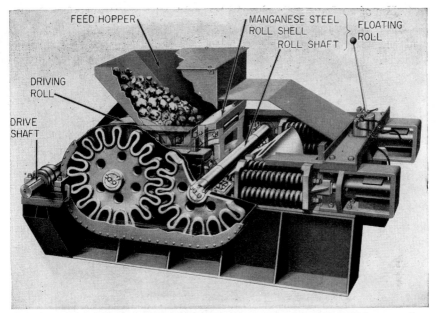

FIG. 11-4. Forty by 22 double roll crusher. The roll crusher is used for secondary reduction, following a primary crusher. A roll crusher produces somewhat more uniform-sized material than jaw or cone crushers. (*Pioneer Engineering Works, Inc.,* photo.)

FIG. 11-5. A portable type of plant, useful for production of road gravel and similar materials. A plant of this type can be used for production of concrete aggregates, as shown here, provided the aggregate is washed and a sand dewatering unit is furnished. (*Pioneer Engineering Works, Inc.,* photo.)

4. *Use of an Impact Crusher.* This machine is sometimes referred to as a cage mill disintegrator. Gravel is fed through a chimney into a metal housing. Inside the housing, a horizontal shaft, equipped with vanes, rotates at high speed. Soft particles are broken up when struck by the

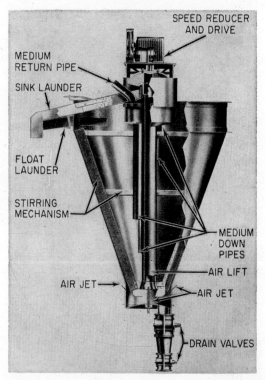

Fig. 11-6. A cone separator for heavy media removal of lightweight aggregate. Feed introduced at the top of the cone is immersed in the ferrous medium of selected specific gravity. The lighter fraction rises to the surface, overflows a weir located opposite the point of entry, and is fed to float drainage and washing screens through a float launder. The heavier fraction sinks to the bottom of the cone and is discharged by internal or external air lift to sink drainage and washing screens. Revolution of the stirring mechanism creates a gentle agitation to maintain uniform suspension of medium particles to provide optimum gravity differential between top and bottom of the cone. (*WEMCO Division of Western Machinery Company photo.*)

vanes, or on impact with the housing. Subsequent screening removes the crushed particles.

Stockpiling

When aggregates are stockpiled on the ground, the ground should first be cleared of all vegetation and rubbish, then leveled. In removing aggregate from the pile, a layer of aggregate should be left on the ground in order that handling equipment will not pick up earth from the original ground. Thickness of this layer or pad depends upon the type of equipment used; an end-loader may require a pad only 6 in. thick, whereas a 12-in. pad should be maintained if a clamshell is being used. Common practice is to spread rejected aggregate of the same size to be stockpiled over the stockpile area to provide a pad in advance of stockpiling operations.

Stockpiles may become contaminated if insufficient area is provided for them, resulting in crowding and overlapping of piles. If there is not

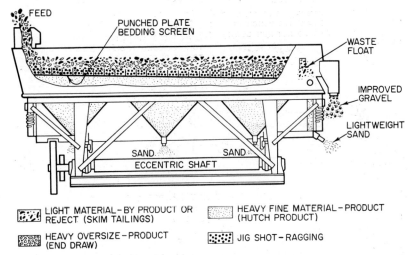

LIGHT MATERIAL–BY PRODUCT OR REJECT (SKIM TAILINGS)

HEAVY FINE MATERIAL–PRODUCT (HUTCH PRODUCT)

HEAVY OVERSIZE–PRODUCT (END DRAW)

JIG SHOT–RAGGING

FIG. 11-7. In the hindered settlement jig, the feed passes over a bed composed of steel shot (ragging) over a punched plate bedding screen. The entire tank is full of water which receives pulsations induced by eccentrics acting on hutches beneath the bed. These pulsations create stratification of the feed, causing the lightweight deleterious material to rise to the top, where it is discharged into waste. Sound gravel is in the second level and is discharged for further processing. Sand passes down through the bed into the hutches, where it is discharged through controllable orifices. (*WEMCO Division of Western Machinery Company.*)

enough room in the area to provide a clear space between piles, separation should be achieved by means of stout partitions or bulkheads.

When moving material into or out of stockpiles by means of a clamshell, the bucket should not be permitted to swing over a pile of one size of aggregate while carrying a different size. For example, if gravel is being removed from a railroad car with a clamshell, the bucket should not be permitted to swing over the sand pile.

Figure 11-8 shows methods of stockpiling gravel that are recommended for minimizing segregation. This figure also shows methods that have been found to be objectionable. Most specifications require that stockpiles be built up in layers not exceeding 4 ft in depth. Piles may be built by dumping directly from trucks, provided:

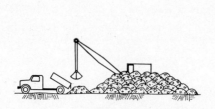
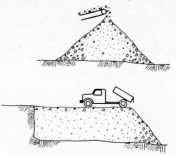

PREFERABLE

CRANE OR OTHER MEANS OF PLACING
MATERIAL IN PILE IN UNITS WHICH REMAIN
WHERE PLACED AND DO NOT RUN DOWN
SLOPES.

OBJECTIONABLE

METHODS WHICH PERMIT THE AGGREGATE
TO ROLL DOWN THE SLOPE AS IT IS ADDED
TO THE PILE, OR PERMIT HAULING EQUIPMENT
TO OPERATE OVER THE SAME LEVEL REPEAT-
EDLY.

PERMISSIBLE BUT NOT PREFERABLE

PILE BUILT RADIALLY IN HORIZONTAL   BULLDOZER STACKING PROGRESSIVE LAYERS
LAYERS BY BULLDOZER WORKING FROM MAT-   ON SLOPE NOT FLATTER THAN 3:1.
ERIALS AS DROPPED FROM CONVEYOR BELT.
A ROCK LADDER MAY BE NEEDED IN THIS
SETUP.

STOCKPILING OF COARSE AGGREGATE

(STOCKPILED AGGREGATE SHOULD BE FINISH SCREENED AT BATCH PLANT)

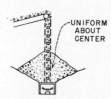
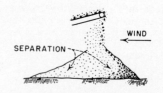

CORRECT

CHIMNEY SURROUNDING MATERIAL FALL-
ING FROM END OF CONVEYOR BELT TO PRE-
VENT WIND FROM SEPARATING FINE AND
COARSE MATERIALS. OPENINGS PROVIDED
AS REQUIRED TO DISCHARGE MATERIALS AT
VARIOUS ELEVATIONS ON THE PILE.

INCORRECT

FREE FALL OF MATERIAL FROM HIGH
END OF STACKER PERMITTING WIND TO
SEPARATE FINE FROM COARSE MATERIAL.

FIG. 11-8. Sand or combined aggregate storage (dry materials). (*U.S. Bureau of Reclamation.*)

1. The pile is protected by mats or otherwise to prevent deposition of oil or mud from the trucks.

2. The trucks do not operate over the same layer repeatedly.

3. The material remains where it is dumped and is not permitted to roll down slopes.

Material is removed from a stockpile by means of a clamshell, end-loader, or a conveyor belt operating in a tunnel beneath the pile. If two or more gates are provided to admit the material to the conveyor, good mixing is usually achieved. When loading out with a clamshell, good mixing can be achieved if the operator takes successive loads from different parts of the pile, rather than removing from one low area where material is continually running down a slope. Use of an end-loader is the least desirable method, as this machine usually removes gravel from the periphery of the pile, near the bottom, causing the gravel to flow down the slope, with resulting segregation.

The greater the size range covered by the gravel in the pile, the greater the danger of harmful segregation. For example, aggregate graded from $\frac{3}{16}$ to $1\frac{1}{2}$ in., when handled as one size of material, tends to segregate more than either the $\frac{3}{16}$- to $\frac{3}{4}$-in. size or the $\frac{3}{4}$- to $1\frac{1}{2}$-in. size.

Sand, being usually handled in a moist condition, need not be subject to the above stockpiling limitations. However, if the sand is dry, it is very difficult to handle. The best remedy is to keep it moist.

Segregation of aggregate is minimized by observing these precautions (illustrated in the accompanying figures):

1. Handle in closely graded sizes, that is, $\frac{3}{16}$- to $\frac{3}{4}$-in. sizes, not $\frac{3}{16}$- to $1\frac{1}{4}$-in. or similar sizes.

2. Handle and move as few times as possible.

3. Avoid high cone-shaped piles.

4. Stockpile in layers.

5. Remove from stockpile in layers, or use a tunnel conveyor with two or more gates under the pile.

6. Use rock ladders in piles and bins.

7. Drop material vertically into the bin.

8. Keep bins full.

9. Use tall and thin bins, preferably circular in plan, with bottom sloping about 50° from the horizontal (see Figs. 11-9 to 11-11).

11-4. AGGREGATE INSPECTING

Sampling

Truly representative samples are difficult to obtain, and the following paragraphs describe methods that will usually enable the inspector to obtain samples as nearly representative as possible.

Considerable judgment is necessary in taking samples and drawing conclusions from the results of tests. Care should be exercised that samples are representative of the materials being tested. ASTM Designation: D 75 gives methods of sampling aggregates from stockpiles, cars,

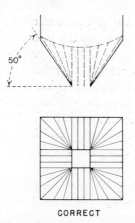
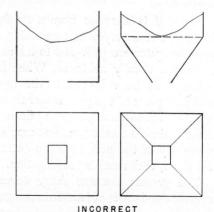

CORRECT

FULL BOTTOM SLOPING 50° FROM HORI-
ZONTAL IN ALL DIRECTIONS TO OUTLET
WITH CORNERS OF BIN PROPERLY ROUNDED.

INCORRECT

FLAT BOTTOM BINS OR THOSE WITH ANY
ARRANGEMENT OF SLOPES HAVING CORNERS
OR AREAS SUCH THAT ALL MATERIAL IN
BINS WILL NOT FLOW READILY THROUGH
OUTLET WITHOUT SHOVELING.

SLOPE OF AGGREGATE BIN BOTTOMS

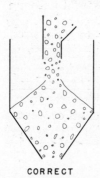
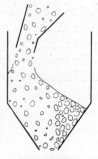

CORRECT

MATERIAL DROPS VERTICALLY INTO BIN
DIRECTLY OVER THE DISCHARGE OPENING
PERMITTING DISCHARGE OF MORE GENER-
ALLY UNIFORM MATERIAL.

INCORRECT

CHUTING MATERIAL INTO BIN ON AN ANGLE.
MATERIAL THAT DOES NOT FALL DIRECTLY
OVER OUTLET IS NOT ALWAYS UNIFORM AS
DISCHARGED.

FILLING OF AGGREGATE BINS

FIG. 11-9. Incorrect methods of handling aggregates cause segregation which results in lack of uniformity in the concrete. (*U.S. Bureau of Reclamation.*)

and other sources. These methods should be followed at all times. In sampling from a stockpile, the composite sample should be made up by taking one shovelful at the top of the pile, four at equally spaced points around the bottom, and four at random about halfway up the slope of the pile, all consisting of material from below the surface. If a short piece of board is held against the pile just above the point of sampling, unwanted material can be kept out of the sample. Individual sieve analyses may be made if it is desired to determine whether or not the materials

Fig. 11-10. Segregation of coarse aggregate in a railroad car, showing concentration of undersize and dirt near bottom of car.

Fig. 11-11. Segregation in a batching plant stockpile. Such aggregate should not be used without finish screening.

are segregated. If an analysis representative of the whole pile is desired, the samples may be combined, then quartered to obtain a sample for testing.

To obtain a representative sample from a conveyor belt, a complete cross section of the stream should be taken for a short period of time, rather than a portion of the stream over a longer time. If possible, the conveyor should be stopped long enough for a sample to be removed, as to take a sample from a moving belt is nearly impossible and somewhat dangerous to personnel. Another practical method is to sample the material as it leaves the belt.

The stream of aggregate emerging from a chute or other opening is seldom uniform in cross section with respect to particle size, hence the need for sampling the entire stream. The sampling bucket or container should not be permitted to overflow, as to do so may result in a sample with more fines than are present in the material being sampled.

Representative sampling of trucks and railroad cars is extremely difficult. It is necessary to dig into the load at several points, obtaining a rather large sample that has to be split down to testing size. The exact procedure is described in ASTM Designation: D 75. Usually, a visual inspection of the car will give a general idea of the condition of material in the car, and can guide the sampler in determining where to take sufficient samples to be representative of the carload of material. Sand, if moist, represents no problem. Coarse aggregate segregates as it is loaded into the car, and this condition may be observed on the surface or by digging into the load.

Samples to be sent to the laboratory should be placed in clean cloth sample bags, plastic-lined burlap bags, or other suitable containers. An identifying card or tag should be placed inside the bag and one on the outside. The bag should be securely tied and sent immediately to the laboratory.

The sampling schedule shown in Table 11-1 was used on a large toll highway project and is included here to illustrate the aggregate control that is sometimes required on a large project. However, any such schedule depends upon the uniformity of the deposit, production capacity, and type of plant. A certain flexibility is necessary to allow for variations in material and production.

The size of sample depends upon the tests to be run and the size of the largest particle. ASTM Designation: D 75 gives the weights of samples required. Generally a sample of 75 to 100 lb of coarse aggregate, or 50 lb of sand, will be adequate for most series of tests.

Quartering Samples

Samples of aggregates, as obtained at the source or processing plant, are usually larger than is convenient for testing. Fine aggregate samples may be effectively reduced to test size by a sample splitter. The quartering method should be used for reducing the size of coarse aggregate samples, and may be used for reducing the size of fine aggregate samples if a sample splitter is not available. In the quartering method, the sample is placed on a hard, clean surface where there will be neither loss of material nor accidental addition of foreign matter. In the field, a piece of canvas may be used. The sample is mixed thoroughly by turning the entire lot over, three times with a shovel, beginning at one end and taking alternate shovels of the material the length of the pile. With the third or last turning, the entire sample is shoveled into a conical pile by depositing each shovelful on top of the preceding one. The conical pile is carefully flattened to a uniform thickness and diameter so that the material will not be transposed from one quarter to another. The flattened mass is then marked into quarters by two lines that intersect at right angles at the center of the pile. Two diagonally opposite quarters are removed and the cleared spaces brushed clean. The remaining

TABLE 11-1. TYPICAL AGGREGATE TESTING SCHEDULE

Test*	ASTM Designation	Frequency†
Screen analysis	C 136	A
Clay lumps	C 142	B
Minus 200 mesh	C 117	B
Organic impurities	C 40	B
Soft particles	C 235	B
Lightweight particles	C 123	C
Specific gravity	C 127 and 128	C
Absorption	C 127 and 128	C
Unit weight	C 29	C
Los Angeles abrasion (coarse)	C 131	D
Soundness	C 88	D
Mortar properties (fine)	C 87	E
Petrographic	C 295	E

* Any and all tests should be repeated whenever the nature of the material in the deposit changes.

† The frequency is as follows:

A. At least once each 100 tons but not more than 10 nor fewer than 1 per day

B. At least once each 2,000 tons, but not more than 1 per day

C. Every 10,000 tons or once every 2 weeks

D. Once for initial source approval, then 1 per 30,000 tons

E. Once per deposit

material is mixed and quartered successively until the sample is reduced to the desired test size (based on Reclamation Bureau method).

The practice of adding or removing small increments of material to obtain a sample of a certain size or weight should be avoided, as these small increments are apt to affect the quality of the sample. Instead, the sample should be split to an amount reasonably close to the desired amount.

Inspecting

It is the responsibility of the aggregate plant inspector to be fully familiar with the specifications and instructions applying to his work. He should be on duty in the plant whenever aggregates are being processed or loaded for the project. He should be cooperative, taking samples and running tests as soon as possible after production of material begins or after notification is received of shipments to be made. Reports should be promptly and accurately made.

The inspector is concerned chiefly with obtaining and testing samples. Additional duties include inspection of the deposit to ascertain that overburden has been stripped ahead of excavation, and inspection of loading out and stockpiling operations. The previous sections in this chapter covering aggregate processing provide information that will enable the inspector to perform his work effectively.

Railroad cars and trucks used for hauling aggregates must be clean and sufficiently tight to prevent loss of material in transit. Hauling equipment should be inspected before loading. Units containing dirt, coal, or the remnants of previous loads should be cleaned out before loading. Sticks, rags, and similar material should not be used for chinking holes in vehicles, as these materials frequently find their way into the batching bins, and subsequently into the concrete. Vehicles that are not in good condition should not be loaded.

The inspector should observe the materials passing on conveyor belts to determine the presence of sticks, roots, trash, clay balls, or other contaminating substances. If the plant is operating in a deposit known to contain a relatively high percentage of chert, soft particles, or other inferior materials, close observation of the finished product is necessary.

Some specifications place a limit on the amount of crushed material in the coarse aggregate. Determination of the percentage of crushed material is accomplished by visual separation of crushed and uncrushed particles, piece by piece, then weighing the two fractions.

11-5. AGGREGATE TESTS

Testing methods, as well as grading and other properties of the aggregates, are spelled out in the job specifications, sometimes by reference to methods of the American Society for Testing and Materials, the American Association of State Highway Officials, American Railway Engineering Association, or similar organizations. The methods described in ASTM Designation: C 33 are generally acceptable.

Specification requirements for aggregate properties are designed to evaluate these properties at the time the aggregates are batched into the concrete. For this reason, control tests of aggregates should be made on samples taken at the batcher. As a practical measure to assist the aggregate producer, it is common practice on large projects to station inspectors at the aggregate processing plant and sample the materials at that location. However, final acceptance is still based on batching plant tests.

Sieve Analysis

The property of aggregate most apt to change from hour to hour is the gradation, or distribution of particle sizes on several specified sizes of sieves. The test for gradation is known variously as sieve analysis, grading analysis, mechanical analysis, gradation, or simply grading.

Sieve analyses are based on per cents retained on or passing square mesh sieves. The material may be sieved through each sieve individually, or, more commonly, by stacking the specified sieves on a mechanical shaker and doing it all in one operation. Slugs, such as steel shot or similar objects, should not be used as sieving aids, nor should individual

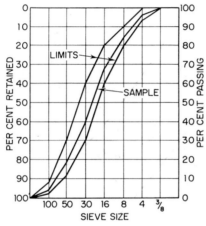

FIG. 11-12. Grading curve with limits.

Sand Grading

Sieve	Limits, % retained	Sieve	Limits, % retained
⅜	0	30	40–70
4	0–5	50	70–88
8	10–20	100	92–98
16	20–40		

particles be manipulated by hand to force them through the sieve openings. The method of making the test is detailed in ASTM Designation: C 136.

Because of the probable variations in gradation, the sieve analysis tests are the ones most frequently performed by the inspector. In a large plant, it may be necessary to make tests as often as once per hour.

Plotting the sieve analysis graphically is of considerable value in visualizing the particle-size distribution of an aggregate, as shown in Fig. 11-12, which is a typical cumulative grading curve for a fine aggregate showing per cents retained (or passing) and the specification limits. Data from coarse-aggregate tests as well as from fine-aggregate tests may be plotted in this manner. Current practice is sometimes to compute and show individual per cents passing one sieve and retained on the next smaller sieve, a practice that appears to be gaining popularity.

The fineness modulus of an aggregate is a measure of its fineness. It is determined by adding together the cumulative per cents retained on a specified series of sieves and dividing by 100. ASTM Designation: C 125 specifies No. 100, No. 50, No. 30, No. 16, No. 8, No. 4, ⅜ in., ¾ in., 1½

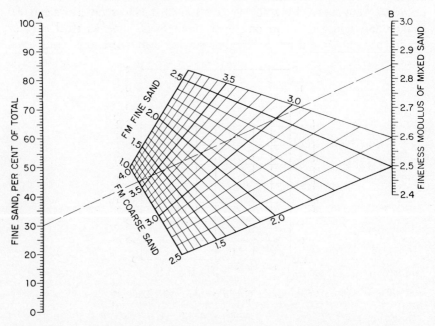

Fig. 11-13. Sand-blending chart. To use this figure, draw a straight line from the specified fineness modulus of mixed sand (Scale B) through the intersection of coarse fineness modulus (FM coarse sand) and fine fineness modulus (FM fine sand) lines, and read, on Scale A, the per cent of fine sand. For example, if the required FM is 2.85, the FM fine sand 2.03, and the FM coarse sand 3.20, then the per cent of fine sand is 30.

in. and larger, increasing in the ratio of 2:1. The fineness modulus (abbreviated FM) does not provide information as to the grading of an aggregate, but is useful in comparing the fineness of different aggregates.

The fineness modulus of sands is useful when attempting to blend a fine sand with a coarse sand to obtain a specified FM. The chart (Fig. 11-13) simplifies the computation. After determining the percentages of the two sands from the chart, the per cents passing or retained on each sieve, for one sand, are multiplied by the percentages of that sand in the mixture and added to similar values for the other sand to give the combined grading of the mixture.

It is usual practice to make more than one test when noncompliance with the specified grading is found, before condemning the material. The recommended procedure is to keep a running average of results from the last three tests, dropping the oldest one and adding the new one each time a test is made, in this way obtaining a more representative evaluation of the material during a given period of production, or contained in any given stockpile or bin.

Occasionally data may be based on round sieve openings instead of square openings. Table 11-2 shows equivalent round and square openings

TABLE 11-2. APPROXIMATE EQUIVALENT SQUARE AND ROUND OPENINGS OF U.S. STANDARD SIEVES

Square hole	Round hole	Square hole	Round hole
3	$3\frac{1}{2}$	$\frac{7}{8}$	1
$2\frac{1}{2}$	3	$\frac{3}{4}$	$\frac{7}{8}$
$2\frac{1}{8}$	$2\frac{1}{2}$	$\frac{5}{8}$	$\frac{3}{4}$
2	$2\frac{3}{4}$	$\frac{1}{2}$	$\frac{5}{8}$
$1\frac{3}{4}$	2	$\frac{3}{8}$	$\frac{1}{2}$
$1\frac{1}{2}$	$1\frac{3}{4}$	$\frac{5}{16}$	$\frac{3}{8}$
$1\frac{1}{4}$	$1\frac{1}{2}$	$\frac{1}{4}$	$\frac{5}{16}$
1	$1\frac{1}{4}$	$\frac{3}{16}$	$\frac{1}{4}$

Note: Measurements in inches.

and will assist in converting from one to the other. The square equivalents may be interpolated on a chart similar to Fig. 11-12. Plotting the per cents of each size will then aid in visualizing the gradation.

Other Tests

Table 11-1 lists various tests routinely performed, with typical frequencies for performing these tests on a large job. Usually, fewer tests will suffice unless the material is quite variable or large quantities are being handled.

Tests that should be performed every day or so are those for clay lumps, material passing the 200-mesh sieve (sometimes called silt, or minus 200-mesh), organic impurities, and soft particles.

Specifications limit the amount of deleterious substances in the aggregate to a total of 4 or 5 per cent by weight, with individual limits on each of the substances classified as deleterious. Soft and unsound fragments, clay lumps, coal, lignite, porous chert, shells, material finer than the No. 200 sieve, conglomerate, and cemented particles are usually classified as deleterious. Other substances may be included, depending on local conditions.

An approximate evaluation of the presence of organic material is made by treating the sand with a 3 per cent solution of sodium hydroxide in a 12-oz graduated bottle. After 24 hr, the color of the clear liquid in the bottle is compared with a standard color. If the sample color is darker than the standard, it indicates the presence of organic

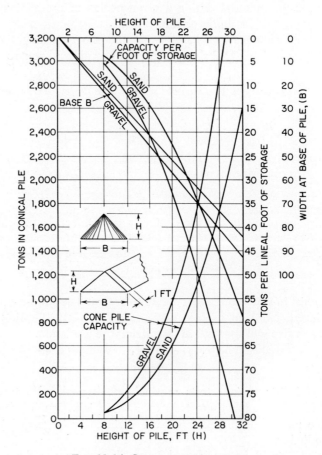

Fig. 11-14. Storage capacity curves.

material in the sand. Further tests, such as for mortar-making properties, should be made, or more intensive washing of the sand should be required.

Specific gravity, absorption, unit weight, abrasion loss, and soundness ordinarily do not change to any considerable extent throughout a deposit, but occasional tests should be made to verify this fact.

If the aggregate has a satisfactory service record in an exposure equal to that of the proposed structure, and the other tests indicate adequate quality, a petrographic analysis is usually not necessary. However, the petrographic analysis sometimes reveals potentially reactive or deleterious materials not otherwise detected, and may point the way to remedial or preventive measures. For example, potentially reactive aggregates will be disclosed, which may make desirable the use of low-alkali cement.

Storage Capacity Curves

The curves in Fig. 11-14 are designed for computing quantities of sand and gravel in either conical piles or in long, tentlike piles. Because of differences in specific gravity, bulking factor, particle shape, and grading, results from these curves should be considered as only approximate.

Three types of computations may be made:

1. Storage capacity of a conical pile. Enter chart at the top or bottom at "Height of pile, ft." Then proceed vertically to intersect the cone-pile capacity curve for the material being computed. Proceed horizontally from this point of intersection to the left, and read capacity in tons. *Example:* A 24-ft-high conical pile of gravel holds 1,750 tons.

2. Storage of long, narrow tentlike piles. The two ends form one conical pile, capacity of which may be computed as above. The intermediate pile is figured from the "Capacities per ft of storage" curve. Enter chart at the top or bottom at "Height, ft." Then proceed vertically to intersect the "Capacity per ft of storage" curve for the material being computed. From this intersection proceed horizontally to the first column on the right, reading tonnage per lineal foot. This multiplied by length in feet of intermediate section gives weight of material. *Example:* A 24-ft-high pile of gravel has 49 tons per foot of storage.

Adding the weight of material in the conical section to that for the intermediate section gives the capacity of the entire pile.

3. The base width of a pile may be determined from the "Base dimension" curves if pile height is known. Enter chart at the height of pile, moving vertically to intersect the proper base dimension line. Next move horizontally from this intersection to the second column on the right, reading width in feet. *Example:* A 24-ft-high pile of gravel will be 70 ft wide.

CHAPTER 12 *Concrete Manufacturing and Inspection*

The amount of inspection and testing to be performed for any job depends upon the requirements of the owner, or upon the customs and instructions of the architect or engineer. As pointed out in Chap. 11, inspection requirements vary widely, depending to a considerable extent upon personal preferences. Many jobs, especially architectural ones, are not inspected to the degree necessary to ensure first-class construction.

Inspection procedures discussed in this chapter are adaptable to any of the batching plant types listed in Table 12-1, with modification to suit individual plants, and may be adapted to whatever degree of control is desired.

12-1. BATCHING AND MIXING

Plant Equipment

Batching and mixing equipment ranges in size and complexity from simple wheelbarrow scales supplying a small portable mixer to complicated automatic stationary plants with a capacity of several hundred cubic yards of concrete per hour. With the greatly increased usage of ready-mixed concrete, the small portable layouts are seen less frequently on construction jobs, especially in the cities. Nearly every town and city has at least one ready-mixed concrete plant, some of which, however, offer virtually nothing in the way of control. Several plants are shown in Figs. 12-1 to 12-5. Figure 12-6 shows an operating console for an automatic plant.

Control is not a function of size. Accurate control of concrete quality is possible with wheelbarrow scales and a three-sack mixer under care-

176

ful operation and qualified inspection. On the other hand, the most modern automatic equipment is of no avail in the hands of sloppy operators and careless inspectors.

With few exceptions, nearly all inspection is performed in one of five general plant classes as shown in Table 12-1.

A wide variety of batching and weighing equipment is available, which may be assembled into diverse combinations subject to one basic requirement: the cement must be weighed separately from other materials. Some plants weigh the cement first on cumulative scales on which the aggregates are weighed, but this is not a desirable method. A satisfactory arrangement is to suspend the cement weigh batcher in the

TABLE 12-1. CLASSIFICATION OF BATCHING PLANTS

1. Semiportable, automatic or manual, of the type used on large highway and airport paving jobs. A plant of this type is set up at a convenient location for the job and upon completion of the contract is dismantled and moved to another location. Concrete is dry-batched into trucks and hauled to the mixer at the paving or structure site. Cement and aggregates may each be weighed in separate plants, the truck making two or more stops to receive a full load of several batches.
2. Permanent, automatic, or manual, serving a fleet of commercial ready-mix trucks delivering a variety of concrete to numerous customers. Concrete may be mixed at the plant and hauled in agitator trucks or may be dumped into truck mixers and mixed in transit.
3. Semipermanent, usually automatic, set up to serve one large job, such as a dam. Although conforming to the criteria for a permanent plant, a plant for this service is dismantled upon completion of the project.
4. A great variety of sizes and types serving prestressed concrete and products casting yards.
5. Small portable job batchers for mixers of 1 cu yd capacity or smaller.

center of, but independent from, the aggregate weigh batcher or hopper. Cement is then weighed first on its own independent scale, followed by the aggregate on their scales.

Batching of aggregates may be cumulative, each aggregate being weighed in turn in one weigh batcher, or batching may be individual, each aggregate being weighed separately in its own weigh batcher. Scales may be either beam- or dial-type for either weighing method.

If the water is weighed, separate scales should be provided for it. Water in most plants is measured volumetrically, either by means of a meter or in a calibrated tank. Water batchers on portable mixers are of the volumetric overflow or siphon type.

Admixtures should be handled in solution and may be measured either by weight or volume. One type of dispenser controls the amount measured by means of a timer which regulates the period of time during

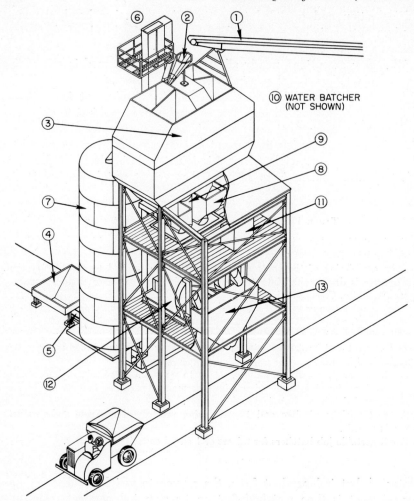

Fig. 12-1. A plant using bulk cement and producing mixed concrete which is moved to the point of placement in agitating or nonagitating trucks (nonagitating truck shown). This is a central-mix plant.

1. Belt conveyor. Transfers aggregates from stockpile (not shown) to top of bin at rate of 460 tons per hr. Belt is 30 in. wide and can be controlled from either ground or top of bin.
2. Pivoted distributor. Directs aggregate flow into any one of three bin compartments. Distributor is manually controlled from ground level by cables.
3. Bin. Portable section bin with 200 bbl central cement compartment and three aggregate compartments, one of 57 cu yd and two of 29 cu yd each.
4. Cement hopper. Receives bulk cement supply from cars or trucks. 30-bbl capacity.
5. Screw conveyor. Transfers bulk cement from receiving hopper or cement silo to elevator boot at 440 bbl per hr.
6. Cement elevator. Vertical, enclosed bucket elevator, with two-way discharge gate, directs cement to central tank in bin or to auxiliary ground storage silo.

which a small pump forces the material through a calibrated orifice. Others depend upon a variable-stroke piston, overflow or siphon tanks, and other devices.

Some specifications, especially on large jobs, require that the plant be equipped with a recorder that makes a graphic record of every batch. Subsequent study of the recorder charts reveals any irregularities in plant operation.

Many permanent and semipermanent plants are equipped with moisture meters. A device of this type consists of two electrodes (sometimes the steel batcher side is one electrode) in the sand weigh batcher, connected electrically to an indicating device at the operating console by which the operator and inspector are informed of the per cent of moisture in the sand being batched so that proper allowances can be made. One type of meter is connected to a recorder so a permanent record of moisture variations is made. This recorder also serves to count the number of sand batches weighed up.

Instruments for measuring the consistency of the concrete in the mixer are also available. One type is a wattmeter that measures the power required to turn the mixer, a dry batch requiring more power than a wet one. Another measures the overturning moment acting on a tilting mixer, a dry batch having a tendency to concentrate in one end of the mixer, rather than level out as a wetter batch would do. Different mixes and different-sized batches require individual calibration.

Mixers may be either portable or stationary, tilting or nontilting, in a large range of sizes from small 3 cu ft laboratory models to those with a capacity of 5 cu yd and larger. The choice between tilting and nontilting is largely a matter of personal preference since either type is capable of mixing concrete efficiently and thoroughly.

The nontilter has a cylindrical drum and is usually charged or loaded by means of a skip or hopper at one end of the drum, with the mixed

---

Gate is cable-controlled from ground level. Elevator capacity is 440 bbl per hr.
7. Cement silo. Stores bulk cement supply. Cement is reclaimed through valve and screw conveyor at bottom of silo. Silo capacity is 829 bbl.
8. Aggregate batchers. Total of three, 4,000 lb capacity each. Rectangular type, fully automatic, air-cylinder operated.
9. Cement batcher. 1,500 lb capacity, fully automatic, air-cylinder operated.
10. Water batcher. (Not shown.)
11. Batch controller. Automatically controls the batch weight of all materials. Includes a graphic recorder that produces a permanent record of all materials batched, with time, date, and batch number of each batch.
12. Mixers. Two nontilting 56-S (2 cu yd) size, automatically controlled by batch controller.
13. Guide spout. Directs mixed concrete from both mixers to common truck charging point. (*C. S. Johnson Co.*)

FIG. 12-2. Semiportable manual plant for producing dry batches for a paving job. Note finish screen on tower adjoining the batcher, on the left.

FIG. 12-3. Semiportable manual plant for producing dry batches for a paving job. No finish screen on this plant. (*U.S. Bureau of Reclamation photo.*)

FIG. 12-4. Small, portable job batcher for weighing three sizes of aggregates. Sacked cement used with this plant.

FIG. 12-5. Portable wheelbarrow scales for weighing concrete aggregates on a small job.

concrete discharged by means of a swinging discharge chute at the other end.

Paving mixers mounted on crawler tracks are a common type of non-tilting mixer. A paving mixer may consist of one or two drums, the dual-drum mixer actually consisting of a long drum divided into two separate compartments by a bulkhead with a swinging chute extending through it. (Recent developments have included the experimental use of a triple-drum mixer.) The advantage of the multiple-drum paver is its greatly increased productivity during any given period of time as compared with a single-drum mixer.

Table 12-2 shows the productive capacity of a 34-E* dual-drum paver operating at various mixing times from 50 to 90 sec, together with materials requirements. Batching-plant capacities for one, two, or three 34-E

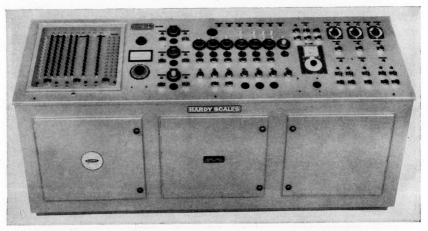

Fig. 12-6. Operating console for an automatic batching plant. This unit contains the following controls: three aggregates, 1 cement, and 1 water, with provision for 13 preset batches. Five weight-selector dials, 1 for each material, to permit batching of special mixes. Three calibrating dials, 1 for each scale. Partial batch system to permit batching partial batches from 7 cu yd to 1 cu yd in ⅛ cu yd increments. Three admixture interlocks, for 3 admixtures. Key reset electrical counter for counting batches. Provision for complete manual operation if necessary. (*Hardy Scales Company photo.*)

dual-drum pavers are shown in Table 12-3. Most specifying agencies require a total mixing time of 60 sec exclusive of the transfer and discharge times.

The series of sketches in Fig. 12-7 illustrates the functioning of a dual-drum paver by following a single batch of cement and aggregate completely through the paver. The steps described in the caption are keyed to the Roman numerals at the left of the sketches.[12.1]†

---

* A 34-E paver has a rated mixing capacity of 34 cu ft of concrete. A mixer in good operating condition will satisfactorily mix a 10 per cent overload, or a total of 37.4 cu ft (1.385 cu yd).

† Superscript figures refer to chapter and reference number. The references are found at the end of each chapter.

Tilting mixers are found in many stationary or permanent plants. The tilter has a bowl-shaped or conical drum and may be charged at either the front or back, depending on the manufacture and installation. Discharge of the mixed concrete is accomplished by tilting the front end downward.

TABLE 12-2. 34-E DUAL-DRUM PAVER PRODUCTION AND MATERIALS REQUIREMENTS

Mixing time, sec................................	50	60	75	90
Cycle, sec per batch...........................	36.5	41.5	49.0	56.5
Batches per hour..............................	98.6	86.7	73.4	63.7
Cu yd concrete per hour......................	136	120	101	88.2
10-in. × 12-ft pavement, lin ft per hr........	369	324	274	238
Cement, bbl per hr...........................	222	195	165	144
Aggregate, tons per hr........................	210	184	156	136
Water, gal per hr.............................	4530	3990	3380	2930

Quantities are based on a 1.385 cu yd batch, consisting of 846 lb cement, 4,250 lb aggregate, and 46 gal water. Comparable output for other pavers: 34-E single-drum, 57%: 16-E dual-drum, 47%: 27-E single-drum, 46%.
SOURCE: C. S. Johnson Co.

TABLE 12-3. RECOMMENDED BATCHING PLANT CAPACITIES

	34-E pavers (dual-drum)		
	One	Two	Three
Cement, bbl per hr..................	195	390	585
Cement, 400-bbl cars per day.........	5	10	15
Capacity cement-handling equipment, bbl per hr.......................	275	440	650
Overhead cement storage, bbl........	254	492	739
Aggregate, tons per hr...............	184	368	552
Aggregate, 50-ton cars per day........	37	74	111
Bin-charging equipment..............	one 1¾ cu yd clamshell	two 1½ or one 3 yd clamshell or 30-in. conveyor	30-in. belt conveyor
Overhead aggregate storage, cu yd.....	70	120	120

Quantities and recommendations based on 60-sec mixing time and 10-hr day.
SOURCE: C. S. Johnson Co.

A relatively new type of mixer, known as a turbine mixer, consists of a large pan or tub in which paddles, operating on a vertical shaft, accomplish the mixing. Advantages claimed are superior mixing in less time than conventional rotating-drum mixers. Another advantage is the low headroom required for installation.

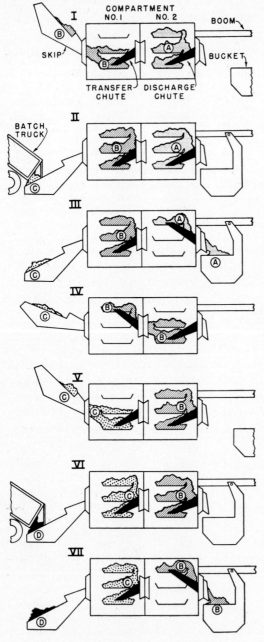

Step I. The skip is up, and batch B is entering compartment 1. Batch A, already in compartment 2, continues mixing. The transfer and discharge chutes are both closed. The empty bucket is returning along the boom.

Step II. Batches B and A continue mixing in compartments 1 and 2, respectively. The skip is down and is receiving batch C from the batch truck. The empty bucket has returned. The transfer and discharge chutes are still closed.

Step III. The discharge chute has opened, and batch A is being discharged from compartment 2 to the bucket. Batch B continues mixing in compartment 1, and batch C is in the skip, which is still on the ground. The transfer chute is still closed.

Step IV. The discharge chute has closed, and batch A is in the bucket, riding out the boom to be dumped. As the discharge chute closed, the transfer chute opened, and batch B is being transferred from compartment 1 to compartment 2. The skip is moving upward with batch C. These four steps complete one paver cycle.

Steps V, VI, and VII. These steps correspond exactly to steps I, II, and III, respectively. They are included in the series to show the progress of batch B through the paver from the skip, in step I, to the bucket, in step VII.

FIG. 12-7. Operation of a dual-drum paver. (*Public Roads, April,* 1960.)

Inspection and Calibration of Equipment

Most specifications require that the batching scales be checked at the beginning of the job, then at regular intervals during the progress of the job. If no frequency is specified, the scales should be checked about once a month. Common practice is for the plant owner to have this checking done by a commercial scale service concern. If the inspector finds it necessary to check the scales, standard 50-lb test weights may be used. This checking should be done by the plant personnel in the presence of the inspector, who makes a record of the test. If the plant is equipped with an autographic recorder that makes a record of the batches, the recorder should be checked at the same time as the scales. The procedure is as follows:

1. See that batching hopper is empty and clean.

2. See that hoppers, fulcrums, knife edges, and all moving parts are free—no binding, no rubbing, no friction. Knife-edge bearings must be centered, and knife edges must be sharp.

3. Balance scales on zero. Be sure recorder, if any, is on zero.

4. Place the weights on the hangers, recording the scale reading and recorder reading at each 250-lb increment. Scales and recorders both must be calibrated together with all equipment in operating condition. Do not disconnect the recorder. Allowance should be made for dunnage, such as planks and hangers to support the weights.

5. Usually the number of test weights will not total the maximum weight desired. In this case, remove all weights and dunnage, balancing the scales and recorder on zero; fill the batcher until the scales indicate the maximum reached under (4); then attach hangers for weights and proceed as under (4).

6. Check operating range of scales and recorder while removing weights also.

7. Caution workmen to place and remove weights carefully so as to cause as little extraneous movement of the scales and recorder as possible.

Scales and batching equipment should be kept clean and in adjustment at all times. Binding of dull or dirty knife edges and fulcrums causes serious weighing errors. Tare weights may vary if material hangs up or sticks in the weigh batcher. Dial scales should be checked at least daily to ascertain that the hand returns to zero when the batcher is empty. Beam scales should balance at no load when only the tare beam is "in."

To check the moisture meter, proceed as follows:

1. Check the zero reading with no sand in the batcher.

2. Load the batcher in the usual manner and note the meter reading.

3. Take a sample of sand (about 1 lb), being sure that it is identical with that surrounding the electrodes.

4. Determine the moisture content of the sand sample by drying.

5. Adjust the meter to correct for any discrepancy between meter reading and moisture content corrected for absorbed moisture.

Actual adjustments to the scales and meters should be made by the plant personnel. The inspector should refrain from operating, adjusting, or otherwise manipulating any of the equipment.

Materials Inspection

The batch-plant inspector, besides being responsible for control of the batching operations, should check all materials delivered to the batch plant. He should assure himself that all materials arriving at the plant have been approved for incorporation in the work. To perform his duties properly, the inspector should be kept informed as to all approved sources of materials and as to expected arrival of shipments.

The inspector should observe unloading of cars, trucks, and barges of cement and aggregates, and handling of materials into and out of stockpiles, being watchful to prevent contamination and segregation; he should collect all shipping reports, test reports, broken car seals, and other pertinent information accompanying each shipment. Any handling or storage that results in contamination or deterioration in quality of the materials may be cause for rejection of the materials.

When aggregates are delivered to the plant by truck, there are two potential sources of trouble. Usually, the material is dumped at the base of a stockpile and cast into the pile with a clamshell. Trucks are apt to carry mud and clay into the stockpile area, or the crane operator may get careless and pick up earth with the aggregate, thus contaminating the pile.

In case the aggregates are placed in a stockpile on the ground, a considerable amount of material at the bottom of the stockpile will, in all probability, be rendered unfit for use because of its becoming mixed with undesirable foreign matter. If aggregates are being taken from the bottom of the pile, unusual care must be exercised in avoiding the use of objectionable material.

Sometimes a truck driver or crane operator will place the wrong material in a pile or bin. The only recourse is to remove the offending material, which may require emptying the bin. Such drastic measures will be avoided if the batching plant is equipped with a finish screen which removes the undesirable material.

Coarse aggregates, in addition to being washed and crushed, are screened into several sizes so that the concrete mixes can be proportioned properly. However, by the time these separated sizes reach the batching plant, they are apt to contain a large amount of undersize caused by numerous handling operations, or they may be seriously segregated. Finish-screening of coarse aggregates at the batching plant largely eliminates the accumulations of undersize and reduces segregation.

The inspector should watch for trash, mud, or other contaminants in the aggregates and have such things removed or require that the aggregate be wasted. Materials used in sealing holes in cars, such as paper, rags, boards, or straw, are frequently picked up by the unloading equipment. Steps should be taken to prevent such materials from getting into the batch. The inspector should inform his supervisor when he finds cars patched in this manner or if aggregates have been loaded into improperly cleaned cars.

When aggregates of different types or sizes are placed in adjoining compartments of the same storage bin, the partition between the two should be built to a height sufficient to prevent material from flowing from one compartment into the other. Partitions should be tight and free from holes through which fine materials might leak from one bin to another.

If cement is inspected at the source or is being shipped on manufacturer's certification, it may be assumed to meet specifications, but cars and trucks should be inspected for evidence of contamination or damage, such as rainwater leakage. The shipping report that accompanies each shipment should be picked up by the inspector. Cement should be used in the order in which shipments are received. Silos and other bulk storage bins should be drawn down completely every month or so and should be cleaned out regularly. Sacked cement should be stored in weatherproof warehouses or sheds, not on planks on the ground, and covered with tarpaulins, except for immediate use.

Other materials, including air-entraining agents, water-reducing retarders, and calcium chloride, if dispensed at the batching plant, should be inspected visually for conformance with specifications. Barrels or cans containing solutions of materials should be inspected for leakage or evaporation that might alter reported concentrations and the contents of each container should be thoroughly mixed before being placed in the dispensers.

Part of the inspector's duties includes taking samples of materials, methods for which were described in Chap. 10. Of special importance are aggregate samples for gradation, or sieve analysis. Methods of sampling and testing are described in Chap. 15, and the application of test results to concrete control is explained in Chap. 16. Samples must be representative. In most plants, it is possible to sample the entire stream of aggregate as it drops from the bin gate into the weigh batcher. Because of probable segregation in the stream of aggregates, the entire cross-section of the stream should be sampled for a short time, rather than taking a portion of the stream for a longer period. Segregation and breakage in the storage bin will be revealed in the results of these tests. Sand, being in a moist condition, is not subject to segregation.

Inspection of Batching Operations

Not all jobs require that an inspector be stationed in the batching plant, but adequate control is not possible without this inspection. In those plants where both proportioning and mixing are done, one inspector can frequently handle all the inspection. However, large central plants with two or more mixers may require more than one man. Inspection procedures vary from plant to plant, depending upon the requirements of the specifications and the type of plant.

At the beginning of each day the inspector should observe and record weather conditions and temperature. He should have all scales balanced or "zeroed" and check operation of batchers, dispensers, meters, valves, gates, etc. If there is a batch counter, he should note the reading thereon. He should make an estimate of the aggregate moisture content and have the scales set accordingly, and he should check the sand moisture meter if there is one. If there is no moisture meter, a sand sample for moisture test should be taken as soon as the first material has been batched out of the bottom of the storage bin and the moisture content has stabilized.

Moisture tests of aggregates, including coarse aggregate when indicated, should be made several times during the shift if there is any variation in moisture content of the material. When mixing is at the site of the work, as on a dry-batch paving job, the batch-plant inspector should keep the site inspector informed as to moisture contents of the aggregates so the correct amount of water per batch will be known.

Aggregates when batched usually have varying moisture contents, depending on length of storage, weather conditions, and other factors. Unless correction is made for these variations, water content of the concrete will vary, with consequent fluctuations in slump and strength. Moisture changes in the aggregate frequently result from the practice of charging the plant feed alternately from wet and dry portions of a stockpile, or alternately from a relatively dry pile, and cars or barges containing wet sand. Operators of end-loaders and cranes should be instructed to avoid charging any one material into the plant from more than one source.

Aggregates should not be used direct from the processing plant, but should be permitted to drain for at least 24 hr. Shipment by rail may be assumed to allow sufficient time for drainage. If it is necessary to moisten coarse aggregate, the operation should be completed several hours before the material is required.

The scales when set at the required weight should be accurately balanced by the load for each batch. Any overload of aggregates, in excess of the allowable tolerance (Table 12-4), should be removed. In weighing cement, care should be taken that all the cement weighed out for each batch is completely discharged. When a dial scale is used, the inspector should make frequent observations to make sure that the indicator returns to the zero reading upon discharge of the hopper. When a beam scale is used, he should make frequent observations to make sure that the tare beam is in balance upon discharge of the hopper when the weigh beams are locked out. Unless otherwise provided for in the specifications, the combined error of weighing and batching each material should not exceed the values shown in Table 12-4.

TABLE 12-4. PERMISSIBLE BATCHING TOLERANCES

Material	Plus or minus batching tolerance, %
Water	1
Cement	$1\frac{1}{2}$
Fine aggregate	2
Coarse aggregate	2
Admixtures	3

Notes: The same tolerances apply to water and admixtures whether batched volumetrically or by weight.

Specifications should be checked before applying any tolerance.

The inspector should observe the dumping of batches into batch trucks and prohibit practices that waste cement or aggregates from batches or that allow materials to spill from one batch compartment to another. He should also inspect the batch trucks to ensure that the interiors are clean. Batch trucks in which material is sticking should be cleaned. Gates should be tight to prevent loss of materials in transit. Batches should be covered with tarpaulins before the trucks leave the plant during rainy weather. Figure 12-8 shows good practices in handling bulk cement in dry-batch trucks. Use of the separate cement compartment is highly recommended. Many agencies now require this method. If separate cement compartments are not used, then the next best thing is to fold the cement into the batch by simultaneously dumping cement and aggregates, covering the load with a tarpaulin for the trip from batcher to mixer.

Transfer of batches to the mixer should be as direct as possible. If conveyor belts are used, care must be exercised in design to avoid flat spots in transfer points, where parts of batches are apt to hang up (see Fig. 12-9).

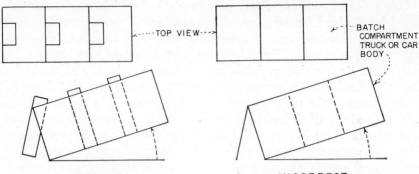

CORRECT	INCORRECT
PROVIDES SEPARATE COMPART-MENTS OF SUITABLE SIZE AND DEPTH ATTACHED TO AND OPERATING WITH EACH BATCH RELEASE GATE.	CEMENT DUMPED ON OR WITHIN AGGREGATE MAY BE BLOWN AWAY, PARTIALLY PREHYDRATED, OR MAY SLIDE INTO ANOTHER BATCH IN DUMPING.

PROVISION FOR CEMENT IN DRY-BATCH COMPARTMENTS

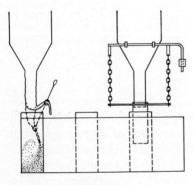 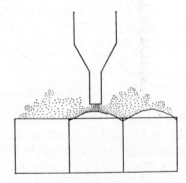

CORRECT	INCORRECT
FALL OF CEMENT CONTROLLED BY ENCLOSING IN KINKED CANVAS DROP CHUTE OR TELESCOPIC FLEXIBLE HOSE TREMIE.	FREE FALL OF CEMENT INTO BATCH CAR OR TRUCK CAUSES WASTE, AND OVERLAP OF BATCHES IS COMMON.

LOADING CEMENT FROM BATCHER INTO BATCH TRUCKS

FIG. 12-8. Proper precautions in handling batched bulk cement prevent waste and dust and result in more uniform concrete. (*U.S. Bureau of Reclamation.*)

Concrete Mixer Inspection

One of three conditions may exist:

1. The mixers and batchers are all located in one plant, the batchers feeding the mixer directly through short conveyor belts, holding hoppers, or other direct means.

2. Dry batches are hauled by truck from the batch plant to the mixer where water and admixtures are added.

3. Dry batches, or dry batches and water, are dumped into truck mixers.

Some modification of the following instructions will be necessary, depending upon which of the three conditions exists. These changes, however, are small, and their need will be obvious.

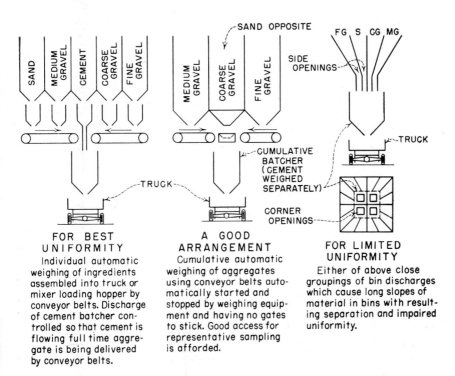

FOR BEST UNIFORMITY	A GOOD ARRANGEMENT	FOR LIMITED UNIFORMITY
Individual automatic weighing of ingredients assembled into truck or mixer loading hopper by conveyor belts. Discharge of cement batcher controlled so that cement is flowing full time aggregate is being delivered by conveyor belts.	Cumulative automatic weighing of aggregates using conveyor belts automatically started and stopped by weighing equipment and having no gates to stick. Good access for representative sampling is afforded.	Either of above close groupings of bin discharges which cause long slopes of material in bins with resulting separation and impaired uniformity.

FIG. 12-9. Batching equipment. Uniformity of concrete is affected by the arrangement of batcher-supply bins and weigh batchers. (*U.S. Bureau of Reclamation.*)

When a new job is started, the mixer or mixers are checked for conformance with specification requirements and overall condition before concreting operations start. Skips, drums, chutes, and other parts should be cleaned of accumulations of cement, aggregates, concrete, and other materials. Mixing blades inside the drum are checked for wear. Most specifications require that blades worn down ¾ in. or more shall be replaced with new blades.

Water-measuring devices should be calibrated carefully and kept in good operating condition at all times. Before an attempt is made to calibrate a water batcher, the valves and other mechanisms should be checked and any necessary repairs made. The water system on a modern paver or mixing plant is so designed that measured water can be drawn off through a special outlet in the discharge line. Calibration is accomplished by passing any given amount of water through the meter or batcher, drawing it off through the special outlet and catching the measured water in a 50-gal drum which is then weighed on a platform scale. Conversion to gallons, if necessary, is accomplished by dividing by $8\frac{1}{3}$, the weight in pounds of 1 gal of water.

The indicator on the measuring tank or meter should be set at a reading below any amount anticipated for use and the water discharged into the barrel, where it is weighed. The indicator should be advanced a gallon or two, the tank refilled, and the water again discharged and weighed. This should be repeated until the capacity of the batcher is reached. Accuracy of measurement should be within the specified tolerance.

After setting the batch timing meter for the specified time, it should be checked while the mixer is operating under load. Time should start when the skip reaches the top of its movement and continue until the discharge gate opens. In the case of a dual drum mixer, the second batch discharged after the start of timing will be the one timed.

Most mixers will tolerate a 10 per cent overload. It is permissible to load mixers to this capacity if the manufacturer's nameplate guarantees that the mixer will handle a batch of this size, and if mixer efficiency tests demonstrate that the concrete is properly mixed.

Variations in water pressure may result in variable amounts of water batched, as the batcher may not fill completely when the pressure is low. A storage tank at the mixer, feeding into the batcher, serves to equalize the pressure, in this way yielding uniform batches of water.

A source of slump variations is sometimes a careless or inexperienced operator who fails to manipulate the weighing and batching equipment properly. Variations in batch weights of the ingredients result, and these variations are reflected in variable consistency of the concrete. Another source of trouble is equipment that is worn out or out of adjustment. A leaky valve on the water batcher or meter can result in wide fluctuations in the amount of water batched, especially if there are variable periods of time between batches.

The sequence of charging materials into the mixer affects the efficiency of mixing, and therefore affects the quality and uniformity of the concrete being produced. A batching sequence should be established for every plant so as to produce concrete of the best and most uniform quality. Water should precede, accompany, and follow the solid ingredients into the mixer. The so-called "ribbon feed," by which the cement and all sizes of aggregate are fed into the mixer simultaneously, promotes thorough blending of all materials in the mixer, and is thus conducive to efficient mixing.

Sometimes cement balls in the concrete result from poor distribution of the cement when it comes in contact with water in the mixer. Specific causes may be feeding cement or water too fast, batch exceeding mixer capacity, worn or improper blading, or holding the unmixed batch in the mixer for several minutes with the mixer not rotating. Once the cement comes in contact with damp aggregates or water, the batches should be mixed and used as expeditiously as possible. A maximum delay not exceeding 2 hr may be permitted, but the specifications should be consulted for specific information. In the case of dry batches hauled in batch trucks or held in a holding hopper, extra cement must be added to the batch if the cement is in contact with the moist aggregate for more than 2 hr. An amount equal to 3 per cent of the original amount of cement in the batch should be added for each hour's delay, starting with 6 per cent for a delay between 2 and 3 hr. Total delay should not exceed 4 hr in hot weather or 6 hr in cold weather.

If cement enters the mixer drum first, it is apt to stick to the interior of the mixer. This trouble is obviated by "leading" a portion of the water ahead of the aggregates and cement, with the aggregates leading the cement slightly.

To promote thorough mixing inside the mixer drum, the blading should be designed so as to cause the concrete to move from one end of the drum to the other, with many crossings of paths, but concrete should not be permitted to drop from near the top of the drum. Mixers for mass concrete containing large cobbles do not require as much blading as mixers for small-aggregate concrete. Incomplete mixing results from too short a mixing time, worn or improper blades, interior of mixer encrusted with old concrete, speed of rotation too fast or too slow, size of batch exceeding the mixer capacity, or improper batching sequence.

A minimum mixing time is usually stated in the specifications. Time starts when all materials, except the last of the water, are in the mixer, and continues for the periods shown in Table 12-5. Overmixing should be avoided, because the grinding action causes objectionable fines in the mix, resulting in a requirement for more water. There may be some loss of entrained air also. During hot weather, overmixing is objectionable because of the heating effect.

Some agencies specify a mixer performance or mortar efficiency test to provide information for adjustments to the mixing time. This test[12.2] compares concrete samples from 3 or more parts of the batch on the basis of unit weight of mortar and percentage of coarse aggregate. Mixing time may be increased or decreased, depending on results of this analysis.

Check List for Batcher and Mixer Inspector

Duties of batching and mixing inspectors may overlap, depending on type and arrangement of plant facilities. For this reason, the following check list includes duties of both. Not all duties are required in every plant.

TABLE 12-5. SUGGESTED MINIMUM MIXING TIME

Capacity of mixer, cu yd	Time of mixing, min
2 or less	1½
3	2
4	2½
5	2¾
6	3

Note: Mixing time in this table should be compared with job specifications.
SOURCE: Bureau of Reclamation data.

At the beginning of each day or shift, the inspector should:

1. Observe and record weather conditions and temperature.

2. Check the batch counter and record the reading.

3. Check the recorder and mark the date on the chart, as well as the mix to be used and the location of concrete placement.

4. Balance all scales and check operation of batchers, dispensers, meters, valves, gates, etc.

5. Make an estimate of the aggregate moisture content and have the scales set accordingly.

The inspector should be in attendance continuously during batching and mixing operations. Additional duties are as follows:

1. Verify that the proper materials, as used in original trial mixes, are being delivered.

2. Test aggregates for grading, cleanliness, and moisture content.

3. Check temperatures of materials and concrete, being sure the concrete temperature is within the specified limits.

4. Verify that the proper mix is being prepared.

5. Verify that batching and mixing equipment is of sufficient capacity for the size of batches proposed.

6. Make an occasional check of the mixing time, with a batch in the mixer.

7. Observe the condition of the mixers—skips, blades, discharge, etc.—and be sure that they are clean and in good condition. Avoid accumulations of cement or concrete in chutes and other places.

8. Adjust the water batcher to produce the required slump of the concrete. Make sufficient slump tests to provide control of the slump.

9. Check operation of the dispenser for air-entraining agent and admixture occasionally, and see that it is cleaned at regular intervals and checked for accuracy.

10. Confirm that the concrete is thoroughly mixed at the time of discharge from the mixer, and see that waste and segregation are avoided (see Figs. 12-10 and 12-11).

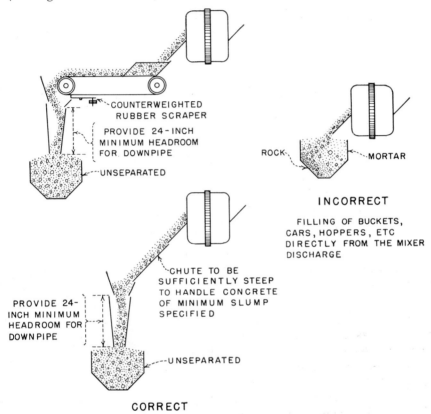

COUNTERWEIGHTED
RUBBER SCRAPER

PROVIDE 24-INCH
MINIMUM HEADROOM
FOR DOWNPIPE

UNSEPARATED

ROCK

MORTAR

INCORRECT

FILLING OF BUCKETS,
CARS, HOPPERS, ETC
DIRECTLY FROM THE MIXER
DISCHARGE

CHUTE TO BE
SUFFICIENTLY STEEP
TO HANDLE CONCRETE
OF MINIMUM SLUMP
SPECIFIED

PROVIDE 24-
INCH MINIMUM
HEADROOM FOR
DOWNPIPE

UNSEPARATED

CORRECT

EITHER OF THE ARRANGEMENTS AT THE LEFT PREVENTS SEPARATION REGARDLESS OF LENGTH OF CHUTE OR CONVEYOR, WHETHER DISCHARGING CONCRETE INTO BUCKETS, CARS, TRUCKS, OR HOPPERS.

Fig. 12-10. Unless discharge of concrete from mixers is correctly controlled, the uniformity resulting from effective mixing will be destroyed by separation. (*U.S. Bureau of Reclamation.*)

11. Determine that the concrete is used within the specified time limit.

12. Make the necessary test specimens and tests of the concrete as required by the specifications, as described in Chap. 15.

13. Keep a record of wasted concrete, including the amount and reasons for wasting.

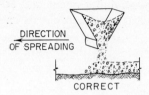
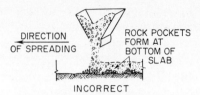

DIRECTION OF SPREADING ←

DIRECTION OF SPREADING ←

ROCK POCKETS FORM AT BOTTOM OF SLAB

CORRECT

TURN BUCKET SO THAT SEPARATED ROCK FALLS ON CONCRETE WHERE IT MAY BE READILY WORKED INTO MASS

INCORRECT

DUMPING SO THAT FREE ROCK ROLLS OUT ON FORMS OR SUBGRADE

DISCHARGING CONCRETE

CORRECT

DROPPING CONCRETE DIRECTLY OVER GATE OPENING

INCORRECT

DROPPING CONCRETE ON SLOPING SIDES OF HOPPER

FILLING CONCRETE HOPPERS OR BUCKETS

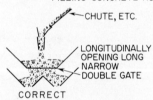
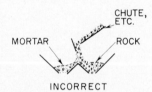

CHUTE, ETC.

LONGITUDINALLY OPENING LONG NARROW DOUBLE GATE

CHUTE, ETC.

MORTAR   ROCK

CORRECT

THE ABOVE ARRANGEMENT SHOWS A FEASIBLE METHOD IF A DIVIDED HOPPER MUST BE USED. (SINGLE DISCHARGE HOPPERS SHOULD BE USED WHENEVER POSSIBLE)

INCORRECT

FILLING DIVIDED HOPPER AS ABOVE INVARIABLY RESULTS IN SEPARATION AND LACK OF UNIFORMITY IN CONCRETE DELIVERED FROM EITHER GATE.

DIVIDED CONCRETE HOPPERS

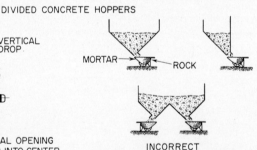

UNSEPARATED   VERTICAL DROP

SQUARE OR CIRCULAR

MORTAR   ROCK

CORRECT

DISCHARGE FROM CENTRAL OPENING PERMITTING VERTICAL DROP INTO CENTER OF BUGGY. ALTERNATE APPROACH FROM OPPOSITE SIDES PERMITS AS RAPID LOADING AS MAY BE OBTAINED WITH OBJECTIONABLE DIVIDED HOPPERS HAVING TWO DISCHARGE GATES

INCORRECT

SLOPING HOPPER GATES WHICH ARE IN EFFECT CHUTES WITHOUT END CONTROL CAUSING OBJECTIONABLE SEPARATION IN FILLING THE BUGGIES

DISCHARGE OF HOPPERS FOR LOADING CONCRETE BUGGIES

Fig. 12-11. Correct and incorrect methods for loading and discharging concrete buckets, hoppers, and buggies. Use of proper procedures avoids separation of the coarse aggregate from the mortar. (*U.S. Bureau of Reclamation.*)

14. Compute the water-cement ratio from data furnished by the batch plant inspector and the amount of water added at the mixer.

15. Keep informed of activities in the vicinity that may affect concrete mixing.

16. Fill out report forms completely and accurately.

In a situation wherein dry batches are hauled by batch truck to a mixer at the site, there are additional duties.

1. Make sure batch trucks, before being loaded, are free of remnants of previous batches.

2. Avoid loss of cement by loading it simultaneously with other materials, making sure it is completely covered with aggregate; or, better, use separate compartments in the truck for cement (see Fig. 12-8).

3. Check batch trucks to determine that they have sufficient capacity for the batches without loss or intermingling of batches. Partitions between batches on trucks should be high enough to prevent parts of batches from moving from one compartment to the next when the truck bed is raised for dumping.

4. Prevent loss of parts of batches when dumping from truck into mixer skip by having the truck maneuvered and placed properly, and by making sure that the mixer skip is large enough.

12-2. READY-MIXED CONCRETE

Equipment

Ready-mixed concrete may be mixed in a central plant and hauled to the jobsite in either agitating or nonagitating truck hauling units or batched into a mixer mounted on a truck and mixed en route to the site; or it may be a combination of partial mixing in the central plant and mixing en route in a truck mixer. These methods are known respectively as *central mixing, truck* or *transit mixing*, and *shrink mixing*.

There are three types of units which may be used either as truck mixers or agitators. They are the horizontal-axis revolving-drum type, the inclined-axis high-discharge revolving-drum type, and the open-top revolving-blade or paddle type. Standards for operation of these mixers are covered in NRMCA publication No. 73[12.3] and ASTM Designation: C 94. The same machine may be used for either truck mixing in transit or hauling of central-mixed concrete, the only difference being that, when used as an agitator, the mixer drum or paddle shaft is rotated at a much slower speed than when used as a mixer. Also, an agitator can handle a batch half again as large as a batch to be mixed.

Another kind of hauling unit consists of a truck-mounted dump body (popularly called a "bathtub" because of the rounded contour of the corners). This is a nonagitating type of unit in which discharge is accomplished by raising the truck body, the concrete sliding out through a gate in the rear of the container.

Mixing speed for the revolving-drum types should be between a minimum of 4 rpm and a maximum of a speed resulting in a peripheral velocity of the drum of 225 fpm. For the open-top types, speed should be between 2 and 6 rpm of the mixing blades.

Each truck mixer should have attached to it in a prominent place a metal plate on which is stamped its rated capacity in cubic yards as guaranteed by the manufacturer, and the recommended speed for mixing. The mixer should be provided with a batch meter and locking device capable of preventing discharge of the concrete prior to the required number of revolutions of the drum, or with a suitable revolution counter for indicating the amount of mixing. An accurate water meter, having indicating dials and totalizer, should be located between the supply tank and mixer.

Inspection and Control

Certain problems in control are inherent in any ready-mixed concrete operation. However, with genuine cooperation between the producer, engineer, and construction contractor, these problems can be overcome and a highly satisfactory job obtained.

The big advantage of ready-mixed concrete is the convenience and saving for the contractor. Storing aggregates and cement on the site, with the consequent congestion of the construction area and waste of materials, is no longer a problem when ready-mixed concrete is used.

From a control standpoint, central mixing is the most desirable method since it enables the inspector to observe all batching and mixing of the concrete. However, most ready-mixed concrete produced in this country is mixed in transit. Because each mixer is equipped with at least one water tank, control of the amount of water and mixing is difficult.

In addition to the instructions previously given in this chapter on inspection of batching and mixing, certain additional points should be covered.

When charging a dry batch into a truck mixer, the ribbon-feed method should be followed. This procedure provides an initial intermingling of the materials and is more rapid than other methods.

Mixing water is usually controlled at the proportioning plant, either by introducing the requisite amount of water into the mixer, or by introducing the required amount of water, and no more, into the mixer tank. The latter arrangement usually complies with specification requirements that all mixing water be added after arrival of the truck at the point of delivery. Some specifications state that no water may be carried on the mixer, all water to be introduced at the site. It frequently happens that a foreman wants more water added to a batch, either at the start of discharge or during discharge. Such action is subject to flagrant abuse and should not be permitted. If the foreman insists on having extra water added, the mixer-truck driver should demand that the fact be noted and acknowledged on the delivery ticket. Under close control and inspection, when the inspector is sure of the amount of water in the batch, additional water may be added provided that the maximum specified water-cement ratio and slump are not exceeded. Whenever supplementary water is added to a batch, the mixer should be operated at mixing speed for at least 20 revolutions after all the water has been admitted.

Wash water is necessary for cleaning out the mixer drum occasionally. Methods of controlling wash water are a frequent source of controversy on the job. If specifications permit it to be carried on the mixer truck, it should be in a special tank or compartment entirely separate from the mixing water.

Sometimes wash water is retained in the mixer drum for use as part of the mixing water for the succeeding batch. Technically, there is no serious objection to such a procedure. However, practical limitations on control make this a poor practice. There are so many variables that it is virtually impossible for anyone to know the amount of water in the batch with any degree of accuracy.

When concrete is central-mixed, the truck-mixer carrying such concrete, acting as an agitator, is set on the slow agitating speed for the trip to the jobsite. Just before discharging the batch, the mixer is operated at mixing speed for a few revolutions. Some mixers agitate and mix in a rotational direction opposite to their discharge rotation.

Concrete has a tendency to lose consistency or stiffen when overmixed, due to generation of heat and the grinding action within the mixer. For this reason, the importance of uniformity in number of revolutions of the drum or paddles is readily apparent. Specifications should place an upper limit on the total number of revolutions. The revolution counter, previously mentioned, provides the necessary information for control.

Careless and improper discharge of concrete from the truck mixer is a cause of segregation. The ideal discharge is at full discharge opening and full drum speed without interruption. This ideal, however, is not always possible to attain. Usually the discharge is intermittent, as into buckets or buggies, and is also at a restricted rate. In any event, the discharge gate should be fully open all during discharge and the rate controlled by varying the mixer speed.

Normal practice is to sample the concrete and make tests at the point of placement. Insofar as control of the job is concerned, it is mandatory that samples be taken after all water has been added and the concrete is being discharged into the forms (discharge into a bucket or buggy may be considered as discharge into the forms).

On some jobs, the producer is required to provide and use a ticket system to account for batches of concrete. Most producers find it necessary to use load tickets, anyhow, for their own information and records. When continuous batch plant inspection is required, the inspector should sign a ticket issued by the supplier that will identify each load of concrete sent to the job. Mix identification and time of day batched are included in the information on this ticket. At the site, the inspector compares the delivery time with the time batched to make sure the allowable elapsed time has not been exceeded. Usual practice is to write arrival time on the ticket and a duplicate, the latter being returned to the plant by the driver.

12-3. PREPARATION FOR PLACING

Foundations

Preparation of surfaces against or upon which concrete is to be placed depends upon the type of foundation material and requirements of the structure. Excavation for foundations should extend into sound, undisturbed soil or rock. If earth is overexcavated, the area must be backfilled with select material and compacted to the specified density. Rock surfaces should be clean and sound. If free water is present, it should be blown out with air jets or otherwise removed. In some cases, it may be necessary to provide a sump (outside the form area) into which the water drains, for removal by means of a pump. Old concrete surfaces must be cleaned of all dirt and laitance, an operation that usually requires wet sandblasting.

Earth foundations should be free of frost and ice when concrete is placed. During dry seasons, the earth should be moist but not muddy. Concrete should not be placed in running water, although underwater placement is permissible in still water if the tremie method is used (see Chap. 13).

Steel shells for cast-in-place piles should be inspected by lowering a light into the shell (see Sec. 5-12). In the same manner, shafts for caissons should be inspected. In belled caissons in earth, it is customary to check the size of the bell and determine the supporting strength of the undisturbed earth in the bottom by means of a penetrometer or other instrument. Figure 12-12 is a typical group of shell piles.

Sometimes, in order to facilitate construction of forms, placing reinforcing steel, and similar work, it may be desirable to place a foundation seal, or sand slab. This is merely a slab of concrete placed in the bottom of the excavation. It is especially desirable when a footing is to be placed within sheet piling below the water table because it seals the bottom of the excavation against the entrance of water. Concrete for the seal is placed so the top of the seal concrete is approximately at the

FIG. 12-12. Shell piles in place and ready to be cut off, after which concrete will be placed in them. These are to support a heavy overpass foundation. (*L.B. Foster Company photo.*)

specified elevation of the bottom of the foundation. Such a seal is placed by the tremie method if it is necessary to place the concrete under water.

Forms

All forms should be so constructed and maintained that the finished concrete will be true to line and grade and of the shape and dimensions shown on the plans. The forms should be constructed so that they can be easily removed without injury to the concrete.

Forms should be mortar-tight, sufficiently rigid to prevent distortion due to the pressure of the concrete and other loads incidental to construction, and so constructed and maintained as to prevent warping and opening of the joints due to shrinkage of the form material. Molding or chamfer strips should be placed in the corners of forms so as to produce beveled edges on permanently exposed concrete surfaces. Interior angles on such surfaces and edges at formed joints do not require beveling unless requirement for beveling is indicated on the plans.

All lumber in contact with concrete should be free from knot holes, loose knots, cracks, splits, warps, or any other defects which would mar the appearance of the finished structure. Any lumber which has defects affecting its strength should not be used.

Forms for concrete surfaces that will be permanently exposed to view should be constructed of plywood or of metal panels. Wood lining for forms should be of such kind and quality, or should be so treated or coated, that there will be no chemical deterioration or discoloration of the formed concrete surface. The type and condition of form lining and the construction of the forms should be such that form surfaces will be even and uniform. The wood lining or metal panels should be placed so that the joint marks on the concrete surfaces will be in general alignment, both horizontally and vertically. Plywood sheets should be placed with the long dimension horizontal.

Plywood sheets less than ⅝ in. in thickness should be placed against a solid wood backing of ¾-in. sheathing. Plywood sheets ⅝ in. or more in thickness may be used without backing, provided the forms are constructed to withstand pressure developed during placing of concrete without producing visible waviness between studs. Plywood sheets should be placed so that joints are tight.

Metal for forms should be of such thickness that the forms will remain true to shape. All bolt and rivet heads should be countersunk. Clamps, pins, or other connecting devices should be such that they will hold the forms rigidly together in place and allow removal without injury to the concrete. Metal forms which do not present a smooth surface or line up properly should not be used. All metal forms should be kept free from rust, grease, or other foreign matter which would discolor the concrete.

Form panels, either of wood or metal, should be constructed and assembled so as to result in tight joints between the panels. Panel joints should match in general alignment the joints of the lining or sheathing.

Forms should be securely tied together with approved rods, and braced in a substantial and unyielding manner. In general, tie rods should be designed to act also as struts or spreaders. Wood struts should not be permitted to remain in the concrete.

For concrete surfaces that will be permanently exposed to view, metal ties or anchorages within the forms should terminate not less than 1½ in. beneath the formed face of the concrete. The ties should be constructed so that removal of the ends or end fasteners can be accomplished without causing appreciable spalling at the faces of the concrete.

Devices which, when removed, will leave an opening entirely through the concrete should not be permitted. Wire ties may be used when both sides of the concrete will be covered with backfill or otherwise not permanently exposed. Wire ties, when used, should be cut off flush with the concrete surface.

All dimensions of forms in place should be carefully checked before concrete is placed. Immediately prior to placing concrete, any warpings or bulging should be corrected and all dirt, sawdust, shavings, or other debris removed. In narrow walls where the bottoms of the forms are otherwise inaccessible, the lower boards or panels should be left loose on the back side so that extraneous material can be removed just prior to placing concrete.

Whenever it is at all possible, the inspector should get down into the forms to make his inspection. While it is true that sometimes the forms are so congested and tight that a man cannot get in, nevertheless, it is difficult to inspect a tall form from the top only. Another point to keep in mind is that dimensional tolerances apply to the concrete, not the formwork, hence the necessity of having the forms constructed well within the tolerances specified.

Forms for suspended slabs and beams are frequently cambered to allow for sagging or settlement, a common allowance being ¼ in. per 16 ft of span. This, however, is something that has to be considered for each individual form, depending upon many factors of form design and construction. It is good practice to install some sort of a telltale beneath a slab or beam form to check on settlement during concrete placement, and to provide information for corrective measures. A satisfactory telltale might be a vertical board suitably marked, or a ruler attached to the center of the span which can be observed by means of a surveyor's level.

In designing formwork and shoring, it is customary to assume the weight of concrete at 150 pcf. Design must consider not only the vertical load resulting from the weight of concrete and other items, but also the lateral pressure on the formwork developed when the concrete is rendered fluid by vibration. An equation developed by ACI Committee 622 is[12.4]

$$p = 150 + \frac{9,000R}{T}$$

where p = lateral pressure on form, psf
R = rate of placement, ft per hr
T = temperature of concrete in the form, °F

This equation is based on the following considerations:

1. Internal vibration of the concrete within 15 min of time of placement
2. A minimum of revibration
3. No external vibration

4. Concrete unit weight of 150 pcf
5. Slump not over 4 in.
6. Rate of placement *R* less than 10 ft per hr

It should be pointed out that this equation is approximate since there are many variables that affect the pressure developed. However, the equation gives conservative results and may be used for either columns or walls. The nomograph (Fig. 12-13) will aid in making quick computations using this formula.

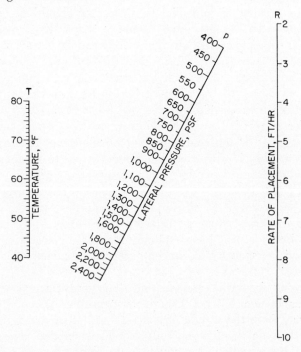

Fig. 12-13. Approximate lateral pressure on forms; $p = 150 + 9{,}000R/T$. (*Based on report of ACI Committee 622.*)

In placing a successive lift of concrete on previously placed and hardened concrete, the horizontal joint between the two lifts is often a source of disfigurement. Two methods of minimizing this are shown in Figs. 12-14 and 12-15. The grade strip shown in Fig. 12-14 should be set accurately with its bottom edge about ½ in. below the finished elevation desired for the lift. Grooves shown in Fig. 12-15 should be straight and continuous across the structure. Their location should be planned beforehand so as to give a pleasing appearance to the completed structure. Form anchorages should be provided about 4 in. below the top of the lift. When the form is set for the succeeding lift, the sheathing should overlap the previous concrete by about 1 in. and should be drawn up snug by means of the anchorage in the concrete below and by ties close to the bottom of the new lift. Proper observance of these precautions will assure a neat-appearing joint in the structure.

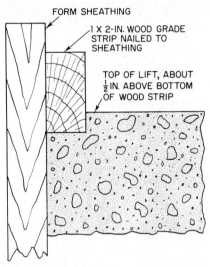

Ornamental concrete should be placed in special wood molds or plaster waste molds. Wood molds should be made of soft white pine or similar wood; they require skilled craftsmanship in their design and construction. More complicated or intricate detail should be cast in plaster waste molds. Waste molds usually require reinforcement with fibre and a wood framework. Great care is necessary in fitting these molds into the formwork. They should be well supported but should not support any of the formwork that is erected above them. Joints within the molds and between the molds and the

FIG. 12-14. Suggested treatment for a horizontal construction joint.

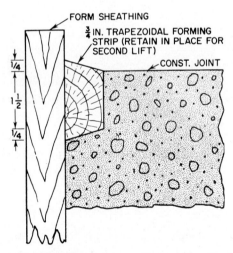

FIG. 12-15. Forming for horizontal groove or rustication strip at construction joint.

formwork should be carefully filled or pointed to eliminate joint marks in the finished concrete. Waste molds should be sized with shellac or lacquer when they are made.

All forms must be treated with a form oil or other coating material which will assure nonadhesion of the concrete. Numerous oils, shellacs, lacquers, and plastic coatings are available, and the choice of one or another is largely a matter of personal opinion. However, in choosing any form coating, the conditions of use must be considered. The material should be formulated for the particular usage and form material intended. The form coating should not interfere with subsequent curing or surface treatments of the concrete, nor should it stain the concrete or cause permanent softening. In applying form oil, care must be taken to avoid getting it on reinforcing steel or construction joints.

Fig. 12-16. Formwork and shoring for arch bridge spans. (*Northern Illinois Tollway photo.*)

Some specifications require that wood board forms be soaked with water for at least 12 hr before the concrete is placed in order to tighten the joints to prevent leakage of grout or mortar. Plaster waste molds should be coated with a thin grease.

Falsework and Shoring

Design and construction of the supporting structure for concrete forms, called falsework, shoring, or centering, are the responsibility of the contractor. Falsework should be designed and constructed so as to carry the full design load with a minimum deflection and settlement. If necessary, camber should be provided to counteract settlement, shrinkage, and deformation (see Fig. 12-16).

Concrete is assumed to weigh 150 pcf when falsework is being designed. In addition, a live load allowance should be assumed, usually 50 psf.

The foundation for shoring is of great importance since settlement must be minimized. In some cases, such as centering for an arch bridge, the falsework should be supported on piling. Mud sills are usually acceptable if they are of adequate area and are carefully placed on firm earth. In a multiple-story building, supports for successive floors should be placed directly over those below. Frequently, the use of jacks or wedges is required to take up any settlement in the falsework, either before or during concrete placement.

Reinforcing Steel

At the time reinforcing steel is embedded in the concrete it should be free of dirt, paint, oil, grease, or other foreign substances. A thin coating of rust or mill scale is not detrimental provided it adheres tightly to the steel. Heavy scaling, to the extent that the bar is pitted and reduced in cross-sectional area, should be cause for rejection of the bar. A check on the usefulness of a bar can be made by cutting and weighing a measured length of bar and comparing the computed area with the nominal area shown in Table 10-3. Dried mortar, splashed on the steel ahead of the concrete being placed, should be removed by wire brushing. If the mortar cannot be removed by vigorous wire brushing, it is probably safe to leave it on the steel. Note that vigorous brushing is required.

The location of splices is shown on the plans, and splices should never be made anyplace else without approval of the structural engineer. When splices are permitted, they should be in an area of low tensile stress in the structure. It is desirable to stagger the splices in adjacent pairs of bars. Splices are made by lapping the bars the specified amount and wiring them securely together. Laps may range from 20 to 40 bar diameters, depending on size of the bar and other factors. Some agencies permit lapped bars to be welded. Butt welds may be made under carefully controlled conditions. When welds are permitted, details must be clearly set forth in the plans and specifications. Because of variations in the chemical composition of the steel, there may be difficulty in welding steel from one source to that from another.

All reinforcing steel should be accurately placed and, during the placing of concrete, held firmly in position. Distances from the forms should be maintained by means of chairs, ties, hangers, or other approved supports. Figure 12-17 shows the types of bar supports commonly used. These described further in Table 12-6.

Layers of bars should be separated by metal spacers of such shape that they will be easily enveloped by the concrete. Bars should be separated from horizontal surfaces by spacers. Vertical stirrups should always pass around the main tension members and should be securely attached thereto. The use of pebbles, pieces of broken stone or brick, metal pipe, wooden blocks, and similar devices for holding steel in position should not be permitted.

If staining resulting from rusting of exposed chairs or supports is undesirable, these items should be made of stainless steel, galvanized steel,

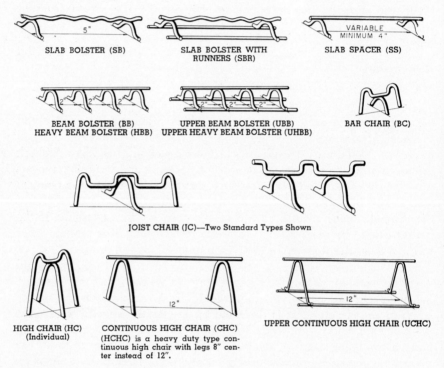

SLAB BOLSTER (SB)

SLAB BOLSTER WITH
RUNNERS (SBR)

SLAB SPACER (SS)

BEAM BOLSTER (BB)
HEAVY BEAM BOLSTER (HBB)

UPPER BEAM BOLSTER (UBB)
UPPER HEAVY BEAM BOLSTER (UHBB)

BAR CHAIR (BC)

JOIST CHAIR (JC)—Two Standard Types Shown

HIGH CHAIR (HC)
(Individual)

CONTINUOUS HIGH CHAIR (CHC)
(HCHC) is a heavy duty type continuous high chair with legs 8″ center instead of 12″.

UPPER CONTINUOUS HIGH CHAIR (UCHC)

FIG. 12-17. Details of bar supports for reinforcing steel. (*Courtesy Concrete Reinforcing Steel Institute.*)

or plastic. Chairs on the ground should be specially designed to prevent settling, by providing a sand plate on which the chair rests, or by other equally effective means. A sufficient number of chairs and supports should be installed to assure rigid support, not only of the steel, but also of construction loads superimposed on the steel, such as by workmen walking or climbing on it.

The inspector should inspect the steel as early as possible, checking for sizes and bends before the steel is wired rigidly in place, thus helping to avoid expensive errors. This inspection can frequently be facili-

TABLE 12-6. SPECIFICATIONS AND STANDARD NOMENCLATURE FOR REINFORCING STEEL BAR SUPPORTS

Symbol	Bar support	Top wire*	Legs*	Description
SB	Slab bolster	No. 4 corrugated	$\frac{3}{4}$ in. high—No. 6 Over $\frac{3}{4}$ in.—No. 5	Legs spaced 5 in. centers—corrugations vertical or flat, spaced 1 in. centers—heights up to 2 in. Stocked in $\frac{3}{4}$-, 1-, $1\frac{1}{2}$-, and 2-in. heights and 5- and 10-ft lengths
SBR	Slab bolster with runners	No. 4 corrugated	Same as SB	Same as SB with no. 7 wire runners
SS	Slab spacer	No. 5 smooth	Same as SB	Legs spaced to provide supporting leg under each bar. Minimum leg spacing 4 in.—heights up to 2 in. Fabricated to order
BB	Beam bolster	No. 7 smooth	No. 7	All legs spaced 2 in. centers—maximum height 3 in. Stocked in 1-, $1\frac{1}{2}$-, 2-in. heights, in 5-ft lengths
HBB	Heavy beam bolster	No. 4 smooth	No. 4	Same as BB except maximum height 5 in.
UBB	Upper beam bolster	No. 7 smooth	No. 7	All legs spaced 2 in. centers—maximum height 3 in. Stocked in 1-, $1\frac{1}{2}$-, 2-in. heights, in 5-ft lengths. Same as BB with no. 7 runner wire
UHBB	Upper heavy beam bolster	No. 4 smooth	No. 4	Same as UBB except maximum height 5 in. No. 7 runner wire. Fabricated to order
BC	Individual bar chair	No. 8	No. 8	Made and stocked only in $\frac{3}{4}$-, 1-, $1\frac{1}{2}$-, and $1\frac{3}{4}$-in. heights
JC	Joist chair	No. 6	No. 6	Made and stocked only in 4-, 5-, and 6-in. widths and $\frac{3}{4}$-, 1-, $1\frac{1}{2}$-in. heights
HC	Individual high chair	No. 5 for 2 to 4 in. No. 4 over 4 to 6 in. No. 2 over 6 to 9 in. No. 0 over 9 in.		Legs at 20° or less with vertical. Width of base to be $\frac{3}{4}$ or more of height. When height exceeds 12 in., reinforce legs with welded cross wires or encircling wire. Stocked in $\frac{1}{4}$-in. increments from 2 to 6 in.
CHC	Continuous high chair	No. 2 for 2 to 6 in. No. 0 for over 6 in.	Same as HC	All legs 12 in. centers (max) with leg within 1 in. of end of chair. Fabricated to order
UCHC	Upper continuous high chair	Same as CHC	Same as CHC	Same as CHC with no. 5 wire runners
HCHC	Heavy continuous high chair	Same as CHC	Same as CHC	Legs 8 in. centers. Fabricated to order

* AS&W wire gauges indicated in this table are the minimum sizes to be used.
SOURCE: Courtesy of the Concrete Reinforcing Steel Institute.[12.9]

tated in deep, thin forms by assembling the steel "curtains" in place after one side form has been erected, but before the opposite form is set in place.

A practice that should be avoided in placing steel for slabs and pavements is that of laying the steel mat or mesh on the bottom form or subgrade ahead of concrete placement, then attempting to lift it through the concrete. Equally undesirable is to place the steel on top of the slab and try to push it down. Correct practice is to support the steel on chairs at the correct elevation, or place concrete to the level proposed for the steel, lay the steel in place, then complete the slab before the concrete below the steel has time to set.

Embedded Items

Most concrete structures have objects and fixtures embedded in them. Among these items are castings for manholes and catch basins, anchor bolts, pipes and conduits, inserts of various types, and instruments. With few exceptions these are fixed in place prior to concrete placement by attaching them to the forms or to the reinforcing steel. Adjustments to the steel location to accommodate these items should be made only as shown on the plans. Nothing should be inserted into the concrete without first considering the effect of the insertion on the strength of the structural member in which the insertion is made.

Some fixtures are to bond to the concrete while others must be permitted to move in some way or another. Whether or not bond is necessary determines the treatment of the contact surfaces. A surface requiring bond should be clean and free of foreign substances. A nonbonding surface may be coated with tar, asphalt, or similar material.

Final Inspection

Performance of all of the inspection discussed in this section requires that the inspector go over the site more than once. Immediately prior to concrete placement, a final inspection should be made, covering all features of foundation, forms, steel and embedded items, clean-up, etc.

At this time, the inspector should check with the contractor's supervisor to make sure that all plants and equipment are ready to go. There should be a sufficient supply of materials at the proportioning plant; transporting equipment, such as truck mixers, batch trucks, buckets, and conveyors should be standing by and should be capable of handling the concrete at the required rate without segregation and at the specified slump; sufficient vibrators, with extra standby units, should be on hand; curing materials should be available. Special protective facilities for hot weather, freezing temperatures, or rain, as the season dictates, should be available. If the work is expected to continue after nightfall, sufficient lights should be in readiness.

12-4. TRANSPORTING CONCRETE

Conveying Methods and Equipment

Of fundamental importance to any method and equipment used for moving concrete from the mixer to the forms is the avoidance of segregation, loss of part of the concrete, or excessive loss of consistency. A slump loss of 1 in. may be tolerated, but anything more than that is excessive.

Buckets, properly designed and operated, are an excellent means of transporting concrete. Capacities range from less than 1 cu yd for structural use to 8 cu yd for mass concrete. Each bucket should have a capacity of at least one batch of concrete as mixed, except that this requirement may be waived when truck mixers are used. Buckets should be capable of discharging low-slump concrete and the discharge rate should be controllable. They should have nonjamming, self-closing gates to permit discharging partial loads. Cylindrical buckets with adequate center discharge gates are the most efficient.

Chutes are one of the most unsatisfactory methods for transporting concrete but may be used if care is taken to avoid segregation. They should be of rounded cross section and of smooth metal to avoid sticking of concrete. They should be of the correct slope so that concrete of the required slump will slide, not flow. End control should be provided so the concrete will drop vertically without segregation from the end of the chute. Two sections of metal drop chute "elephant trunk" will serve to control end segregation. A mere baffle is not adequate. Care should be exercised to prevent water, used for flushing the chute, from entering the forms.

Belt conveyors are satisfactory provided segregation and slump loss are avoided. Loss of mortar on the return belt should be prevented by a rubber or other suitable scraper. Scraped mortar should be fed into the concrete-receiving hopper.

The use of long chutes and conveyor belts should be avoided whenever possible, but if used, they should be covered to protect the concrete against the hot sun or rain. Flow of concrete should be as continuous as possible.

Pumping through a pipeline (Pumpcrete) is also a satisfactory method of transporting concrete. It requires a continuous supply of uniform, plastic, workable concrete. Air-entrained concrete may require more sand and water than non-air-entrained concrete to be handled satisfactorily, especially in a long line. Maximum size of aggregate should not exceed 2 in., although under favorable conditions, 2½-in. aggregate can be handled. Undersanded mixes should be avoided, as well as either wet or dry batches. Optimum slump is between 3 and 4 in., with the higher limit during hot weather. Loss of slump during pumping is about 1 in. per 1,000 ft of line. Line plugging is usually worse in hot weather but will be kept to a minimum by following the above precautions. On a long line, shading from the sun may be of benefit. Usual practice when starting a pumping operation is to precede the concrete with a cubic yard or so of mortar to lubricate the line.

Buggies and wheelbarrows are frequently used for distributing concrete into the forms. Concrete may be deposited in holding hoppers by any of the methods of transportation, with the buggies making the final distribution.

Pneumatic concrete placers are available and are especially useful in tunnel-lining operations. However, serious segregation of the concrete is apt to occur at the discharge, owing to the high velocity of the concrete as it emerges. Segregation can be minimized by keeping the end of the discharge line buried in the concrete, once the placement has been started.

Segregation

One of the most important considerations in handling concrete, as has been pointed out several times in this section, is the avoidance of segregation, or separation of the coarse aggregate from the mortar.

Concrete is not a homogeneous material and is subject to forces attempting to separate the component materials. Separation should be prevented before it happens, not corrected afterwards. Regardless of the type of equipment it is coming out of or into, concrete should drop vertically. It should be confined in a metal drop chute or elephant trunk for all but the lower few feet of drop, and the final drop should be vertical and in the clear. Concrete should not be dropped through reinforcement steel or other objects that tend to separate it, nor should it be directed against the forms. Figure 12-18 illustrates several methods of minimizing segregation when discharging concrete from a belt or chute. If such end controls are employed, there should be little trouble with segregation in transporting concrete.

Hauling buckets of concrete on trucks or cars for a considerable distance, especially if the buckets are subject to appreciable jolting or bumping, causes segregation.

Loss of Slump

The popular term used to describe a drying, or loss of consistency, of concrete is "slump loss." Slump loss is especially apt to be troublesome

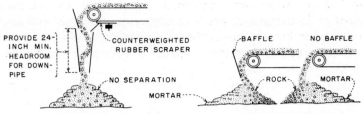

CORRECT	INCORRECT
THE ABOVE ARRANGEMENT PRE-VENTS SEPARATION OF CONCRETE WHETHER IT IS BEING DISCHARGED INTO HOPPERS, BUCKETS, CARS, TRUCKS, OR FORMS.	IMPROPER OR COMPLETE LACK OF CONTROL AT END OF BELT. USUALLY A BAFFLE OR SHALLOW HOPPER MERELY CHANGES THE DIRECTION OF SEPARATION.

CONTROL OF SEPARATION OF CONCRETE AT THE END OF CONVEYOR BELT

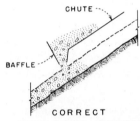 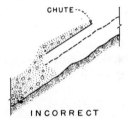

CORRECT	INCORRECT
PLACE BAFFLE AND DROP AT END OF CHUTE SO THAT SEPARATION IS AVOIDED AND CONCRETE REMAINS ON SLOPE.	TO DISCHARGE CONCRETE FROM A FREE END CHUTE ON A SLOPE TO BE PAVED. ROCK IS SEPARATED AND GOES TO BOTTOM OF SLOPE. VELOCITY TENDS TO CARRY CON-CRETE DOWN SLOPE.

PLACING CONCRETE ON A SLOPING SURFACE

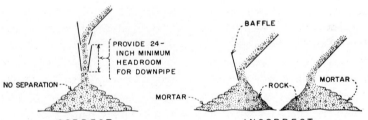

CORRECT	INCORRECT
THE ABOVE ARRANGEMENT PRE-VENTS SEPARATION, NO MATTER HOW SHORT THE CHUTE, WHETHER CONCRETE IS BEING DISCHARGED INTO HOPPERS, BUCKETS, CARS, TRUCKS, OR FORMS.	IMPROPER OR LACK OF CONTROL AT END OF ANY CONCRETE CHUTE, NO MATTER HOW SHORT. USUALLY A BAFFLE MERELY CHANGES DIRECTION OF SEPARATION.

CONTROL OF SEPARATION AT THE END OF CONCRETE CHUTES

THIS APPLIES TO SLOPING DISCHARGES FROM MIXERS, TRUCK MIXERS, ETC AS WELL AS TO LONGER CHUTES, BUT NOT WHEN CONCRETE IS DISCHARGED INTO ANOTHER CHUTE OR ONTO A CONVEYOR BELT.

FIG. 12-18. Control of separation. (*U.S. Bureau of Reclamation.*)

during hot, dry, windy weather, especially when concrete is hauled long distances or is transported on long chutes or conveyors exposing concrete to the drying effects of wind and sun. If it is necessary to transport concrete in this manner, the belts and chutes should be covered or shaded.

Dry aggregates in the mix will absorb water quite rapidly for a short time and will cause a loss of consistency. For this reason, all aggregates should be moist at the time they are batched.

The following measures are of value in hot, dry weather:

1. Organize the job well, with plenty of labor and equipment to handle the concrete, and proper coordination of all steps to prevent delays.

2. Precool aggregates with cold water or cold air jets in the batcher bins.

3. Use chipped ice in the mixing water. This is also valuable in holding concrete temperature below maximum specified. All ice should have melted by the time the concrete leaves the mixer.

4. Paint truck mixers white (better than aluminum or a light color).

5. Avoid overmixing.

6. Work at night.

7. Shade water lines and tanks, and paint them white.

8. Expedite movement of materials and concrete.

9. Investigate the possibility of false set in the cement, and avoid such cement.

The reader is referred to Chap. 2 and to Sec. 13-1 for further discussion on these subjects.

12-5. PLACING CONCRETE

The correct term to describe the act of depositing and consolidating concrete in the forms is "placing." Concrete is not "poured," although this expression is commonly accepted in construction jargon, owing its beginning to the days when sloppy, wet concrete really was poured and permitted to flow into place.

The first uses of concrete were in dams, heavy foundations, and other relatively massive structures in which an earth-moist concrete was compacted in place with much hand labor. Later, when reinforced concrete was introduced, the narrow forms containing reinforcing steel required a wet, plastic consistency, and concrete passed into the era of very fluid mixes which were poured in place. However, research was pointing out the faults and shortcomings of high water contents. Then, about 1930, the introduction of high-frequency vibration for consolidating concrete presented a practical way of handling relatively dry and unworkable mixes. Today, practically all concrete, regardless of its application, is consolidated by vibration and the need for wet mixes no longer exists.

It should be kept in mind that the slump of the concrete is prescribed by the specifications and is not to be determined by the condition or type of construction equipment. If the equipment will not handle concrete of the specified maximum slump, then the correction lies in the direction of proper equipment, not wetter mixes.

Depositing Concrete in the Forms

A basic rule is that concrete should be deposited as nearly as possible in its final location. It should be dropped, as nearly as possible, vertically. Figures 12-18 and 12-19 show correct and incorrect methods of placing concrete under various conditions. As long as the concrete is deposited near its final position without undue segregation, any method is acceptable. The use of drop chutes, or elephant trunks, may be necessary to guide the concrete through congestions of reinforcing steel or other items. Use of a crane bucket, moving along the top of a wall form, is entirely satisfactory as long as the concrete falls freely between the curtains of reinforcing steel. Any reasonable height of unconfined fall is acceptable provided the fall is vertical and segregation does not occur. In practice, it is usually necessary to limit free fall to a few feet because of obstructions in the form. As a practical safety measure, specifications usually limit the height of free fall.

Placing should be rapid enough to cover encrustation of mortar on steel or forms before the mortar dries. In using elephant trunks, the workmen should be cautioned to avoid pushing the bottom section at a considerable angle from the vertical. The bottom section should be vertical, although upper sections may be at an angle to facilitate placing of the concrete.

Concrete in walls, footings, beams, or any other structural components of appreciable height, should be placed in horizontal layers not exceeding about 18 in. in depth, unless another thickness is specified, starting at the ends or corners of the forms and working toward the center. The first layer on a rock foundation or construction joint should be preceded by a layer of mortar, not over ½ in. thick, well-broomed into the surface,* or by a layer of concrete containing one-half the amount of coarse aggregate in the regular mix, spread to a thickness of at least 2 in. Subsequent layers, continuing to the full height of the structure, should be placed before the underlying layer has hardened. As the top of the placement is approached, a drier concrete consistency should be used.

---

* A satisfactory mortar is made by omitting the coarse aggregate from a batch of concrete, using just enough water to provide a soft, mushy consistency. Any admixture used in the concrete should be included in the mortar batch also.

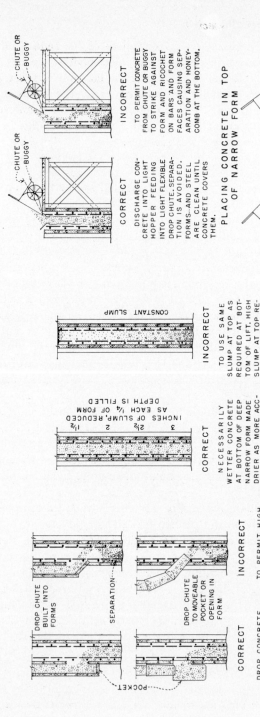

CHUTE OR BUGGY

CORRECT

DISCHARGE CONCRETE INTO LIGHT HOPPER FEEDING INTO LIGHT FLEXIBLE DROP CHUTE. SEPARATION IS AVOIDED. FORMS AND STEEL ARE CLEAN UNTIL CONCRETE COVERS THEM.

CHUTE OR BUGGY

INCORRECT

TO PERMIT CONCRETE FROM CHUTE OR BUGGY TO STRIKE AGAINST FORM AND RICOCHET ON BARS AND FORM FACES CAUSING SEPARATION AND HONEYCOMB AT THE BOTTOM.

PLACING CONCRETE IN TOP OF NARROW FORM

CORRECT

TO DUMP CONCRETE INTO FACE OF CONCRETE IN PLACE.

INCORRECT

TO DUMP CONCRETE AWAY FROM CONCRETE IN PLACE.

PLACING SLAB CONCRETE FROM BUGGIES

CORRECT

INCHES OF SLUMP, REDUCED AS EACH ¼ OF FORM DEPTH IS FILLED

3   2½   2   1½

NECESSARILY WETTER CONCRETE AT BOTTOM OF DEEP NARROW FORM MADE DRIER AS MORE ACCESSIBLE LIFTS NEAR TOP ARE REACHED. WATER GAIN TENDS TO EQUALIZE QUALITY OF CONCRETE. SETTLEMENT SHRINKAGE IS MINIMUM.

CONSTANT SLUMP

INCORRECT

TO USE SAME SLUMP AT TOP AS REQUIRED AT BOTTOM OF LIFT. HIGH SLUMP AT TOP RESULTS IN EXCESSIVE WATER GAIN WITH RESULTANT DISCOLORATION, LOSS OF QUALITY, AND DURABILITY IN THE UPPER LAYER.

CONSISTENCY OF CONCRETE IN DEEP NARROW FORMS

DROP CHUTE BUILT INTO FORMS

SEPARATION

POCKET

CORRECT

DROP CONCRETE VERTICALLY INTO OUTSIDE POCKET UNDER EACH FORM OPENING SO AS TO LET CONCRETE STOP AND FLOW EASILY OVER INTO FORM WITHOUT SEPARATION.

DROP CHUTE TO MOVEABLE POCKET OR OPENING IN FORM

INCORRECT

TO PERMIT HIGH VELOCITY STREAM OF CONCRETE TO ENTER FORMS ON AN ANGLE FROM THE VERTICAL. THIS INVARIABLY RESULTS IN SEPARATION.

PLACING IN DEEP NARROW WALL THRU PORT IN FORM

Fig. 12-19. Placing concrete in narrow forms and in slabs. (U.S. *Bureau of Reclamation.*)

216

For placing concrete in high, thin walls or similar structural units, it is common practice to provide ports or windows in the forms (Fig. 12-19). If possible, these windows should be made on a surface that will not be exposed to view in the finished structure, such as the back side of a wingwall on a highway structure. When the level of the fresh concrete within the structure approaches the window, the hole should be closed as tightly and neatly as possible. Because of the danger of segregation resulting from a high velocity stream of concrete entering the form at an angle, and because of the surface blemishes usually resulting in the area where the hole was closed, it is best to avoid use of these ports, if at all possible.

Concrete in cast-in-place piles and deep caisson footings must, of necessity, be dropped a considerable distance. Placement should be as nearly continuous as possible, as consolidation in the lower portion of the footing depends upon the impact of succeeding increments of concrete. A plastic consistency of about 4-in. slump is adequate.

In placing a slab, batches of concrete should be placed against or toward the preceding ones, not away from them. Batches should not be dumped in separate, individual piles. If the slab is on a slope, placing should start at the lower end of the slope.

In a structure consisting of monolithic columns, beams, and slabs, concrete should be placed to the top of the columns or beams, then allowed to set for 2 or 3 hr, depending on the weather, for settlement to take place; then the slab may be placed. If this procedure is not followed, cracks are liable to form where the slab joins the beam or the beam joins the column.

Waste molds or other molds for intricate architectural details should be protected from accumulations of mortar or other damage while the underlying concrete is being placed. One method of accomplishing this is to cover the inside of the mold with canvas or similar material.

Mass concrete in dams and similar massive structures is usually placed in lifts of 5- or 7½-ft depth, each lift consisting of several layers as previously described. In order to avoid cold joints, these layers are carried across the form in a series of steps, the first step being the mortar, then step no. 2 and so on until the final step at the top. Concrete contains cobbles as large as 6 in. in diameter, has a low cement content, and is placed at a slump of 1 or 2 in. or even less. Segregation is an ever-present problem. Buckets, which may have a capacity of as much as 8 cu yd, should have full-opening bottoms that discharge the concrete vertically and quickly.

Placing concrete during a rain is always a thorny problem. Usually a quick decision is necessary, so trouble may be forestalled by proper preparation and planning. A supply of protective coverings should be available nearby. Placing of concrete should not be commenced during a rainstorm but should be delayed until there is reasonable assurance that the placement can be completed before rain starts. If rain starts while concrete placing is in progress and the work must be continued because a construction joint cannot be made, no damage will be done during a light drizzle provided the following precautions are taken:

1. Place the concrete at a slightly lower slump.
2. Dry up puddles of water collected on the foundation or old concrete in the joint before new concrete is placed.
3. Cover the working area with tarps or tents, and keep them in place until the concrete has set.
4. Keep the surface of the new concrete on a slight slope so water will run off.
5. Avoid working the surface of the new concrete. After the concrete reaches grade, a slight slope should be provided, if feasible, for drainage.
6. If the rain is so heavy that it is not possible to dry up the puddles or keep the rain from washing the surface, discontinue work. The inspector should consult his supervisor regarding the placing of bulkheads and dowels and making a joint.

During thundershowers of short duration, it may be possible to cover the forms with a temporary cover and suspend work until the storm passes.

Consolidation

Once the concrete has been deposited in the forms, it has to be consolidated to make it into a solid, uniform mass without voids, rock pockets, or sand streaks. Many years ago, consolidation was accomplished with laborers wielding a variety of spades, tampers, and similar tools. Now nearly all concrete is consolidated with high-frequency vibrators. The report of ACI Committee 609, Consolidation of Concrete,[12.5] lists nine types of vibrators, but for this discussion these can be grouped into three general classes:

First are the internal spud vibrators, to be immersed in the concrete, operating at speeds of 5,000 to 10,000 rpm or more, ranging in size from $\frac{3}{4}$ in. diameter to $6\frac{3}{4}$ in. diameter with lengths from 10 to 28 in. The larger ones for mass concrete require two men to handle them. Most vibrators are either electric or air-powered, and some are driven by small gasoline engines. The motor may either be in the head of the vibrating unit, or the vibrating unit may be connected to the motor by means of a flexible shaft. This classification includes the gang-mounted and tube vibrators used on paving machines, as well as vibrators for structural concrete.

The second group includes surface, pan, or screed vibrators that operate on the surface of a floor, slab, or pavement. Minimum frequency should be 3,000 rpm. Consolidation of the concrete in thin slabs is accomplished by drawing the vibrating unit slowly over the surface. Slabs up to 8 in. thick can be consolidated adequately. Thicker slabs may require additional internal vibration. Screed lengths as long as 40 ft have been used.

The third group comprises the external vibrators, or form vibrators. As their name implies, these vibrators, operating at a minimum speed of 3,600 rpm, are attached to the exterior of the mold or form. They are used in locations where it is not possible to use internal vibrators, such as in tunnel linings or heavily congested forms. They are also used for making pipe, masonry units, and many other types of precast concrete.

Concrete should be consolidated to the maximum practicable density, so that it is free of pockets of coarse aggregate and entrapped air, and closes snugly against all surfaces of forms and embedded materials. Vibrators should be applied to the concrete immediately after it is deposited. In consolidating each layer of concrete, the vibrator should be operated in a nearly vertical position and the vibrating head should penetrate and revibrate the concrete in the upper portion of the underlying layer. Application of vibrators should be at points uniformly spaced, amply close together to ensure complete consolidation (usually not more than twice the radius over which the vibration is visibly effective), and of sufficient duration to consolidate the concrete thoroughly, ordinarily 5 to 10 sec per insertion. Vibrators should not be dragged through the concrete nor should they be used to move the concrete about in the forms. Vibrators cannot recombine concrete that has already segregated. If segregation has occurred because of improper handling techniques, concentrations of rocks should be broken up by shoveling the rocks onto areas of concrete containing a sufficiency of sand (see Fig. 12-20).

Completion of vibration is indicated when the surface of the concrete takes on a flattened glistening appearance, the rise of entrapped air bubbles ceases, the coarse aggregate blends into the surface but does not disappear, and the vibrator, after an initial slowdown when first inserted into the concrete, resumes its normal speed.

Overvibration can and does occur, especially when overly wet mixes are being placed. The correction is to reduce the slump rather than the amount of vibration. If concrete has been overvibrated, the coarse aggregate will have sunk below the surface, and the surface may have a frothy appearance.

Revibration occurs when the vibrator, in consolidating a layer of concrete, penetrates into the layer below. The general effect of revibration is

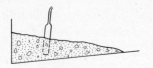 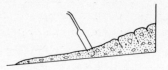

CORRECT

START PLACING AT BOTTOM OF
SLOPE SO THAT COMPACTION
IS INCREASED BY WEIGHT OF
NEWLY ADDED CONCRETE.
VIBRATION CONSOLIDATES.

INCORRECT

TO BEGIN PLACING AT TOP OF
SLOPE. UPPER CONCRETE TENDS
TO PULL APART, ESPECIALLY
WHEN VIBRATED BELOW, AS VIBRA-
TION STARTS FLOW AND REMOVES
SUPPORT FROM CONCRETE ABOVE.

WHEN CONCRETE MUST BE PLACED IN
A SLOPING LIFT

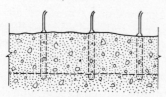 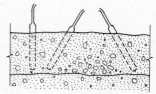

CORRECT

VERTICAL PENETRATION OF
VIBRATOR A FEW INCHES INTO
PREVIOUS LIFT (WHICH SHOULD
NOT YET BE RIGID) AT SYSTEM-
ATIC REGULAR INTERVALS
FOUND TO GIVE ADEQUATE
CONSOLIDATION.

INCORRECT

HAPHAZARD RANDOM PENETRA-
TION OF THE VIBRATOR AT ALL
ANGLES AND SPACINGS WITHOUT
SUFFICIENT DEPTH TO ASSURE
MONOLITHIC COMBINATION OF
THE TWO LAYERS.

SYSTEMATIC VIBRATION OF EACH NEW LIFT

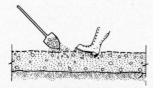 

CORRECT

SHOVEL ROCKS FROM ROCK
POCKET ONTO SOFTER, AMPLY
SANDED AREA AND TRAMP OR
VIBRATE.

INCORRECT

ATTEMPTING TO CORRECT
ROCK POCKET BY SHOVELING
MORTAR AND SOFT CONCRETE
ON IT.

TREATMENT OF ROCK POCKET WHEN PLACING
CONCRETE

FIG. 12-20. Use of vibrator; and eliminating rock pockets. (*U.S. Bureau of Reclamation.*)

improved strength—compressive, flexural, and bond—durability, and appearance. It tends to reduce water pockets under horizontal reinforcing steel and reduces the appearance of settlement cracks. In moderation, the net effect of revibration is beneficial.

In some instances, as in certain architectural work when the surface must be as nearly flawless as possible, vibration may be supplemented by rodding or spading along the forms, especially in corners and angles.

12-6. JOINTS

Construction Joints

A construction joint is the plane surface between two increments of concrete, the second increment having been placed against or on the first after the first had hardened. A construction joint may be horizontal, as in a wall or column, or it may be vertical, as in a slab or adjacent blocks of a dam. Locations of construction joints are shown on the plans. If, because of a stoppage of the work for several hours or longer, it becomes necessary to install a joint, the joint should be made in a plane normal to the main reinforcing bars and in a region of minimum shear. Minimum shear in simply supported slabs or girders is at or near the center of the span. The design engineer should be consulted with respect to location of construction joints, as a wrongly located joint can seriously alter the load-carrying properties of the structure.

Reinforcing steel is normally continuous across a construction joint, or dowels are provided. Some designs call for shear keys in the joint. Shear keys, formed in the run of concrete comprising the lower portion of a horizontal joint, may be formed by inserting and subsequently removing beveled strips or blocks of wood which were saturated with water prior to insertion. Keys in a vertical joint may be formed by affixing beveled blocks or trapezoids to the forms.

After the first run of concrete at a vertical construction joint has gained sufficient strength, the form or header board should be removed and the concrete washed with a jet of water of sufficient volume and velocity to wash the cement paste from the surface. This washing should be done at such a time that the aggregate will not be loosened. Horizontal joints should be similarly washed. If this is not done, it is permissible that the concrete surface be cut later by wet sandblasting.

Roughness is not essential to a good joint. In fact, a better joint is obtained if the surface is regular and smooth, avoiding large pieces of aggregate protruding above the surface, or depressions such as footprints. The ideal cleanup exposes particles of fine aggregate but does not cut deep enough to expose the coarse aggregate.

Formed construction joints should be avoided whenever possible, as they are planes of weakness and potential sources of leakage of water through the structure. Waterstops should be installed if leakage of water through the joint must be prevented.

Immediately prior to placing the second run of concrete, the joint surface is thoroughly washed to remove all sand, mortar, nails, and other foreign materials, then concrete placing is done as previously described.

Heretofore, when preparing a concrete surface to which a subsequent lift is to be bonded, practice has been to keep the surface wet for several hours or for a day or so. Recent research,[12.6] however, indicates that a stronger, tighter, and better joint results if the joint mortar is spread on dry but thoroughly clean concrete, or even if the concrete is spread on

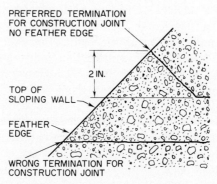

Fig. 12-21. Horizontal construction joint intersecting a sloping surface.

a dry surface, without mortar, at least as far as mass concrete is concerned. However, thorough cleaning of the joint surface is essential. If the joint surface has been treated with a retarder, incomplete removal of the retarded layer does not impair the integrity of the joint.

Where a horizontal construction joint meets a sloping form, it is a good idea to bevel the concrete slightly by building the first lift up against the form slightly, in this way avoiding the formation of a feather edge (see Fig. 12-21).

Contraction Joints

Large areas of concrete require contraction joints, sometimes called dummy joints or weakened plane joints, in order to control cracking. Location of joints is designated in the plans or specifications. In pavements and other slabs subject to heavy loading, lubricated dowels are installed ahead of concrete placing along the line of the proposed joint.

There are several methods of making contraction joints. In one method, a small groove is tooled in the fresh concrete surface, a common practice in sidewalk and floor construction. The joint may be sawed in the hardened concrete; this method is widely used in highway and airport pavement (see Chap. 14) and is coming into use for other slab construction. In still another method, a forming strip of wood or metal is embedded in the fresh concrete and subsequently removed, leaving a groove in the concrete.)

In making a groove in fresh concrete, the edges should be slightly rounded and care must be taken to make sure that the groove is free of projections of concrete or aggregate particles. Joints made by sawing or a forming strip are filled with a mastic material to prevent foreign material from entering the joint and to seal against passage of water.

Expansion Joints

The object of an expansion joint is to provide for movement of the concrete caused by changes in volume. Expansion joints in bridges are quite complicated because of the amount of movement that occurs during the changing seasons, and because of the necessity of providing a relatively continuous surface for traffic. Expansion joints are also provided in large buildings and slabs, such as at the joint between a floor and a wall or footing.

Expansion joints may be formed by installing preformed strips at the time concrete is placed, the exact procedure and location being designated in the plans and specifications. Sliding or moving joints are sometimes lubricated with a bituminous material to facilitate movement. Inspection includes checking to make sure that dowels and joints are properly aligned, as a misaligned dowel or joint is sure to cause spalling during subsequent movement of the joint. Care should be exercised in placing concrete to avoid moving any part of the joint assembly. Fins and projections of concrete should be removed before the concrete becomes hard.

12-7. REMOVAL OF FORMS AND SHORING

Essentially, the effect on the concrete is the basis for determining the time to remove forms. Forms should be stripped as soon as possible after placing of concrete has been completed so that repairs can be made to the concrete, and curing started without delay. However, there must be no damage to the concrete as a result of the form removal, nor should there be any evidence of deflection of the structure, except that which is allowed for in its design.

Forms on the top side of a sloping wall can be removed within 2 or 3 hr, but forms supporting such structural elements as beams and slabs obviously have to remain in place until the concrete has sufficient strength to carry both the dead load and any live load that might be imposed, with a safety factor of 2. Because of the great variety of field conditions that exist, job-cured strength specimens should be used for determining strength for this purpose. Table 3-3 shows typical strength values for removal of forms in different situations. However, this table is only a guide, and an adequate factor of safety must be provided, based on an analysis of the particular situation and using field-cured specimens.

The practice of leaving the forms in place for curing the concrete is not well advised because there is a tendency for the concrete to shrink away from the forms, thus permitting a loss of moisture. If it is necessary to leave the forms in place, the concrete should be kept wet and water permitted to seep into the space between the concrete and the forms. However, in cold weather, it may be desirable to leave the forms in place until the concrete has cooled because of the danger of cracking caused by sudden cooling.

Removal of supporting forms and falsework should be done in such a manner as to cause the concrete to assume the load gradually and in a systematic manner. Such structural elements as arches require a carefully thought-out plan of removal to preclude distortion and uneven application of load.

12-8. FINISHING

Classification of Finishes

The amount of finishing and dressing to be applied to a concrete surface, either formed or unformed, depends upon the type of surface and whether it is to be exposed to view. The following classifications, based on practice of the Bureau of Reclamation and the Concrete Industry Board of New York City, should be considered when preparing specifications for concrete work. In these classifications, the "F" finishes apply to formed surfaces, and the "U" finishes apply to unformed surfaces.

Finish F-1. Finish F-1 is applied to surfaces where roughness is not objectionable, such as surfaces to be backfilled, permanently submerged, or otherwise concealed from view. The only surface treatment after removal of forms is filling of tie-rod holes on walls under 12 in. thick, or on all surfaces to be waterproofed, and repair of defective concrete. Forms may be quite rough, as long as they do not leak mortar.

Finish F-2. This is used for all permanently exposed surfaces where a higher-quality surface is not specified, such as external portions of bridges (except grade separations); hydraulic structures such as tunnels, canals, culverts, siphons, spillways, and dams; retaining walls not subject to close public view; docks and wharves; and certain rough buildings. Forms must be carefully and accurately built, without conspicuous offsets or bulges. Sheathing may be plywood, shiplap, or steel (not thin sheet steel). Surface treatment includes removal of mortar fins, filling of tie-rod holes, and dressing of offsets greater than $\frac{1}{4}$ in. and bulges greater than $\frac{1}{2}$ in. in 5 ft.

Finish F-3. Finish F-3 is used for all surfaces subject to close public view such as inside and outside of buildings (except those surfaces with special architectural treatment), parapets, grade separation structures, and power houses. Forms must be carefully and accurately built by skilled workmen, without visible offsets or bulges. Sheathing should be plywood or tongue-and-groove boards. Special care is required at construction joints. Uniform color and texture are necessary, which may necessitate sack rubbing, grout cleaning, or other treatment, as specified. Materials should be from the same source throughout the work, except for surfaces to be painted.

Finish F-4. Finish F-4 provides a special smooth surface for conduits carrying high-velocity water where cavitation might occur. Forms must be especially tight, strong, and smooth, without perceptible offsets or bulges. Surface treatment consists in removal of all rough spots, offsets, and bubble holes by filling or grinding.

Finish F-5. This is a special rough surface for bonding to plaster or stucco. Concrete is cast against rough, unoiled form boards. Surface treatment includes removal of fins and projections, and repair of defective areas.

Finish U-1. Finish U-1 is screeded only, and it is used for surfaces to be backfilled, construction joints, base for two-course floor, and rough exposed slabs. Also, it is the first stage for further finishing. See Sec. 13-5 for a description of finishing operations.

Finish U-2. Screeded and floated, finish U-2 is used on all outdoor concrete, unless another finish is specified, such as tops of bridge piers, outside decks at industrial buildings, hydraulic structures such as canals and tunnel inverts, and reservoirs.

Finish U-3. This finish is screeded, floated, and troweled and is used for inside floors; at tops of walls and parapets subject to close public view; and for roof slabs, sidewalks, and pools.

Finish U-4. This is a special simplified trowel or slipform finish for canal linings. It is equivalent to bullfloat or darby slab finish.

Finish U-5. Various special finishes designated in the specifications, requiring certain finishing procedures in each case, come under this category. It is also used for architectural finishes.

Formed Surfaces

Normally, no finishing is required for formed surfaces, as the type of form used should provide the specified surface. However, it is necessary to remove fins of concrete that developed between form boards or panels and to perform the treatments required for each of the finishes just described.

Some specifications require a rubbed finish on certain F-2 or F-3 exposed surfaces. Forms should be stripped as soon as possible since rubbing of green concrete is easier and produces a better finish than rubbing of concrete that has been cured and dried out. After any necessary repairs have been made, the surface is wetted thoroughly, then rubbed vigorously with a carborundum stone of No. 16 grit, which removes all fins and roughness, fills all pits, and produces a smooth uniform surface. The paste resulting from the rubbing is spread uniformly over the surface and allowed to set, after which it is again moistened and rubbed with a No. 30 stone until the surface is uniform and smooth. Normal curing should then be applied. Because of the amount of labor involved, workmen frequently fail to do a thorough job of rubbing with the result that the dried paste scales and peels. Curing compound should not be applied to a surface that is to be rubbed later.

Sometimes, if it is stained with excess form oil, architectural concrete requires grout cleaning, or it is not of uniform color. Grout for cleaning consists of 1 part cement with 1½ parts fine mason's sand and sufficient water to produce a consistency of thick paint. (It may be necessary to use some white cement to give the correct color.) After the concrete surface has been thoroughly moistened, the grout is spread, then vigorously floated with a cork float; care must be taken to fill all holes in the concrete. After the grout has partially set, a sponge rubber float is used to remove excess grout. Finally, after the surface has dried thoroughly, it is rubbed again, this time with dry burlap to remove all dried grout.

Unformed Surfaces

Tops of slabs, pavements, canal linings, and floors are unformed surfaces; that is, the finish is obtained by working the surface of the concrete, before final set, with certain tools to provide the type of surface desired.

The amount of surface manipulation that will give the desired finish should be kept to a minimum. A screeded finish is all that is necessary on a surface to be covered with backfill. Smoothing with a darby or bullfloat should be adequate for a construction joint. More elaborate finishing operations for floors are described in Sec. 13-5, and pavement construction is treated in detail in Chap. 14.

12-9. CURING

Fresh concrete, when placed in the forms, contains more than enough water for combining with the cement during hydration. One function of curing is to preserve or replenish this water for a suitable time until the concrete has reached the strength and hardness desired. Curing should also maintain the temperature of the concrete at the required level throughout the structure for the required period of time and provide protection from impact, loading, and other mechanical disturbances.

Water Curing

In theory, water curing is the ideal way to cure concrete, assuming that satisfactory temperature conditions prevail. In practice, however, this ideal is seldom realized because of the difficulty in keeping the concrete continuously wet. Far too often, water is sprinkled intermittently by some laborer who has too many places to cover or too many other jobs to do, or someone removes the hose to use someplace else. As a result, water curing does not work out as well as it should. Water-saturated mats in intimate contact with the concrete are probably the best way to keep the entire surface continuously wet. Water should be continuously available by means of sprinklers, soaker hoses, or other means. Pieces of burlap loosely draped over the concrete, whether wet or dry, are of little value in curing.

Unformed top surfaces should be moistened by wet burlap or other effective means as soon as the concrete has hardened sufficiently to withstand the treatment without damage. This is especially important for construction joints, which cannot be cured with sealing compound.

Wood forms offer a good measure of insulation against cold weather, but, as mentioned previously, leaving the forms in place is no guarantee of good curing.

On such structures as dams and high piers, it is sometimes the practice to attach spray pipes to the lower edge of the forms. As the forms are raised for successive lifts, water curing is applied to the freshly exposed concrete. However, water running over the lower portions of the structure for a long period of time is apt to stain the concrete.

Flat slabs may be cured by constructing small earth dikes around the perimeter and flooding the area with water, or by the application of several inches of earth or sand kept in a wet condition. Placing of moist backfill on footings or against below-grade walls also provides good curing, as soon as the structure can withstand the earth pressures developed.

Blankets and Sheet Materials

Various types of pads and blankets of jute, cotton, or burlap are available which are placed in contact with the concrete, especially slabs, and maintained in a wet condition. Impermeable sheets of heavy paper or polyethylene sheeting are available which provide a watertight covering, preserving the moisture in the concrete. In using any of these materials, care must be exercised to see that the pad or sheeting is in intimate contact with the concrete and that separate pads or sheets are lapped between 6 and 12 in. The surface of the concrete should be wetted before the impermeable sheet is placed.

Any of these curing materials can be reused if they are kept free of oil, dirt, and encrustations of mortar and if holes are patched so as to retain a continuous covering.

Wetted straw is sometimes used, especially on sidewalks and pavements. With this method, wetted burlap is first placed on the slab, then covered with clean straw to a depth of 8 to 12 in. The straw is kept wet for the specified curing period. This method is prohibited in some areas because of the litter sometimes resulting.

The length of time the concrete should be kept wet is usually stated in the specifications. A minimum should be 7 days for Type I cement at normal atmospheric temperatures. For Type III cement this curing period can be reduced to 3 days. Type II and other slow-hardening cements require more time.

Sealing Compounds

Either the pigmented or clear sealing compound may be used. Usually, the white pigmented material is used on pavements, canal linings, and similar slabs with large areas exposed to the sun because of its heat-reflecting property. The clear compound is used on structures and walks, one reason being that it weathers more uniformly than the white and does not present a mottled appearance after a few weeks.

Compound should be applied to unformed surfaces as soon as the water shine disappears but while the surface is still moist. If application of the compound is delayed, the surface should be kept wet with water until the membrane can be applied. The compound should not be applied to areas on which bleeding water is standing.

Compound should be applied to formed surfaces immediately after removal of the forms. If the concrete surface is dry, it should be moistened and kept wet until no more water will be absorbed. As soon as the surface moisture film disappears, but while the concrete is still damp, the compound should be applied, with special care taken to cover edges and corners. Patching of the concrete is done after the compound has been applied. Compound should be sprayed, not brushed, on patched areas.

Brush application should never be permitted on unformed surfaces since the surface is still soft enough to be injured by the brush, and the compound will penetrate excessively into the concrete. Brush application may be permitted on formed surfaces in limited instances.

If curing compound is applied to a dry concrete surface, it is apt to "strike into" or penetrate into the surface. A soft, dusty concrete surface usually results.

Pressure tank equipment should be used for spraying the compound, and the compound should be agitated continually during application. The coverage of about 135 to 150 sq ft per gal should be made in one coat, consisting of two passes of the spray nozzle at right angles to each other. Rough concrete requires slightly more compound than smooth concrete. On rough surfaces, particular care is necessary to ensure complete coverage.

Compound should never be thinned. However, during cold weather, it may be necessary to heat the compound if it becomes too viscous for application. Heating should be done in a hot water bath, never over an open flame, and the temperature should never exceed 100°F. When being heated, the container should be vented and there should be room in the container for expansion of the compound. The compound should be agitated during heating.

REFERENCES

12.1 How a Dual-drum Paver Operates, *Public Roads*, U.S. Bureau of Public Roads, April, 1960, p. 11.
12.2 Variability of Constituents in Concrete, *Concrete Manual*, 6th ed., U.S. Bureau of Reclamation, 1955, pp. 447–451.
12.3 Standards for Operation of Truck Mixers and Agitators, National Ready Mixed Concrete Association, March, 1957.
12.4 Formwork for Concrete, Report of ACI Committee 662, *J. Am. Concrete Inst.*, March, 1961, pp. 993–1040.
12.5 Consolidation of Concrete, Report of ACI Committee 609, *J. Am. Concrete Inst.*, April, 1960, pp. 985–1011.
12.6 Tynes, W. O.: Investigation of Methods of Preparing Horizontal Construction Joints in Concrete, Technical Report No. 6-518, U.S. Army Engineers, Waterways Experiment Station, July, 1959.
12.7 Curing Concrete, Report of ACI Committee 612, *J. Am. Concrete Inst.*, August, 1958, pp. 161–172.
12.8 Recommended Practice for Measuring, Mixing, and Placing Concrete, (ACI 614), American Concrete Institute, 1959.
12.9 Reinforced Concrete—A Manual of Standard Practice, Concrete Reinforcing Steel Institute, March, 1961.

CHAPTER 13 *Special Concreting Techniques*

13-1. HOT-WEATHER CONCRETING

High-temperature Effects

Concrete mixing and placing can proceed during hot weather with no detrimental effect on the concrete provided certain precautions are taken. These precautions seek to protect the fresh concrete from damage because of high temperatures, provide adequate curing so the concrete will develop the strength and durability of which it is capable, and minimize shrinkage and cracking.

Of basic importance is to limit the concrete temperature to 85°F when the concrete is deposited in the forms. The reasons for this are that the ultimate strength of concrete mixed and cured at high temperatures is never as high as that of concrete mixed and cured at lower temperatures. Also, the water requirement is higher at the higher temperatures, contributing to greater drying shrinkage. For each 10° rise in concrete temperature, the water requirement for concrete increases about ¾ gal per cu yd.

Shrinkage cracking tendencies are greater at higher temperatures because of the greater difference between placing temperatures and later temperatures. Concrete placed at a high temperature is not as durable as concrete placed at a lower temperature. Resistance to cycles of freezing and thawing, or wetting and drying, is appreciably less. Loss of slump or workability is magnified at higher temperatures. The effect of delays in transporting and handling is manifested by evaporation of water from the fresh concrete and rapid setting or hydration of the cement.

Use of Admixtures

Strength accelerating admixtures, such as calcium chloride, should be used sparingly, or not at all, during hot weather. The same holds true for high-early-strength cement.

Set-retarding admixtures may be used to considerable advantage, as they not only lengthen the time that the concrete remains in a workable condition, but most of them also reduce the water requirement. A retarder should be used whenever the air temperature exceeds 75°F.

When, because of the necessity of putting a structure in service as soon as possible, high-early-strength cement must be used, a retarder may be used with confidence. Retardation may not be as pronounced as with normal cement. Strength gain will be at the usual rate for high-early-strength cement, so the early-strength requirement will be safely met.

Temperature Control

There are a number of steps that can be taken to prevent excessively high concrete temperatures. Water tanks and supply lines should be shaded or insulated; in extreme cases, flake or chipped ice may be used in the mixing water. On a large canal-lining job in the West, tank trucks delivering water to the mixer were insulated, and blocks of ice were used to cool the water in the tanks. Mass concrete plants for large dams are provided with refrigeration plants to produce flake ice which is introduced into the mix with the water. Because of the latent heat of liquefaction, ice is several times as effective as cold water in cooling capacity. If ice is permitted to enter the mixer, the amount should be adjusted so that the ice will be entirely melted before mixing is completed. Of course, the ice is considered as part of the mixing water.

Other measures include cooling the coarse aggregates with water or cooled air, sprinkling water on mixer drums, working at night, and shading the work area (Fig. 13-1). Mixers, especially truck mixers, should be painted white or a light color. Overmixing should be avoided by carefully scheduling truck mixers to keep at a minimum the time between charging the mixer and depositing the concrete in the forms. Not only is heat absorbed from the air during mixing, but the work of mixing generates heat in the batch.

Use of hot cement should be avoided. Cement temperature should not exceed 150°F at the time the cement is batched. Accelerated cooling of cement in the average batching plant is nearly impossible, and it is necessary to rely on natural loss of heat to the atmosphere.

Placing and Curing

Sprinkling the working area with water causes a lowering of temperature by evaporation, but care is necessary to avoid mud and standing water, especially in the forms. Sun shades are also helpful. Sometimes it is possible to cover the work area with tarpaulins supported on a frame-

FIG. 13-1. A temporary cover protects the work area from the hot sun as well as providing shelter from possible showers.

work or poles. Methods for preventing cracking that were discussed in Sec. 7-2 should be employed.

On the Dunvegan Bridge over the Peace River in Alberta, use was made of curing compound followed by white polyethylene sheeting to protect the concrete from the hot, dry air and sun.[13.1*]

False strength indications will result if test specimens are permitted to dry out or become too hot (see Sec. 15-6).

13-2. COLD-WEATHER CONCRETING

In the past, it was customary to curtail concrete work during the winter in areas subject to temperatures below freezing for considerable periods. In recent years, however, with a better understanding of the effects of cold weather, and with improved methods of protection, cold weather is no longer a serious obstacle to construction progress. There is no reason why good concrete cannot be made in the winter, provided the effects of cold weather are understood and proper precautions are taken.

Low-temperature Effects

The effects of frost and freezing on strength and durability were discussed in Chaps. 3 and 5. At temperatures above freezing, the rate of

* Superscript figures refer to chapter and reference number. The references are found at the end of each chapter.

hardening depends upon the temperature (Fig. 13-2), hence the need to maintain the concrete temperature well above freezing until the concrete gains sufficient strength to suffer no damage. In addition, it is necessary to protect the concrete from freezing and minimize thermal stresses.

Low temperatures may even affect the quality of aggregates. One case is reported in which freezing of the moisture in the sand caused it to stick to the bed of the dump truck used for hauling aggregates. When dry stone was hauled in the same truck, dumping the stone in the truck broke the frozen sand loose, resulting in contamination of the stone. A little care in inspecting the hauling vehicles would have prevented such an occurrence.

A case of bond failure occurred when warm concrete for a thin floor topping was placed on cold, hardened concrete. Subsequent cooling and shrinkage of the topping, simultaneously with warming and expansion in the surface of the old concrete as equilibrium in temperature was established, caused failure of bond between the two.

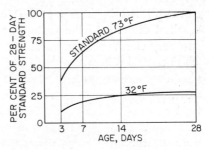

Fig. 13-2. Concrete cured at low temperatures gains strength more slowly than concrete cured at standard temperature.

Temperature Limitations

Preparation for cold weather concreting should be made before the cold weather arrives, not afterwards. Facilities for heating and protection should be on hand, as well as an adequate supply of calcium chloride to be used as an accelerating admixture.

Temperature limitations are stated in the specifications or building code. Lacking these, the following limitations are suggested: in moderate weather when the mean daily air temperature is above 40°F, concrete temperature should be above 40°F when it is placed. When the mean daily temperature is below 40°F, the concrete temperature should be between 50 and 65°F at time of placement. The temperature at which the concrete is mixed should be the minimum necessary to provide a reasonable margin of safety above the minimum specified placing temperature. Heat loss during transporting and handling rarely necessitates a mixing temperature above 80°F.

Overheating of the concrete should be avoided since the water requirement for any given slump increases as the temperature increases. Overheating also causes an excessive loss of slump and accelerates hydration of the cement.

Aggregates should not be heated if heating of the mixing water alone will ensure delivery of concrete of the required temperature. Because the specific heat of water is approximately five times that of aggregate and cement, each pound of water provides five times as much heat as a pound of aggregate or cement. Temperature of the water should not exceed 150°F at the time of mixing with the other ingredients.

When the air temperature is below freezing, frozen aggregates should be thawed before entering the mixer. Heating of aggregates is best accomplished by steam or hot water circulating in pipes. Steam jets applied directly to the material should not be used, even though they are very effective, because the resulting variable moisture content makes close control difficult.

Proportioning and Mixing

There are no special rules necessary in proportioning concrete during cold weather. The same mixes that are suitable in moderate weather are suitable in the winter, except that air-entrained concrete should be used, and usually an accelerator is used. The batching and mixing plant must be heated for proper operation of the equipment and personnel efficiency.

Close liaison is necessary between the plant and placing site to assure expeditious handling of the concrete with a minimum of delay. This is especially important when ready-mixed concrete is being used.

Accelerators

Calcium chloride, by its catalytic action, hastens the hydration process, causing the concrete to gain strength more rapidly than concrete without the salt, thus enabling the concrete to withstand freezing temperatures sooner. Calcium chloride may be used in the concrete during freezing weather in an amount not exceeding 2 per cent by weight of the cement; usually 1 per cent is sufficient. In lieu of calcium chloride, Type III cement may be used. Either of these expedients requires close control to avoid a flash set and rapid loss of workability, especially when the water or any of the ingredients is heated.

The practice of adding dry calcium chloride to the batch in a truck mixer after arrival at the jobsite should be discouraged because the probability is that the salt will not be thoroughly mixed throughout the batch. Then, too, there is danger of lumps of the salt failing to dissolve, resulting in subsequent disintegration of spots in the concrete. (Because of its hygroscopic nature, calcium chloride lumps easily on exposure to the air, even in apparently dry weather.) Calcium chloride should be introduced in solution with the mixing water. A good procedure is to mix lots of 50 or 100 gal of a solution containing 1 or 2 lb of salt per gallon of solution. Then measured amounts of solution assure uniform addition of the accelerator to the concrete. Automatic measuring devices are available (Fig. 13-3). The volume of solution should be considered as part of the mixing water.

There is no material presently available that can be used as an antifreeze in concrete without damage to the concrete. Even as much as 4

Fig. 13-3. Components of an automatic dispenser for calcium chloride solution. The amount of solution batched is regulated by the timer. (*J. W. Materials, Inc., photo.*)

per cent of calcium chloride has a negligible effect in lowering the freezing point.

Placing and Protection

All frost and ice must be removed from the forms, reinforcing steel, embedded materials, and similar items before concrete placing is started. Concrete should never be placed on a frozen subgrade, since to do so is apt to result in loss of support when the ground thaws. If concrete is placed against frozen ground without forms or on a frozen subgrade, the ground may take sufficient heat out of the concrete to cause it to freeze, or the concrete may harden very slowly, even though the air temperature is relatively warm.

Common practice is to enclose the entire structure in tarpaulins or transparent polyethylene sheeting (Figs. 13-4 and 13-5). Bridges, buildings, and other types of structures may be enclosed in this manner. The enclosure should be at least a foot away from the fresh concrete. Heat

Fɪɢ. 13-4. Polyethylene sheeting protects this bridge from cold weather. Heat is supplied by salamanders, and the deck is protected with insulated pads and straw.

Fɪɢ. 13-5. This structure was entirely enclosed within the heated tent. (*Illinois Tollway photo.*)

should be provided before, during, and after placing. Heat is best supplied by releasing moist steam within the enclosure. If dry heat is used, the concrete must be protected from drying out by means of curing compounds, blankets, or wet burlap.

Salamanders are an excellent source of heat but must be used with great care. Fire is an ever-present hazard. Salamanders must be vented to the outside to remove the danger of carbonation of the concrete surface. (Carbonation causes a soft, weak concrete surface.) Blower types of heaters and pipe coils or radiators are frequently used. With any of these heaters, protection must be provided to avoid concentrations of heat on concrete surfaces. The exhaust from blowers should not impinge directly on the concrete. Salamanders should be insulated from the slab on which they are standing.

After placement, the concrete should be maintained at a minimum temperature of 50°F for at least 5 days, 3 days if an accelerator or Type III cement is used. After this initial protection, it is good practice to maintain a temperature of 40°F for 4 more days. Discontinuance of protection from freezing must be gradual so that the drop in temperature of any portion of the concrete will not exceed 40°F in 24 hr.

When placing a slab or floor, the tarpaulin or plastic cover should be supported on horses or a framework in such a way that the covering follows closely behind the placing. If it is necessary to open the covering for finishing, only small areas of the slab should be exposed at a time, and then for very short periods.

Insulation

In the last few years, the use of insulation on forms has come into common practice. Insulating bats, consisting of rock wool, glass wool, fiberglass, or balsam wool, covered on each side with heavy asphalt-impregnated paper, are attached to the outside of the forms, and the normal heat of hydration of the cement serves to keep the concrete adequately warm, even in zero weather. Straw or bats are used on horizontal surfaces also.

The insulating material should be attached to the forms with wood cleats or similar means and should be tight against the forms so as to prevent circulation of air under the insulation. It should be in place before concrete placing is started and should overlap previously placed concrete by at least 1 ft. Tears and holes in the covering should be patched with waterproof tape. The insulation must be kept dry.

The ACI Recommended Practice for Winter Concreting[13.3] contains detailed instructions for insulation of forms and other winter concreting practices. Even in the coldest weather, the insulation must be used as directed because there is actually danger of permitting the concrete to get too hot. A case of cracking was discussed in Chap. 7 in which the cracks were traced to the use of too much insulation on the forms, followed by rapid cooling.

Special care is necessary to protect corners and edges of the concrete as well as thin members.

Figure 13-6 shows that actual temperatures in a concrete bridge pier placed during very cold weather were adequate to promote strength development at a satisfactory rate.

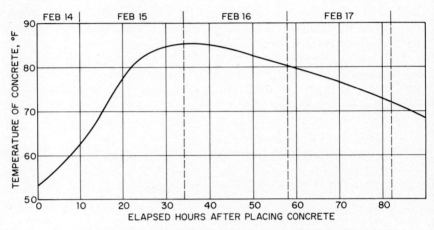

FIG. 13-6. Concrete temperature inside insulated form.

Air Temperatures, °F

Date	Max	Min
Feb. 14..........	25	0
Feb. 15..........	7	−10
Feb. 16..........	5	−12
Feb. 17..........	5	−4

Mix: $5\frac{1}{2}$ sacks cement; 1 per cent $CaCl_2$: 4 per cent air. 41 cu yd concrete placed in 5 × 5-ft column. Forms insulated with $1\frac{1}{2}$-in. balsam wool.

13-3. CONCRETING UNDER WATER

General

Underwater placing of concrete should be avoided if at all possible. Most specifications prohibit such placement except in special cases and under close control. Concrete should never be placed in running water.

Cement content of the mix should be increased by at least $\frac{1}{2}$ sack per cubic yard; some specifications require 1 additional sack, and others require 10 per cent additional cement. A plastic, wet mix is required as no working or vibrating of the concrete is done. Slump should be about

5 or 6 in. The concrete should not be disturbed after it has been placed. Use of a densifying and water-reducing admixture is recommended.

Tremies

Two methods of placement are used: bottom-dump buckets and tremies, the tremie being far superior to any other method. A tremie is a pipe, at least 10 in. in diameter, consisting of sections joined together by means of flanged and gasketed couplings, with a funnel-shaped section at the top to receive the concrete. The tremie should be supported so as to permit free movement of the discharge end over the area in which concrete is being placed, and also to permit rapid lowering to regulate or stop the flow of concrete. Usual practice is to have one crane with the sole function of handling the tremie, using another crane to handle concrete buckets and other items.

To place concrete with a tremie, the bottom of the pipe should be kept continuously immersed in the concrete. Movement of the tremie should be regulated so as to accomplish this end, and at the same time the concrete should be placed in approximately horizontal layers. The tremie should be kept full of concrete at all times and the flow regulated by raising or lowering the tremie. Once concrete placing has started, there should be no interruption until the placement has been completed.

The principal advantage of tremie concrete placement is that dewatering of the foundation area is unnecessary, a feature of great value that permits placing a foundation seal in a deep, underwater excavation. Subsequent structural concrete can then be placed in the dry. Also, tremie placement permits rapid placing of a large volume of concrete at considerable depth.

Inspection of the results is, of course, virtually impossible, except when the top surface is subsequently exposed. Laitance formation is usually excessive. Quality of the concrete throughout the mass is apt to be nonuniform, especially at the edges.

Buckets

Use may be made of a watertight bucket which discharges concrete from the bottom. If an open-top bucket is used, the top should be covered with heavy canvas or other sheet material to protect the concrete. The bucket should be lowered slowly while under water. Considerable care is necessary in manipulating the discharge gate, which should not be opened until the bucket comes in contact with the foundation or previously placed concrete. After the concrete has been discharged, the bucket must be raised slowly until it is well away from the concrete.

13-4. PRESTRESSED CONCRETE

Prestressing is accomplished when two stressed materials are joined in such a manner that a force acting in one is balanced by an opposite force in the other. Thus in prestressed concrete a tensile force applied to steel tendons embedded in the concrete generates a compressive force in the concrete. The reason for prestressing concrete is to enable it to withstand tensile stresses; concrete is weak in tension, its tensile strength being roughly one-tenth of its compressive. This permits the use of smaller, lighter concrete members. Prestressing imparts greater stiffness to the member and enables the designer to take advantage of high-strength steel. Because the concrete is in compression, applied loads can be greater than for reinforced concrete members of the same size before actual tensile stresses are set up in the concrete.

In any prestressing operation, the procedure follows good concreting practices in regard to materials, mixing, placing, curing, and other phases of concrete making. Additional work involves placing and tensioning strands or wires, and, in the case of pretensioning, release of tension at the proper time.

Control of prestressed concrete includes the usual inspection and control procedures for any good concrete. Uniformity of the concrete is especially important since nonuniform concrete results in variations in camber and other features of the finished units. Concrete strength as high as 8,000 psi is frequently specified.

Steel forms are almost universally used. They should be stoutly built and should close tightly to prevent leakage of mortar when the concrete is placed in them. Because forms are used repeatedly, they are apt to warp and bend, resulting in mortar leaks and uneven surfaces.

Prestressed units require conventional reinforcing steel, the same as nonprestressed concrete. Stirrups in girders and beams should be accurately placed as shown on the drawings. Frequently, special steel is installed to control certain types of cracking.

Pretensioning

Prestressing is accomplished by two general methods: pretensioning and posttensioning. In pretensioned concrete, the steel tendons are placed in the forms and a tensile load is applied to them by means of jacks. The concrete is then placed and, after it reaches a certain specified strength, the tendons are cut loose at the ends. This transfers the load to the concrete as a compressive force, and it is held by means of the bond between the concrete and the steel.

Steel for pretensioning consists of twisted strands, usually made up of seven wires, although some two- and three-wire strands are used also.

The high-carbon, stress-relieved steel wire has an ultimate tensile strength of over 250,000 psi. The strands are anchored in grillages at the ends of the casting bed and are elongated by means of hydraulic jacks. All the strands in a member may be stressed simultaneously, or the strands may be stressed one at a time. The trend is now toward single-strand tensioning. Figure 13-7 is a view of a large stressing bed for bridge girders.

FIG. 13-7. A large prestressing bed for three lines of forms. The reels in the foreground contain stressing strand. (*Illinois Tollway photo.*)

Detailed inspection procedures are given in reference 13.4, but certain general rules are presented herein.

Knowing the properties of the steel, tensioning requirements, and dimensions of the stressing bed, it is not difficult to compute the required pressure to apply to the stressing jacks, or the elongation to be obtained. Differences in the modulus of elasticity of different lots of steel or inaccuracies in pressure gauges on the stressing jacks are sources of error in measuring stressing loads. These measurements are complicated when deflected or draped strands are used. All equipment should be calibrated at regular intervals, preferably under operating conditions. Any measurements should be checked occasionally with a dial gauge extensometer applied to the wire during the stressing operation.

The modulus of elasticity of steel for prestressing is in the neighborhood of 28 million psi, and if specified, is usually specified to be a minimum of 28 million. This is apt to vary as much as 7 or 8 per cent from lot to lot, thus introducing a possible error in stress values computed from strain measurements. By using jack pressure for computing stress, a check is obtained. As long as the two are within reasonably close agreement, there is no question of the accuracy of the stress measurement. Each job will have to set up its own standards and tolerances.

The following computation shows how to compute the tensioning load in a group of strands being stressed simultaneously. If single-strand stressing is being used, the equations are still valid, in which case $N = 1$ and $J = 1$.

Let A = area of one strand, sq in.
a = net area of jack ram, sq in.
d = unit deformation or strain, in./in.
E = modulus of elasticity of strand, psi
e = total change in length l, in.
J = number of jacks
L = net length of stressing bed, ft
l = length, in.
M = measured movement of jack-end anchorage, in.
N = number of strands in one group
P = jack pressure, psi
S = unit stress applied to strand, or required, psi
T = total slippage, in.
W = total load on N strands, lb

The number of strands N is the group of strands being stressed at one time by a group J of jacks. This will vary with different plants, but will probably be the number of strands in one beam, assuming that the bed consists of several beams in tandem. The unit stress S is determined on the basis of the physical properties of the steel being used, and this will be the basis for the field computations. The modulus of elasticity E is determined from laboratory tests and is the basis for determining the change in length of the strands in the bed.

When a tensile load is applied to a piece of steel, the steel starts to stretch or elongate. This elongation (called strain) is proportional to the applied load (called stress) up to a point called the proportional elastic limit. If the load is now released, the wire will resume its former length. If the load is carried beyond the elastic limit, the wire is permanently stretched to a degree depending on the load. This is called permanent set.

In prestressed concrete, it is desirable to elongate the strands to a stress just below the elastic limit, generally about 175,000 psi.

The modulus of elasticity E is a measure of the elasticity of a material. It is equal to the unit stress S divided by the unit deformation or strain d.

To obtain the jack pressure reading P required to produce the unit stress S in the strand, we have:

$$W = ANS$$

then
$$P = \frac{W}{Ja} = \frac{ANS}{Ja} \tag{1}$$

In using E to determine the total elongation of the strands, it is necessary to consider the amount of slippage of the strands in the anchors, both at the dead end of the bed and at the jack end. As the load is applied, there will be a slight movement in the anchors at each end as they grip the strand. This is normally of the magnitude of $\frac{1}{4}$ in. To find what it is, mark each strand, under no load, just where it emerges from the anchor, using crayon, soapstone, or similar material. After the bed has been stressed, measure the distance the marks have moved away from the ends of the anchors. The sum of the slippages at each end is the total slippage T.

From the relationships

$$d = \frac{S}{E} \quad \text{and} \quad d = \frac{e}{l}$$

we get
$$e = \frac{Sl}{E} = \frac{12SL}{E} \tag{2}$$

e being the total required elongation in a bed of length L. Movement of the ram

$$M = \frac{12SL}{E} + T \tag{3}$$

The slippage T should be checked for each operation. Once the pressure and elongation have been set up, there will be no change unless there is a change made in the other constants. In some plants it will be possible to measure the elongation e directly, without measuring slippage. In this case, use Eq. (2).

The following example illustrates the computations.

A certain plant has a stressing bed 400 ft long using one jack with a net ram area of 32 sq in. It is planned to stress a string of beams using 16 strands of 0.035 sq in. area. The steel has an elastic modulus of 28,000,000 psi and the strands will be stressed to 175,000 psi. Slippage in the anchors is ¼ in. at the jack end and ¼ in. at the dead end. Compute required jack pressures and movement of jack-end anchorage.

From the above:

$$A = 0.035 \qquad N = 16$$
$$a = 32 \qquad\quad J = 1$$
$$E = 28,000,000 \quad S = 175,000$$
$$L = 400 \qquad\quad T = \tfrac{1}{2}$$

$$P = \frac{ANS}{Ja} = \frac{0.035 \times 16 \times 175,000}{1 \times 32} = 3{,}062 \text{ psi}$$

$$M = \frac{12SL}{E} + T = \frac{12 \times 175,000 \times 400}{28,000,000} + \tfrac{1}{2} = 30.5 \text{ in.}$$

In practice it is necessary to apply a slight load to the strands in order to take up all the slack and give a reliable starting point for measuring elongation. This is done by applying a small load, say 100 psi, to the jack which will take the catenary or droop out of the strands through the forms. The stress in the strands can be computed from Eq. (1) and the initial elongation by proportion.

Using values from the above example, for a 100-psi initial jack load: From Eq. (1)

$$S = \frac{PJa}{AN} = \frac{100 \times 1 \times 32}{0.035 \times 16} = 5{,}714 \text{ psi}$$

$$\frac{5,714}{175,000} = 0.0325$$

Elongation at 100 psi = $(M - T) \times 0.0325 = 30 \times 0.0325 = 0.98$ in.

After the initial 1-in. elongation resulting from the 100 psi jack load, the strands are elongated an additional 29½ in., thus achieving the full 30½ in. of elongation.

The foregoing computations apply to a bed with straight strands. Many prestressed units, on the other hand, contain deflected, or draped, strands. A draped strand is one that extends for a predetermined distance near the bottom of the beam or unit being made, for equal distances each side of the center of the span, then rises and emerges from the ends of the beam near the top. The purpose of draping is to provide a better stress distribution in the beam.

Elongation and load computations are made as for a straight strand. However, it is usually not possible to stress a deflected strand from one end only, because of friction in the hardware holding the strand down and up at several points through the length of the bed (Fig. 13-8). In this case, the full load is applied to one end of the strand and the elongation noted. The jack is then moved to the other end of the bed and the full load applied at that end, the elongation there being noted. The sum of the two elongations should equal the computed total elongation within 5 per cent.

As a check on stressing, for either straight or deflected strands, the use of load cells is recommended. A load cell makes use of electric strain gauges (SR-4 gauges) for measurement of loads.

Strain gauges applied directly to the strand are useful to determine the uniformity of tension along a deflected strand. This procedure is used when checking a new tensioning system but is impractical as a routine check.

The sudden release of energy that occurs when a strand breaks or an anchor fails causes rapid recoil of the strand and other hardware in the stressing bed. For this reason, inspectors and workmen must be alert for any unusual occurrences during stressing.

Fig. 13-8. "Hold-downs" for holding down draped or deflected strands. Note that some of the strands are straight.

After the strands have been tensioned, concrete is placed in the conventional manner, following good construction and control practices. Mixes are usually quite rich, containing as many as 8 sacks of cement per cubic yard, and are placed at a low slump, in some cases at a slump of less than 1 in. Vibration may be either internal, external, or both.

Concrete test cylinders should be made during the time that concrete is being placed. The exact number will depend on the manufacturing schedule set up by the contractor, but a minimum of six cylinders should be field-cured with the concrete members, and the time of releasing stress on the wires determined by the strength developed in these specimens. Cylinders should be made for standard curing also. Specimens for standard curing may be cast in either cardboard or metal molds, but the field-cured ones should be cast in metal molds.

Steam curing is almost universally practiced in prestressed concrete work. The start of steaming should be delayed 2 to 4 hr after the last concrete is placed, and the temperature should never exceed 160°F. After the expiration of the steaming period (determined by field-cured cylinders), the stressing jacks are released and the members removed from the casting bed. When the air temperature is below 50°F, the concrete should be cooled at a rate not exceeding 5° per hr. Steam should be wet, as evidenced by the presence of free moisture on the concrete during the entire steaming period (see Sec. 3-6).

As soon as the concrete reaches the specified strength for transfer of stress to the concrete, the strands are released, or detensioned. This may be accomplished by releasing the jacks when multiple-strand tensioning has been applied to straight strands. Single-strand tensioning and the presence of draped strands make other methods necessary. One method is to cut the strands individually with an acetylene torch, using a sequence or pattern that has to be developed for each type of unit and stressing bed (Fig. 13-9).

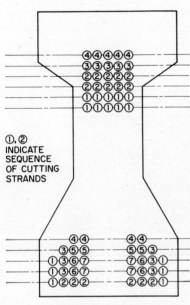

①, ② INDICATE SEQUENCE OF CUTTING STRANDS

Fig. 13-9. Typical strand-cutting sequence. Section near end of 48 × 28-in. bridge girder, showing 64 strands (30 deflected).

The relationship between curing, release of tension in the strands, stripping of forms, and release of strand hold-downs, is important in the control of cracking in the units. Forms should be loosened as early as possible in the curing cycle, but in any event while the concrete is warm, and before detensioning is done. Next, the strand hold-downs are released, then the strands are detensioned. All of this should be done as rapidly as possible to minimize cooling of the concrete before the bed has been completely released, otherwise undesirable cracking may result.

Posttensioning

Prestressing by the posttensioning process is accomplished by forming ducts through the concrete at the time it is cast. When the concrete has reached the required strength, as indicated by field-cured cylinders, the stressing wires are inserted in the ducts, tensioned, anchored, and grouted (Fig. 13-10). Whereas pretensioned members are manufactured at a central casting yard or plant, posttensioned units are frequently made at the site. One reason for posttensioning is that there is no need to transport the units over highways and streets, hence the logistics of getting the units in place does not impose a limitation on size. Pretensioned girders are rarely over 100 ft long for this reason.

The same care is necessary for production as for pretensioning. Frequently the ducts are curved or draped, a condition that is apt to lead to friction on the wires while they are being stressed. For this reason, it is especially important to check jack pressure and elongation at both ends.

Individual wires are usually used in posttensioning, instead of the strand commonly used in pretensioning. By means of special equipment, a group of wires is forced through the duct and anchored by means of special wedges. In another type of posttensioning, the wires are accurately measured and assembled into groups in a length of flexible metallic tubing. Each wire is then upset on each end, forming small buttons which bear against a special perforated plate. The entire tube and

Fɪɢ. 13-10. Stressing jacks posttensioning wires in a 54-in. prestressed pile.

wire assembly is located in the forms and the concrete placed. After the concrete has developed the required strength, a special jack grips the perforated plate and elongates the wire, which is then anchored, and the tube is grouted.

Still another type of posttensioning is applied to cylindrical objects, such as large concrete pipe and concrete tanks. After the pipe or tank has been cast in a conventional manner and has attained the necessary strength, special machines wrap high-tensile wire around the object, stressing the wire to the required tension. The entire outer surface is then coated with pneumatically applied mortar.

13-5. FLOORS

General

A floor finish may be applied to the top of a structural slab, in which case it is called a monolithic floor, or a special topping mix, in the form

of a thin overlay, may be applied to the hardened slab. A good floor can
be obtained by either method, the two-course topping method being
used for especially heavy-duty floors, and for certain decorative effects.

A satisfactory floor begins with proper preparation of the subgrade
and base. Soft, spongy soils must be stabilized or removed. Acceptable
materials are granular materials such as bank-run sand or sand and
gravel, gravel, crushed stone, crushed blast furnace slag (weighing at
least 70 pcf), or similar granular materials. Placing and compaction
must be done in accordance with good construction practices. The subgrade and base must be free of frost when the concrete is placed.

Monolithic Floor

Only high-grade materials should be used for concrete, and concreting should follow good practices, as described in Chaps. 10 and 12. Suggested proportions are shown in Table 13-1.[13.6] After screeds, bulkheads,

TABLE 13-1. REQUIREMENTS FOR CONCRETE FOR ONE-COURSE FLOOR

	Maximum water, gal per sack	Minimum sacks cement per cu yd	Maximum slump, in.	Air content, %		Minimum 28-day compressive strength, psi
				Aggregate		
				1½-in. max	¾-in. max	
Floors to Be Covered with Tile and Subjected to Foot Traffic Only						
Job-mixed concrete......	6½	5½	4	5 ± 1	6 ± 1	3,500
Ready-mix alternate 1*..	6½	5½	4	5 ± 1	6 ± 1	
Ready-mix alternate 2*..			4	5 ± 1	6 ± 1	3,500
All Other One-course Floors on the Ground						
Job-mixed concrete......	5½	6	3	5 ± 1	6 ± 1	4,500
Ready-mix alternate 1*..	5½	6	3	5 ± 1	6 ± 1	
Ready-mix alternate 2*..			3	5 ± 1	6 ± 1	4,500

* Ready-mixed concrete should conform to the requirements of ASTM Designation:
C 94.

and joint materials have been set in place, the concrete is placed, beginning at a bulkhead or edge form.

Concrete should be consolidated by vibration, then struck off or
screeded to the required grade by means of the working straightedge.
This screeding consists of removal of excess concrete by moving the
straightedge back and forth with a sawing motion as it is advanced

along the forms or screeds, which are metal or wood strips set accurately to the desired grade (Fig. 13-11). A small amount of concrete should be pushed ahead of the straightedge to fill in low spots. Sometimes a vibrator is mounted on the straightedge, helping to consolidate the concrete as well as bringing it to the required elevation. A typical vibrating screed is shown in Fig. 13-12, smoothing and consolidating concrete for a bridge deck.

After screeding, the concrete is smoothed with a bull float or a darby (Figs. 13-13 and 13-14). A bull float is usually of wood, and has a handle several feet long to permit the finisher to work from the edge of

FIG. 13-11. One type of screed for striking off concrete surfaces. Note the excessively wet consistency of the mix, as evidenced by the extent the workmen sink into the fresh concrete.

the slab. A darby is a special float 3 or 4 ft long. Both tools serve the same purpose—to smooth the concrete immediately after the screeding. The slightly rough surface that is left after this operation is frequently satisfactory.

Subsequent finishing operations are delayed until the concrete starts to stiffen and the water sheen has left the surface, sometimes as long as 2 to 8 hr after placing. The first of the delayed finishing operations is edging and grooving. Edging is accomplished by running a special hand tool back and forth to produce a small radius on the edge of the slab, which improves appearance and protects the edge from spalls and nicks. Then the slab is grooved, or jointed, using another hand tool with a bit in the center that makes a groove about ¾ in. deep in the concrete. A straight board laid on the concrete should be used as a guide for the grooving tool, otherwise unsightly irregularities will be produced.

Fig. 13-12. This heavy-duty vibrating screed, working on a bridge deck, has the far side traveling on a rail, and the near side moving along a pipe screed rail flush with the finish grade elevation. (*Stow Manufacturing Co. photo.*)

Fig. 13-13. A darby for smoothing concrete.

Floating is the next operation and should preferably be done with power-driven equipment. Temperature, humidity, slump of the concrete, and other factors all influence the time for floating, and only experience can provide the knowledge and judgment to tell when the concrete is ready. For hand floating, an aluminum or magnesium float should be used rather than a wooden one, especially on air-entrained concrete, as the metal has less tendency to stick and drag on the concrete. Because air-entrained concrete bleeds less than plain concrete, the floating may be done sooner. Air-entrained concrete requires less floating than non-air-entrained concrete. Usually it is best to use the magnesium float in a fairly flat position.

Floating removes marks left by the edger and groover, smooths the surface, and embeds the large aggregate particles, making a thin layer of dense mortar on the surface.

Fig. 13-14. Bull floating sidewalk concrete after striking off with a vibrating screed. (*Stow Manufacturing Co. photo.*)

The final operation normally employed is troweling, which follows immediately after floating. Troweling may be done more than once, depending on the degree of smoothness desired. A short period of time should elapse between successive trowelings. The trowel blade, especially for the first troweling, should be kept as nearly flat on the surface as possible. When doing the final "hard troweling" the trowel produces a distinctive ring when held at the correct angle as it passes over the surface.

A troweled surface is quite smooth, a condition that is desirable in hydraulic structures carrying water at high velocity. However, the smooth surface may be dangerously slippery for traffic, either foot or wheeled, especially if it becomes wet. For this reason, the surface should be made nonslipping or nonskidding by roughening it. This may be done by drawing an ordinary push broom over the surface as soon as troweling has been completed. Different degrees of roughness can be obtained by using different types of brooms or brushes.

In some cases, especially those jobs involving large areas of slabs, instead of grooving the concrete for contraction joints, the joints are sawed using a power saw equipped with a special diamond or abrasive blade. This sawing is done several hours after the concrete has set, depending upon the weather and other factors (see discussion in Sec. 14-8).

The following points are mentioned here again for emphasis:

1. Timing is of extreme importance in all finishing operations. If the work is done too early, it is apt to bring too much soupy mortar to the surface, resulting in hairline cracks and scaling. If it is delayed too long, the proper finish is extremely difficult, or impossible, to attain.

2. Water or mortar should never be sprinkled on a surface that is too dry to finish (or on a surface that the finisher *thinks* is too dry).

3. Dry cement should never be spread on an area that is too wet to finish.

4. No finishing should ever be done on a surface where free water is standing.

5. The use of accelerators or retarders, and different types of cement, will affect the timing.

6. Concrete finishing is hard work, requiring considerable physical effort for its proper execution.

Floor Topping

The base slab should be struck off about ¾ or 1 in. below the finished grade elevation and should be free of laitance, oil, free water, or other contaminants when the topping is applied. The topping may be applied the same day that the base concrete is placed, or it may be delayed until a more convenient time. Whenever conditions and the type of machinery to be installed permit, it is good practice to delay application as long as possible to obviate damage or staining of the surface when installing machinery or performing other work in the building.

Aggregate should be hard and tough, consisting of quartz, granite, or similar natural rock particles, or it may be a manufactured product such as silicon dioxide. It should all pass a ½-in. sieve.

Mix proportions should be 1 part cement, 1 part sand, and 1½ or 2 parts of coarse aggregate by volume. After the mix proportions have been determined, batching should be by weight. Sufficient water should be used to provide a very stiff consistency that can just be worked with the straightedge. The topping should form a ball when squeezed in the hand. In any event, no more than 4 gal of water per sack of cement should be used.

After a thin, neat grout has been broomed into a small area of the base slab, the topping is placed, straightedged, and tamped or rolled. The area should be as large as can be covered at one time before the grout starts to dry out. The process of spreading grout and applying topping over the small areas is continued until the entire slab is covered, taking special care that edges to be lapped are well bonded, and cold joints are avoided. Meanwhile floating, preferably with a power float, should be commenced as soon as possible (Fig. 13-15). Temperature

Fig. 13-15. Finishing zero slump floor topping. Machines in the background are floating and troweling ahead of the hand finishers who are doing the final troweling. (*Nardoni Floor Co. photo.*)

difference between base slab and topping should not be excessive when the topping is applied. Finishing should then be done as previously described in Sec. 13-5. Finally, the slab is cured.

Special Floor Finishes

There are many attractive finishes that can be applied to a concrete floor.

Terrazzo is made by using selected coarse aggregate of the desired color and particle size in the topping. Marble chips are usually used. Cement may be either white or colored by means of mineral pigments. After the terrazzo topping has been spread and tamped or rolled, additional aggregate should be spread on the surface, if necessary, so the surface consists of at least 70 per cent aggregate. Finishing and curing are then done.

Upon completion of curing, the floor is ground with a 24-grit stone, then with an 80-grit stone. Loose material should be washed off, and a grout of the same composition as in the topping is applied. After 3 or 4 days of curing, a final rubbing is done with the 80-grit stone, followed by thorough washing of the surface and additional curing. Interior terrazzo floors may be waxed, after the concrete has thoroughly aged and dried out.

An exposed aggregate finish, suitable for outdoor walks, is accomplished by embedding selected, uniform-size aggregate particles in the surface, similar to the terrazzo technique. After the surface has been floated, a retarder is applied to the surface, and several hours later the aggregate is exposed by brushing with a bristle broom and washing with water (see "Exposed Aggregate" in Sec. 13-9).

A travertine finish is accomplished by brooming the surface after the slab has been bull-floated. Then a mortar with a consistency of thick paint is dashed on the surface, making an uneven surface. After the slab has hardened to the proper degree, it is troweled, smoothing parts of the surface and leaving other parts rough. The travertine mortar consists of 1 part cement, 2 parts mortar sand, and sufficient mineral pigment to produce the desired color. Sufficient water is used to give the correct consistency.

In applying any special finish, care is necessary to achieve uniformity in effect and color and to avoid staining or disfigurement from the curing materials. Thorough curing is essential.

Heavy-duty Surfacing

For exposure to especially severe abrasive conditions that exist, for example on a floor carrying many steel-wheeled trucks, it is usual practice to apply a "dust" or "dry shake" coat of abrasive-resistant material to the surface just prior to final finishing. Abrasive material for this usage might consist of aluminum oxide, silicon carbide, or malleable iron particles, the size of particles depending upon traffic conditions and type of finish desired. Particles are seldom larger than those passing a No. 8 screen or smaller than those retained on a 50- or 60-mesh screen.

In using a dry shake, recommendations of the manufacturer should be followed. In the absence of such recommendations, a mixture may be made consisting of 2 parts dry abrasive and 1 part cement. About two-thirds of the required quantity of shake should be broadcast over the surface immediately before power floating. After the material has been blended into the surface with the power float, the remaining material is spread, taking care to make the complete coating as uniform as possible, then the surface is power-floated again, followed by machine troweling, then hand troweling. No water should be used during any of these finishing operations.

Sometimes blisters, bubbles, or scaling result from improper finishing or application of dry shake. On one job where metallic dry shake was used on a suspended slab, a thin layer of the finished surface scaled in several large spotty areas several days after construction. There were two basic or primary causes for this scaling and probably other factors were involved. First, the cement and metallic aggregate mixture may have been placed on the concrete base too soon. If so, the base was probably softer than it should have been for ideal conditions for application. This would result in some of the metal being worked beneath the surface of the concrete with the consequent thin layer of cement and water on top. It appeared that this surface cement-water paste scaled. Overworking of the surface material by the finishers may also have contributed to the scaling.

A minor factor was the fact that artificial heat during placing and curing was furnished from beneath by three portable blower-type heaters. This caused uneven drying of the concrete from the bottom up, resulting in some areas of the slab being drier than others. Seven days after placing the concrete, the heat was discontinued and the surface of the slab froze. This freezing could possibly have aggravated the condition.

The thin layer of cement and water that was apparently formed over the surfacing material in the areas that scaled produced a condition similar to that resulting when a finisher dusts dry cement on the surface of a slab to dry it up so that he can finish it. Such a procedure, of course, results in eventual failure of the surface. In all probability, the areas that scaled on this floor eventually would have dusted or scaled.

Dusting

Probably one of the worst faults of concrete floors is dusting. In time, when exposed to especially heavy traffic, even a good floor will wear away to some extent.

Dusting of a floor results from weak concrete which owes its origin to the use of overly fluid or wet mixes, or excessive working of the surface during finishing, causing laitance. Usually it is a combination of these, bringing an excess of water and fines to the surface, producing a weak sand-cement mortar as the wearing surface. The excessive finishing may be in either the screeding, floating, or troweling operation, as any of these is capable of bringing fines to the surface.

Another cause of dusting is failure to cure adequately, which stops the chemical process of hydration by allowing the water to escape through evaporation, preventing the concrete from attaining the strength intended. Rapid evaporation also causes surface shrinkage resulting in crazing and surface cracking. During cold weather, carbon dioxide from poorly vented heaters, if it comes in contact with the fresh concrete during the first few hours, will carbonate the concrete, resulting in a soft, chalklike surface.

Little can be done to repair a badly dusting floor, except replace it. Sometimes the application of a chemical hardener gives temporary relief. One of the following methods is suggested:

1. Coat the dry concrete with sodium silicate or potassium silicate, making several coatings with a warm, dilute solution, allowing each coat to dry thoroughly. Then follow with a coating of 1.5 per cent hydrofluoric acid solution.

2. Apply a silicone treatment which consists of a spray or brush coat of silicone solution.

3. Apply three coats of a solution of magnesium fluosilicate in water, using 1 lb of fluosilicate per gal of water for the first coat, and 2 lb per gal for subsequent coats, allowing each coat to dry thoroughly. Excess crystals should be removed by brushing and washing after the final coat has dried. This treatment is also effective for hardening a new floor.

4. In extreme cases, remove the old concrete down to good, sound concrete, and install a new concrete topping.

Method 4 is obviously the most effective, but it is also the most costly. The fluosilicate treatment (method 3) is the best of the chemical methods.

A long-lasting, skid-resistant surfacing for a heavy-duty floor may be made by bonding abrasive aggregate with an epoxy adhesive. The floor is first thoroughly cleaned, preferably by sand blasting, to remove all dirt, oil, and grease, after which the epoxy adhesive is brushed or sprayed on the surface. While the adhesive is still wet, the abrasive aggregate is broadcast uniformly over the surface. Suitable aggregates are silicon carbide, aluminum oxide, and silica sand.

13-6. TILT-UP CONSTRUCTION

This is a special type of precast construction in which wall panels are cast in a horizontal position at the site, tilted to a vertical position, and moved into final location as part of the building.[13.7] As a rule, the concrete floor of the building serves as the casting platform. Columns are usually cast in place after the panels have been erected. Panels may be of solid concrete, or of sandwich construction, in which relatively thin, high-strength, conventional concrete surfacing layers are separated by a core of low-density insulating material. Tilt-up is used for small residential construction as well as for commercial and industrial buildings.

Fabrication is accomplished by first placing a bond breaker on the casting floor. Liquids of various types are generally used, although sheets of plywood, metal, or paper can be used. Liquids consist of special formulations for this purpose, curing compound, and waxes, which are applied in two coats, the second coat being applied shortly before the panel concrete is placed. Uniformity of application is important.

Side forms are usually of lumber. Forms for window and other openings may be metal or wood, with metal preferred because the swelling of wood frames makes them difficult to remove and may crack the concrete.

Placing of reinforcing steel and inserts, and placing of the concrete, are done in the same manner as for slabs. Many special finishes can be applied while the concrete is still plastic, including the embedment of architectural details and ornamentation.

Various types of cranes and gin poles have been used to lift the panels into place. The panels are tilted on to a layer of mortar on the foundation and braced temporarily until the columns have been constructed.

The inspector should verify that the casting floor is perfectly smooth and uniform because any imperfections in the floor will show on the wall. Paper and felt bond breakers nearly always wrinkle, and asphalt materials will stain the concrete; hence they should be avoided. Inspection of forms, steel, concreting, and all operations should follow good practices described in Chap. 12.

Tilting places unusual stresses on the panels which should be considered in the design. The inspector should make sure that the panel has reached the required design strength with a factor of safety before the panel is tilted. Field-cured cylinders will provide this information. Pickup points must be carefully located and lifting equipment designed so as to avoid high localized stresses in the panel that cause cracking, splitting, or spalling of the concrete. Vacuum lifting attachments are sometimes used.

Considerably more lifting force is required to break the panel loose from the casting floor than is necessary to lift the panel after movement has started. For this reason, it is a good idea to move the panel slightly, if possible, before lifting. This can be accomplished with jacks operating in a horizontal direction, sliding the panel a fraction of an inch to break the bond.

13-7. SLIPFORMS

A slipform, or sliding form, is a movable form that is raised vertically as the concrete is placed. Concrete is placed continuously in thin layers and the form is raised by means of jacks operating on smooth steel rods that are embedded in the concrete as the structure rises. The area at the top of the form is enclosed to provide a working platform. Suspended below the form are platforms on which the finishers work. As the form rises, the finishers are enabled to repair and finish the emerging concrete surface. Curing may be applied by means of water or sprayed-on curing compound. Figure 13-16 is a view of slipform construction of a group of grain storage silos.

Fig. 13-16. Simultaneous placing of concrete in a large group of grain storage silos is accomplished by the slipform technique. (*Macdonald Engineering Co. photo.*)

Of great importance is getting the form set up in a perfectly plumb and level condition at the beginning. It is extremely difficult to plumb a form that has drifted off the true vertical, although manipulation of the jacks may provide some correction. Operation of the jacks can be varied to keep the platform level.

Formerly used only on such structures as silos and bins, sliding forms have in recent years been used in building construction.[13.8] It is, of course, impossible to have any projections beyond the face of the wall during slipforming, but there is practically no limit to the variety of inserts, blockouts, and openings possible within the limits of the wall. These inserts and openings provide for windows, doors, and attachment of beams and other structural items.

Slipform construction requires careful inspection and execution of the work by supervisors and workmen experienced in this type of work, including farsighted planning of the whole operation. Concrete mixes should be well proportioned, with a slump between 3 and 5 in., depending on the weather, size of wall, presence of steel or other items in the wall, and similar considerations. Concrete is usually spaded into place, although some careful vibration may be used. Revibration of previous layers below the one being placed must be avoided. A sufficient and steady supply of concrete must be available and the placement made so there is not much more than an hour's delay between layers, or lifts. Once a placement has been started, it should be continued, 24 hr a day, until completion.

Reference 13.9 is an excellent description of slipform technique.

Another type of slipform has been used extensively for placing concrete lining in canals and ditches, especially on irrigation projects in the West. A machine of this type operates on rails set to grade on the berm of the canal. Most of them are self-propelled by means of traction wheels, although some of the small ones are pulled along by means of winches or tractors.

Concrete is distributed across the forms by means of a bucket and aprons or downspouts. As the form moves ahead, vibrators consolidate the concrete. Finishers, working on outriggers behind the form, make the necessary repairs to the surface and make contraction joints. A special carriage, following at the proper time, provides a platform for the application of curing compound.

A recent development is a slipform paver for highway pavement (see Chap. 14).

13-8. LIFT SLABS

In the lift-slab technique, the building floor serves as a casting floor, as in the tilt-up method, but here the similarity ends. Raising is accomplished by means of jacks mounted on top of the building columns, openings being left in the slabs to enable them to rise along the columns. Several slabs may be involved, stacked one on top of the other, each of them raised individually to its required elevation.

Forming, casting, finishing, and curing follow closely the procedures for any slab production methods. To raise the slab, suspension rods, reaching down from the jacks on top of the columns, are first attached to collars on the slab, one collar encircling each column. All jacks are synchronized, and operate on a short stroke of the magnitude of an inch or two. Follower nuts automatically hold the slab when the jacks are retracted. Raising is accomplished by extending the jacks, holding the slab with the nuts while the jacks are retracted, then extending the jacks, repeating the cycle until the slab comes to the required elevation, where the collars are attached to the columns. Usual jacking rate is between 5 and 15 ft per hr.

Lift-slab construction is fairly new, and methods are developing rapidly. Of special importance to the inspector and construction superintendent is the need to keep the slabs level and to avoid overstressing any portion of the slab.

13-9. SPECIAL ARCHITECTURAL FINISHES

In the great majority of cases, the surface of concrete produced by well-built forms is satisfactory, as described in Sec. 12-8. However, there are occasions when certain special effects are desired, such as exposed aggregate or coloring, which may be applied either to slabs or formed surfaces. Other special effects and relief are obtained by casting concrete against plaster waste molds. Recently, plastic forms have been introduced that give a smooth, glassy surface to intricate castings.

Colored Concrete

Color can be imparted to concrete by the use of mineral oxide pigments added to the concrete. Organic pigments should not be used, as they will fade, react with calcium hydroxide, or dissolve in water. When color is specified, samples of the colored concrete should be prepared for approval ahead of time, and the same materials used throughout the job. The inspector should see that no changes are made in the sources or proportioning of materials. Pigment should be weighed for each batch and mixed with the cement before placing these materials in the mixer. Uniformity of materials and methods is essential; all batches must be identical in all respects, and all methods of handling the concrete, including finishing and curing, must be unchanged throughout the job.

Hardened concrete can be stained by the application of chemical stains. This work is highly specialized and is usually done by the chemical manufacturer under a guarantee. Staining is especially applicable to interior floors, where the floor can be kept waxed.

Paint

Almost any type of paint can be applied to concrete and will give satisfactory service if properly applied.

Concrete should be permitted to age several months if possible before application of any paint. This results in more uniform suction over the surface and overcomes the effect of residual form oil adhering to the concrete. The paint is less apt to craze, and the danger of efflorescence is lessened.

Concrete should be clean when paint is applied. This requires washing with water, and probably some scrubbing. Efflorescence, if any, should be removed with acid. In special cases, sandblasting or rubbing may be necessary.

Portland cement paint should have a thick, creamy consistency (the first coat may be thinner) and should be applied to the slightly damp concrete with scrub brushes or calcimine brushes. Batches of paint should be used up in 3 to 4 hr. However, some commercial paints contain calcium chloride and so will have to be used sooner. Painting is best done during moderate weather.

Curing should be done by fog-spraying the surface several times a day for at least 2 days. Properly applied and cured cement paint should last for several years.

Failures of portland cement paint may consist of rapid chalking, caused by too low a cement content, or poor curing. Other failures are peeling or flaking, resulting from painting glassy-smooth, dirty, or dry surface. Some are also caused by unhydrated lime. Pinholes result from insufficient brushing or sprayed coating. Crazing is usually not serious and may result from crazing of the underlying concrete. Efflorescence comes from painting the concrete before it has aged sufficiently.

Other paints include oil-base paints consisting of opaque pigments suspended in a vehicle of drying oils and thinner (linseed oil paints); resin-emulsion paints consisting of water-reducible pigment paste in an emulsified oil-extended resin, usually glycerol phthalate; and synthetic-rubber paints, either the emulsified synthetic-rubber resin type or the rubber-solution type. The newer plastic types of paints are also satisfactory.

Paint should be applied as directed by the manufacturer, after a proper pretreatment of the surface. The best pretreatment for concrete on which oil paint is to be applied is to permit the concrete to age for about a year. The surface must be clean and dry when the paint is applied. If earlier painting is necessary, a suggested pretreatment consists of a solution of 2 per cent zinc chloride and 3 per cent phosphoric acid in water applied as a wash. As soon as the surface has dried thoroughly, the paint may be applied.

Exposed Aggregate

A rough surface, exposing the aggregate particles, is obtained by treating the concrete surface with a concentrated retarder solution. Usually special aggregate is embedded in the slab in a manner similar to that for preparing a terrazzo floor. Best results are obtained if the aggregate particles are rounded or cubical in shape, avoiding splintery or flat pieces, and of uniform size, usually not over $\frac{1}{2}$ in. in diameter. As soon as the slab has been finished, the retarding solution is applied uniformly to the surface. After the underlying concrete has hardened, the surface is hosed with water, at the same time being gently brushed to remove the cement and mortar. This is best done 12 to 24 hr after placing the concrete, if a depth of $\frac{1}{8}$ in. is desired. Considerable care is necessary to avoid loosening the coarse aggregate, at the same time uniformly removing cement from the aggregate particles. The time for washing is best determined by trial on a small inconspicuous area because it depends upon temperature and other factors. This method produces an attractive rustic finish, especially adaptable to walks and patios.

Another method is the aggregate transfer method, adaptable to formed surfaces. This method consists of attaching the special facing aggregate to plywood liners by means of a special adhesive. The liners are positioned in the forms, after which normal procedures are followed in placing the structural concrete. When the forms are stripped, the liners are removed, leaving the aggregate embedded in the concrete. After the concrete is about 2 wk old the aggregate is exposed by brushing with a power-driven wire brush, or by sandblasting. If a smooth polished surface is desired, it is obtained by grinding.[13.10]

13-10. VACUUM CONCRETE

Vacuum processing of concrete is accomplished by applying a vacuum to fresh concrete surfaces, either formed or unformed. This patented process removes as much as 40 per cent of the water from a few inches of the concrete surface, producing in effect a "case-hardened" concrete. It also removes the large bubbles or "bug holes." The result is high early strength, enhanced durability, better wear resistance, less shrinkage, and higher density. In addition, there is a saving in time and cost because forms can be removed and reused sooner. However, the process is costly and is normally used only in special cases.

Vacuum is administered by means of mats applied to the surface of slabs or form panels on formed areas. The panels or pads consist of plywood faced with two layers of metal screen cloth covered with muslin, or fiber cloth. Vacuum, applied within about 30 min after placing the concrete, should continue for 1 or 2 min per in. of slab thickness. After 2 min, the concrete is usually quite hard. Concrete should be vibrated during the first part of the vacuum treatment.

The treatment is most effective on fairly lean mixes with a minimum sand content. Sticky mixes containing an excess of fines should be avoided.

Improvements to the technique and equipment are constantly being made. Sometimes porous rubber sheets are used for lining the mats or forms.

The inspector should check the condition of the mats, for they have a tendency to become clogged with cement. He should also observe the amount and time of vacuum and the amount of water extracted.

13-11. LIGHTWEIGHT CONCRETE

There are two general classes of lightweight concrete: lightweight structural concrete, and lightweight insulating concrete.

Structural Lightweight Concrete

With the improvements in materials and techniques during the last few years, the use of lightweight aggregates for cast in place, structural concrete is becoming widespread. Strengths of 5,000 psi and higher are made without difficulty by concrete weighing 110 pcf. By entraining the proper amount of air, obtaining durable concrete is no longer a problem. Air entrainment also serves to overcome poor workability, segregation, and bleeding properties often associated with lean lightweight concrete. The amount of air-entraining agent necessary to produce the desired results may be several times as much as is required for normal-weight concrete.

The most important reason for using lightweight concrete of a structural grade is the reduction in weight of the structure, with the resulting saving in cost by permitting smaller footings and a lighter supporting structure. Corollary advantages are its thermal and acoustical insulating values. Values of thermal conductivity (k) of lightweight concretes are between 2 and 4 Btu per hr per sq ft per in. of thickness per °F, the lower values being associated with lighter densities (see Sec. 4-2).

Proportioning and Handling

Proportioning and control of lightweight concrete present some difficulties not encountered in normal-weight concrete control. For one thing, the absolute volume method of proportioning is inaccurate and difficult to apply, the principal reason being that lightweight aggregates may absorb as much as 20 per cent moisture by weight. Most of this absorption occurs within the first few minutes of contact with water, but continued absorption causes a significant loss of slump when dry aggregates are batched for concrete. Another disadvantage of using dry aggregates is segregation and loss of fines that occur during handling of the aggregates.

Some producers solve this problem by using saturated aggregate, a solution that is satisfactory if the concrete is not to be exposed to freezing and thawing action. Even with air entrainment, the durability of concrete made with some lightweight aggregates in a saturated condition is not good. If the aggregate contains about two-thirds to three-fourths of its potential absorption, its tendency to segregate is greatly reduced, and the slump loss can be kept within reasonable bounds. In addition, this will produce concrete with good durability.

The appearance of fresh lightweight concrete should be similar to that of normal-weight concrete. Coarse aggregate particles should be evident but not segregated from the mortar. Mortar should be sufficient to coat the coarse aggregate and hold it in suspension. The amount of fine aggregate should be between 42 and 60 per cent of the total aggregate by volume. Entrained-air content should be at least 6 per cent.

The aggregates are lighter in weight than the concrete in which they are used, hence the need for careful handling and avoidance of wet consistencies. Because of its lower density, lightweight concrete does not slump as much as normal-weight concrete at the same workability, and can therefore be handled with 2 in. less slump than normal-weight concrete. A slump of 3 in. is adequate for any structural work, and 2 in. or less is sufficient for flat slabs.

The inspector should require that the aggregates are uniformly prewetted before a placement is commenced.

Lightweight concrete may require somewhat more mixing than normal-weight concrete. If truck mixers are being used, the mixer should first be charged with the aggregate, air-entraining agent, and about three-quarters of the water, then mixed for several revolutions until the initial water demand is satisfied. Cement, admixture if any, and the necessary water to give the slump are then introduced into the mixer, and the mixer is rotated for 60 additional revolutions at mixing speed. If there is a delay between completion of mixing and discharge, the mixer should be given an additional five revolutions at mixing speed just prior to discharging the concrete.

The inspector should check the unit weight of every truckload of concrete delivered to the job and compute the yield. As long as the unit weight is uniform, the concrete contains the correct proportions of materials. If the unit weight is in error by more than 2 pcf, the air content should be determined. If the air content is off, correction to the air-entraining agent should be made. If the air content is correct, then the moisture content or density of the aggregates should be checked. Duplicate tests should be run whenever any irregularities are found. Air content should be determined by means of the volumetric method, ASTM Designation: C 173.

Concrete should be consolidated by means of vibration. In walls, columns, and similar structural elements, this is accomplished with internal vibrators. Special care is necessary to prevent segregation and the formation of honeycomb. A vibrating screed should be used on flat slabs. However, lightweight concrete can be overvibrated, hence vibration should be kept to the minimum that will consolidate the concrete properly.

Finishing is acomplished in the same manner as for normal-weight concrete.

Good curing is essential to satisfactory performance and should be continuous for 7 days.

Insulating Concrete

Concretes possessing densities between 15 and 90 pcf are classified as insulating concrete. This concrete is used for thermal insulation in roofs and other areas, and as fire protection for certain structural portions of buildings. Insulating concrete has but little structural value since its 28-day compressive strength ranges from less than 100 psi to slightly over 1,000 psi, depending mainly on the materials, mix proportions, and curing. Thermal conductivity (k value) ranges from less than unity to about 4, depending on density and material.

Aggregates consist of expanded perlite, vermiculite (expanded mica), or conventional lightweight aggregates. Entrained air is as much as 35 per cent. Very low density concrete is obtained by introducing chemical foam into the mix.

Concrete containing mineral aggregates may be mixed in paddle-type mixers, or in conventional concrete mixers, including truck mixers under close control. Valore[13.11] reports that several types of mixing are employed for cellular or foamed concretes: (1) high-speed mixing during which air entrainment is effected by the beating action of mixer paddles upon the ingredients in the presence of a foaming (air-entraining) agent; (2) moderate to high-speed mixing or blending, in which a stable air-foam is the mix ingredient that provides the cellular structure; and (3) moderate to high-speed mixing of mixtures containing such gas-forming chemicals as aluminum powder or hydrogen peroxide and calcium hypochlorite. When a gas-forming chemical is used, the mixture increases in volume while in the forms. For field applications, the so-called "foam" concretes, either "mix-foamed" or "prefoamed," may be more convenient to use and their densities more easily controlled than is the case with "gas" concretes.

Vermiculite concrete may consist of varying proportions of aggregate, as shown in Table 13-2.[13.12]

Water requirements vary quite widely because of variations in air content, slump, yield, and absorption by the aggregate, and are best determined by placing conditions. Both perlite and vermiculite mixes are usually quite plastic, with high slumps, and are usually placed (or "poured," in this case) with a minimum of manipulation.

Density and strength are determined on oven-dried samples. The procedure recommended by the Vermiculite Institute is to cast three 2-in.

TABLE 13-2. VERMICULITE CONCRETE

Mix	Cu ft vermiculite per sack cement	Minimum compressive strength, psi	Oven-dry density, pcf	Use
A	4	350	35–40	Roof decks
B	6	125	25–30	Insulation
C	8	100	20–25	Insulation

cubes, by pouring the mixture into the molds, vibrating or tapping lightly, but not rodding; or to cut 2-in. cubes from hardened concrete. The wet density should be noted and recorded. The specimens are cured under standard conditions until time to dry them for a 28-day test. Drying is done to constant weight in an oven at 220 to 230°F. The cube is positioned in the testing machine so the load is applied to the top and bottom,

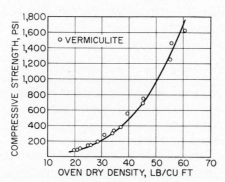

FIG. 13-17. Compressive strength verses oven-dry density, using Vermiculite Institute testing specifications.

using a capping compound, if necessary, and the load applied so failure will occur in 20 to 80 sec. The report should include wet density, oven-dry density, and strength, in addition to the normal identification of the specimen.

Relationships between oven-dry density and strength for vermiculite concrete are shown in Fig. 13-17. Similar values may be expected from perlite concrete.

13-12. HEAVY CONCRETE

Formerly, heavy concrete was used for counterweights, especially on movable railroad and highway bridges, where it was desirable to obtain the maximum weight in a minimum volume. During the last few years, a new use has been found for heavy concrete in the biological shielding of nuclear reactors. Ordinary concrete is a good shielding material for neutron and gamma rays, if a sufficient thickness is used. However, heavy concrete made with special high-density aggregates is more effective and requires less thickness than ordinary concrete. Increasing the density of concrete increases its effectiveness against penetration of neutrons in proportion to *e* (the base of natural logarithms) raised to the power of the density.[13.13] By using special aggregates, concrete weighing as much as 300 pcf can be produced. Information relative to design of reactors and shields is available in numerous booklets published by the National Bureau of Standards and Department of Commerce.

With respect to shielding requirements, Henrie[13.14] says:

Nuclear rays and particles commonly shielded against are gamma rays, x-rays, alpha particles, beta particles, and neutrons. Gamma-ray and x-ray shields require mass primarily, and therefore must be made of high-density material if they are to be compact. Concrete is one of the more common gamma-ray and x-ray shielding materials. Alpha and beta emitters are dangerous contaminants and require good containment but little shielding, hence concrete is not generally used for this purpose.

Neutrons are the most difficult of the above types of radiation to shield against. They must be slowed down or thermalized and then captured in the nucleus of an atom. Hydrogen is the most effective element in slowing down neutrons over the entire energy spectrum. Carbon is also quite effective, but has a low neutron capture cross section and is not commonly used as a shielding material. Most other elements are relatively ineffective in slowing down neutrons below certain energy levels. Heavy elements are generally quite effective in slowing down fast or high energy neutrons. Therefore, a combination of materials is required to effectively thermalize neutrons over the entire spectrum. Capture of a neutron produces a new isotope which may be unstable and might therefore release energy in the form of gammas, betas, alphas, or even other neutrons. Some are released immediately and some at a slower controlled rate. This capture and secondary release may occur when a neutron is almost through the shield and could result in a serious leakage, particularly of secondary or captured gamma rays. The shield may become radioactive due to the production and decay of unstable isotopes, and this presents a design problem where the inner shield surfaces must be intermittently accessible to personnel.

Therefore, in general, the neutron shield must be able to (1) thermalize fast neutrons, (2) capture the thermal neutrons, (3) produce secondary particles or rays which can be shielded against relatively easily, (4) effectively shield against the secondary particles produced, and (5) minimize the build-up of long-lived activity. To thermalize fast neutrons, a shield must contain light atoms such as hydrogen (usually in the form of water) to slow down neutrons by elastic or "billiard ball" type scattering and heavier nuclei (such as iron) which absorb some of the neutron's energy by the process termed inelastic scattering as it passes through the nuclei. To effectively capture the thermal neutrons, the shield must contain atoms such as boron or cadmium having high neutron capture cross sections (a measure of their ability to absorb additional neutrons). Property 3 is best displayed when the neutrons are predominantly captured in atoms which liberate energy primarily by the release of alpha particles (n–a reactions) rather than hard gamma rays (n–y reactions). As an example, captures in boron result in n–a reactions while captures in cadmium and iron result in n–y reactions. Property 4 is best achieved by dense materials since the important secondary energy release requiring special shielding is in the form of gamma rays. Property 5 is achieved by materials such as boron and lithium which have high capture cross sections and produce stable or short-lived isotopes on the capture of a neutron. If Property 5 is of major importance for access reasons, certain materials having long half-life products must be limited. (In a recent design of an experimental reactor shield where inside access will be necessary after the reactor has operated, limits of 4.3 percent iron, 0.12 percent zinc, 0.029 percent antimony, and 0.0004 percent cobalt in the concrete shield were established.)

Proportioning and Handling

Proportioning of mixes for heavy concrete follows conventional methods, with about the same proportions by volume as for normal concrete. Parts by weight are, of course, considerably different for the aggregates because of their high density. Cement contents may range from 5 to 7 sacks per cubic yard, with water-cement ratios approximately the same as for normal concrete of similar quality.

Compressive strength and elastic modulus values are similar to those of normal concretes of similar cement contents and water-cement ratios. Durability of heavy concrete exposed to freezing and thawing is rather poor in some cases. For example, barites produce a concrete of low durability. If entrained air can be tolerated, the durability of exposed concrete is greatly improved. Concrete inside of buildings, or in a moderate climate where freezing and thawing do not occur, needs no protection.

Materials used for heavy aggregates are iron ores, such as magnetite and limonite, barite, scrap steel punchings, and steel or iron shot. Colemanite, a boron ore, is sometimes added to the concrete because of the ability of the boron to capture the originally fast neutrons as they become thermalized, and thereby reduce the buildup of secondary gamma rays.[13.14] However, boron slows the hydration of cement appreciably.

Mixes should be proportioned by volume and the components converted to parts by weight for batching. Half-size batches should be used to avoid excessive wear on equipment and segregation of the concrete. Good construction practices should be followed throughout the construction, including design of forms to withstand the greater pressure resulting from heavy concrete.

Most of these heavy aggregates are angular: this coupled with their high density makes a concrete that is less workable than normal concrete of similar characteristics. Mixes should be as stiff as can be placed, using vibration for consolidation.

Pipes and other embedded items are spaced so close together in some installations that conventional concrete placing techniques cannot be followed, and it is necessary to resort to the intrusion method. In this method, the coarse aggregate is first placed by hand in the spaces to be concreted, and grout pipes are installed at the same time. Subsequently, the space is filled with grout, pumped in under pressure, starting at the lowest portion of the forms.

13-13. CONCRETE PRODUCTS

Materials that are classified as concrete products include masonry blocks, cast stone, pipe, joists, girders, lintels, posts, piles, and similar products that are produced in a central manufacturing plant for many users, as contrasted with concrete that is cast in place at the structure site.

In all but a few special cases, it is customary to sample and test the products from stock at the producer's plant or upon delivery to the job-site, rather than to provide inspection in the plant during fabrication. An exception is the production of special items in relatively large quantities, such as a large quantity of precast wall panels, prestressed concrete units, pipe, or piles.

Masonry and Cast Stone

Blocks and bricks for masonry construction are made in special machines that vibrate, jolt, press, and otherwise consolidate a concrete of barely moist consistency. Standard ASTM specifications are available for these products, describing strength, absorption, and appearance requirements. Each sample of masonry units for compressive strength test should consist of five specimens: if maximum absorption is specified, five additional specimens are necessary. Strength specimens are capped and tested dry. Moisture absorption specimens are immersed in water for 24 hr, weighed, then dried to constant weight. The number of samples required is shown in Table 13-3.

Cast stone is an especially high-quality precast concrete usually specified to have an absorption of 6 per cent or less, and a minimum compressive strength of 6,500 psi when tested in 2-in. cubes or cylinders. It may be manufactured by either the dry-tamped or wet-cast process. Because of the very special ornamental requirements, a sample with the desired appearance should be available before fabrication is commenced.

TABLE 13-3. NUMBER OF CONCRETE MASONRY SAMPLES

No. of units in lot	No. of specimens
10,000 or less	5
10,000–100,000	10
Over 100,000	5 per 50,000

Note: Double the number of specimens if both strength and absorption tests are required.

Inspection of masonry and cast stone consists of examining the products for compliance with specifications as regards appearance, finish, and workmanship, and obtaining samples for laboratory testing.

Concrete Pipe

Methods for making pipe include tamping, compression by means of a revolving packerhead, vibration, centrifugation, and certain combinations of these processes.

Unreinforced irrigation and sewer pipe may be made by the packerhead process, in which the barely moist concrete is fed into a stationary split cylindrical jacket or form, standing on a base ring that forms the groove end of the section of pipe. As concrete is fed into the form, a rapidly revolving shoe, or packerhead, compacts the concrete against the outside form and makes a smooth interior on the pipe. The packerhead starts at the bottom of the form and is slowly raised as it rotates. The form and pipe are removed from the machine, placed in a curing room, and the form immediately removed from the new pipe.

A split form is used for the tamping method also. While the form and base plate rotate about a stationary core, concrete is fed into the annular space and compacted by steel-shod hardwood tamping bars striking at a rate of 500 to 600 blows per minute. A smooth interior on the pipe results from the troweling action of the stationary core, which is withdrawn as soon as the pipe is completed. The form is removed from the new pipe as soon as it is placed in the curing area. Both reinforced and unreinforced pipe are made by this process.

In the centrifugal process, zero or very low-slump concrete is placed in the horizontal mold as it rotates at slow speed, just fast enough to hold the concrete against the mold by centrifugal force. The rotational speed is gradually increased, compacting the concrete and expelling excess water. The optimum spinning speed varies with the size of pipe being made and is best found by trial for the particular materials and equipment in use. It may be a peripheral speed of 3,000 fpm or more. During the spinning period, water and lightweight particles migrate to the interior of the pipe and are removed by light brushing or troweling. No interior form is required for spun pipe. After a suitable curing period, the exterior form is removed.

In another method, known as the "vibrocast" process, pipe is cast, using plastic mixes in vertical forms, in much the same manner as structural concrete, and the recommended practices for good concrete construction should be followed. Pipe made by this process is usually 48 in. in diameter or larger. Concrete should be placed in shallow lifts and well consolidated by means of high-speed (7,500 rpm) form vibrators. Vibrators on the lower portion of the form should be operated until the level of the concrete in the form is well above them, then stopped.

Another process is one in which the pipe is made by a combination of vibration, centrifugal force, and rolling. The dry-mix concrete is fed into a horizontal, rotating form in a manner similar to that for centrifugally spun pipe. After the necessary amount of concrete has been fed into the rotating form, a heavy roller is brought to bear against the concrete and vibration is applied to the form. This process is frequently used for making hollow sections for prestressed piles.

Steam curing is almost universally employed for concrete pipe. For large pipe units, such as vibrocast pipe 6 ft in diameter by 24 ft long, portable housings, which can be moved about with a crane, are provided.

Figures 13-18 to 13-22 are views of various pipe manufacturing operations.

Failure of pipe to pass hydrostatic or crushing tests specified in the several ASTM designations is rare. After inspection and testing of several hundred miles of various types of concrete pipe for irrigation projects, covering 4 years of intensive pipe production in a number of plants, it was found that more pipe is rejected because of cracks, spalls, roughness, and similar defects than for test failures.

With respect to the packerhead pipe in 12- and 15-in. diameters, the normal amount of cull pipe was small. At the start of the job, one producer used a $\frac{1}{16}$-in. oversize packerhead (to compensate for wear) which made a thin-wall pipe. Failure to center and align the jacket, or mold almost perfectly caused a slight irregularity which produced a pipe thin enough on one side to be a reject. This happened to 100 per cent of the production for the first few days of operation of the plant. After that, with a packerhead of the proper diameter and care in placing the jacket in position, this trouble was nearly eliminated. On normal days, the percentage of culls was less than 2 per cent; these culls were caused mostly by rough handling producing cracks and spalls.

The amount of culled tamped pipe was large, due primarily to carelessness in handling. For instance, during 1 month, the daily percentage of

Fɪɢ. 13-18. Tamping 36-in. bell and spigot pipe. (*U.S. Bureau of Reclamation photo.*)

cull 18-in. reinforced pipe ranged from 7 to 32 per cent averaging 17 per cent, and the 21-in. ranged from 4 to 27 per cent averaging 14 per cent. Causes of rejects were circumferential cracks, longitudinal cracks, ragged tongues, and rough interiors.

Subsequently, several steps were taken to reduce the number of culls. Pipe was inspected as soon as the jacket was removed, and the defective ones knocked down immediately, hauling the concrete back to the pipe machine. Fog sprays were provided in the curing rooms. By turning on the sprays progressively across the room as it was filled with pipe, the pipe did not dry out before steaming. Finally, it was decided to make the smaller sizes (15-in. or smaller) in 3-ft lengths instead of 4-ft lengths.

Besides cracks and spalls due to rough handling, other defects were circumferential cracking of reinforced tamped pipe. Sometimes these

Fig. 13-19. Removing jacket from newly made pipe in curing yard. (*U.S. Bureau of Reclamation photo.*)

Fig. 13-20. General view of centrifugal spinning operation. (*U.S. Bureau of Reclamation photo.*)

cracks were in the form of a helix. They were caused by reinforcing cage hoops poorly welded to longitudinals, inexperienced or careless strippers, poorly graded mix containing insufficient gravel, or twisting of cage during tamping that was released when the pipe was stripped. Cracks in

FIG. 13-21. "Cenviro" machine, using a combination of centrifugal force, vibration, and rolling to form the pipe.

FIG. 13-22. Lightweight sheet aluminum boxes for covering pipe sections during steam curing. (*U.S. Bureau of Reclamation photo.*)

general were caused by drying of pipe before initial steaming, careless stripping, mix too wet, or length-diameter ratio too great (as 4-ft lengths of 15-in. pipe).

Rough interiors resulted from poor aggregate grading or using a mix that was too wet or too dry. Pin holes, causing hydrostatic failures, sometimes resulted from using sand lacking in fines.

The greatest weakness of the vibrocast pipe was the spigot end (which was the top of the pipe as cast). It is estimated that 90 per cent of the pipe had repairs of the spigot end, many of them minor, a few probably unnecessary. Many of the spigots had a fine, circumferential crack near the top, caused by settlement of fresh concrete, overheating while steaming in forms, overvibration, or use of high-slump concrete. Poor quality of concrete in the spigot (segregated, resulting in all mortar and no rock) was caused by overvibration, too much entrained air, or concrete too wet. The most common defect, broken, spalled, or chipped spigots, resulted from removal of core or jacket too early and rough handling during stripping. Poor quality of concrete in the spigot contributed to the breaking and spalling.

Many of the spalls in the spigot ends were in the shoulder on the outside of the pipe, where the concrete would frequently stick to the form.

Improper manufacturing procedures caused cracking of the pipe in locations other than in the spigot. Some of the causes of cracking in general were thermal stresses during steam curing, removal of core or form before concrete was strong enough, rough handling during stripping and tipping, poorly designed concrete mixes, improper slump, overvibration or undervibration, and shrinkage of concrete.

Other defects were soft spots in the bell, caused by an excess of form oil accumulating in the bottom of the form, dimensional inaccuracies caused by careless setting of forms, wear on forms or improper filling of forms with concrete, and sticking of concrete to the form.

The most common defects in spun pipe were seam cracks, caused by leakage of mortar through jacket gate during spinning; broken or spalled spigots, which developed during spinning or stripping; exposed steel, usually due to faulty alignment of the cage rather than to faulty cage dimensions: inside diameters not within allowable tolerances; rough interior, frequently caused by attempting to fill an underfilled pipe after it had spun several minutes, or lightweight aggregate particles; crooked gasket ring in spigot, misalignment of the ring ends, or ring not perpendicular to axis of pipe; and rough, sandy spots resulting from excessive form oil.

At times blisters, or drummy areas, in which the interior concrete separated from the main body of the pipe wall, occurred in spun pipe. These blisters were attributed to a number of conditions, including concrete too soft or too wet (high slump), insufficient spinning, starting steam curing too soon after spinning, and steaming at too high a temperature (above 155°F).

Blisters were usually worse during wet, cold weather than at other times. Probably all the above factors contributed to their formation at times. It was found that by giving the pipe its initial steam curing in a vertical position, or at least steeply inclined, the blisters were largely eliminated. The effect of lower-slump concrete was definite in reducing the incidence of blisters.

13-14. PNEUMATICALLY APPLIED MORTAR

When cement mortar is sprayed on a surface, the product is variously known as pneumatically applied mortar, shotcrete, or "Gunite." The process consists essentially of mixing dry sand and cement in a mixer, then placing this mixture in the delivering equipment, the first part of which is a vertical, double-chambered vessel wherein the mixture is placed under pneumatic pressure. Under pressure, the mixture flows through a rubber hose to the gun or nozzle, where water joins the material, wetting the

Fig. 13-23. One-half-in. shotcrete nozzle.

mixture as it leaves the gun under high velocity. Velocity of the material as it leaves the nozzle should be within the following limits:

¾- or 1-in. nozzle	375 to 500 fps
1½-in. nozzle	425 to 550 fps

Smaller nozzles are sometimes used, as in Figs. 13-23 and 13-24, which show a small job-made gun used for patching work. With the exception of the jacket (which can be machined from a piece of tubing) all parts are standard pipe fittings. This small gun was used successfully for patching concrete pipe and similar work.

Uses of Shotcrete

Application of mortar by the pneumatic method is adaptable to either new construction, the application of a coating or covering, or repair of existing structures.

New construction includes linings for canals, reservoirs, tunnels, and pipe; coating over stressing wire in circularly prestressed tanks and pipe; and thin slabs and walls.

Coatings may be applied to deteriorated concrete or masonry, after removal of unsound, deteriorated material; to rock surfaces to prevent scaling or disintegration of newly exposed surfaces; and to steel and timber for fireproofing.

Almost any type of deteriorated concrete surface can be repaired by application of shotcrete.

Preparation of Surface

In new construction, the forms, compacted earth, or other surface must be clean and sufficiently rigid to withstand the shooting, and stout enough

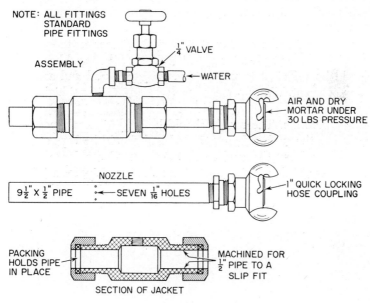

Fig. 13-24. One-half-in. shotcrete nozzle.

to carry the load. In repair of old concrete or masonry, all the old unsound material must be removed so the shotcrete is applied to a sound surface. Heavily corroded steel should be sand-blasted, using the shotcrete equipment for this purpose. Reinforcing should be securely doweled or bolted in place.

Application

Shotcrete requires expert and conscientious workmanship, and should be done under careful supervision and inspection, employing only experienced workmen.

On vertical or overhanging surfaces, the mortar should be applied in layers not exceeding ¾ in. in thickness. On horizontal, or nearly horizontal surfaces, the thickness may be as much as 3 in. Excessively thick layers will cause the mortar to slough, or sag. Sagging may also occur if insufficient time elapses between layers. Time between successive layers should be at least 30 min, but should not be so long as to permit the previous layers to set completely.

Shotcrete can be finished the same as any concrete or mortar. However, finishing should be kept to a minimum.

Factors that affect quality of the work are the following:

Materials and Mix. Only first-class materials should be used conforming to ASTM standards for cement, concrete sand, and water. If the nozzle is small, mortar sand should be used; otherwise ordinary concrete sand is suitable. The mix should be 1 part cement to 3 or 4 parts of sand by volume. Sand should contain from 3 to 5 per cent moisture.

Water. The amount of water added at the nozzle should be a minimum, but should be sufficient to prevent excessive rebound and assure hydration of the cement. Water pressure should be 10 to 15 psi higher than the air pressure.

Nozzle Operation. The nozzle should be held as nearly perpendicular as possible to the surface being treated and should be kept at a uniform distance away from the surface at all times. For a large nozzle, the distance is about 3 ft, ranging down to as close as 12 in. for a ½-in. nozzle in close quarters.

Air Pressure. An adequate supply of air is essential. Pressure should be uniform, in the range of 50 psi for heavy work or long hoses and 25 to 50 psi for finishing. A pressure of about 30 psi is adequate for the ½-in. nozzle.

Rebound

A portion of the mortar bounces from the surface where it is being applied, the amount varying with air pressure, quality of sand, placement conditions, and the cement and water contents. The amount of rebound varies from about 30 per cent when shooting vertical surfaces to about 20 per cent from horizontal or sloping surfaces. This rebound material should not be reused because of its variable quality and low cement content.

Inspection and Testing

Six- by twelve-in. cylinders for compressive strength tests are made by shooting the mortar vertically into molds made of ½-in. mesh hardware cloth. The excess material is trimmed off the outside of the mold immediately after filling, and the hardware cloth is removed before the cylinders are tested. Cylinders should be handled and stored under standard conditions. Twenty-eight-day strength should be at least 4,000 psi.

The presence of hollow spots or areas containing an excess of rebound included in the shotcrete can be detected by sounding the surface of the finished work with a hammer. Imperfections should be removed and replaced with new shotcrete.

13-15. REPAIR OF CONCRETE

In spite of all the precautions and quality control measures that are taken in the production of concrete, there are occasions when concrete suffers damage and deterioration. Repair is greatly complicated if inferior concrete was placed originally, although protective measures may be effective in controlling spread of the damage.

Diagnosis

The first step in repair is to diagnose the damage (see Maintenance of the Structure in Sec. 1-4). This includes determination of the cause of deterioration and an evaluation of the extent of damage. Causes of deterioration are discussed in Chap. 5. In general, they may be inferior materials, poor design, faulty workmanship in construction, chemical activity within the concrete, exposure to aggressive substances, long exposure to weathering, freezing and thawing action, or accidental damage. The next step is to determine the extent of the damage, and the necessary repair measures.

Three methods of repair are available: dry pack, concrete replacement, and mortar replacement or shotcrete.

Preparation for Repair

Whatever the method of repair, the first step is removal of all unsound and disintegrated concrete. This requires rigorous and uncompromising removal of any concrete of doubtful soundness. Surface of the old concrete should be clean, and the fractured face should be bright and crystalline in appearance. A dull, dead-appearing surface will not do. While good work can be done with hand tools, a faster and better job is done with pneumatic chipping hammers. Edges are best made with a saw, making the cut at a slight angle so as to key the patch in place. Note, however, that edges for shotcrete should slope outward slightly to avoid inclusion of rebound.

Reinforcing steel exposed during the concrete removal should be sandblasted and rigidly fixed in place. If additional steel is required within the repair area, it should be tied to existing steel and anchored by means of expansion bolts set in the old concrete.

Dry Pack

Cavities of small area but relatively deep, such as those resulting from form bolts, are best filled with a dry-pack mortar, consisting of 1 part cement to $2\frac{1}{2}$ parts of sand passing the 16-mesh sieve. Usually, it is necessary to use part white cement for a good color match. The mixture should contain just enough water so it will form a ball when squeezed gently in the hand. Too much water will result in shrinkage and consequent loosening of the patch. Too little water will not make a sound patch.

If the patch is applied shortly after the form is removed from new concrete, it is not necessary to moisten the cavity. Old concrete should be saturated, then permitted to become surface-dry before the cavity is filled.

After the cavity has been cleaned of all loose material, unsound concrete, and oil, the mortar is tamped in layers about $\frac{1}{2}$ in. thick. For good compaction and bond between layers, tamping should be done by hammering on a hardwood stick. The surface of the patch should be finished to match the existing concrete. However, even when matching a steel-formed surface, a steel trowel should never be used on the patch because this leaves a dark surface that is impossible to remove.

Concrete Replacement

This method is used for repairs involving large and deep areas of more than a few square inches in area and 6 in. in depth. It is especially suitable for restoring large areas of hydraulic structures, where it has become necessary to remove concrete to an appreciable depth over an extended area.

Repairs in horizontal surfaces may be made without forms, except where replacement of corners and edges is required. Sloping and vertical surfaces require forms to confine the concrete.

Forms must be mortar-tight and must fit snugly to the old concrete to avoid loss of mortar or an offset around the perimeter of the patch.

The old concrete should be nearly dry when a $\frac{1}{8}$-in. coating of mortar of the same proportions and water content as the replacement concrete is applied, preferably by shotcrete or hand-rubbing into the surface.

Concrete placement follows immediately after the mortar coating. Concrete with a slump of 2 to 3 in. should be deposited in lifts, or layers, each layer consolidated by vibration using immersion vibrators if possible, otherwise by means of form vibrators (provided the forms are constructed to withstand form vibration).

Under carefully controlled conditions, a small amount of aluminum powder (2 or 3 g per sack of cement) may be added to the concrete to prevent shrinkage (see Chap. 4).

Pneumatically Applied Mortar

Shotcrete is especially adaptable to thin areas of large extent, such as scaled areas. Preparation of the area and application of the shotcrete should be performed as previously described.

Bonded Overlay

Scaled areas of pavements and similar flat slabs may be repaired by application of a thin overlay. This process, developed by the Portland Cement Association, is described in detail in reference 13.15.

After removal of unsound concrete, the area to be patched is cleaned, preferably with a muriatic acid wash and thorough scrubbing and washing. After the surface becomes surface-dry, a thin layer of mortar is spread, followed by air-entrained concrete containing coarse aggregate no larger than about one-third of the thickness of the overlay. Slump should not exceed 1 in. The concrete should be thoroughly tamped, then finished to match the original surface. Joints should be provided over joints in the original concrete.

Bonding Agents

The mortar coatings previously mentioned in this section may be classed as bonding agents, for their purpose is to promote the bond between the old concrete and the new.

Epoxy resin may be used as a bonding agent, applied to the old concrete immediately ahead of the new concrete. The resin must be applied to dry concrete and should be used in accordance with the manufacturer's instructions.

There are available latex materials which, when added to the fresh mortar or concrete as an admixture, or mixed with the bonding grout, serve to improve bond. Among these are polyvinyl acetate and copolymers of butadiene and styrene (see Chap. 10). Bonding agents are usually mixed with the cement grout and scrubbed into the old concrete immediately ahead of application of the patching mortar or concrete. In some cases, when patching spalls and nicks, the bonding agent is mixed in the patching mortar or concrete.

Curing

All patches require thorough curing. This may be done by keeping the patch continuously wet for at least five days, by the use of liquid curing compound, or by covering with waterproof paper or polyethylene.

Sealing Leaks

Sodium carbonate (washing soda) is a powerful accelerator and is useful as an admixture in mortar to seal a leak in concrete. Using about 10 per cent of the carbonate by weight of cement will cause the cement to set hard in a few minutes. Tests should be made with the materials first. Calcium oxychloride (less than 10 per cent of the cement) is also an accelerator. Soluble silicates and fluosilicates and mixtures of aluminous and portland cement all act as accelerators. Any of these materials must be used with caution, as lowered ultimate strength and durability usually accompany their use. They are especially useful for emergency temporary repairs and sealing of leaks in hydraulic structures, basements, and walls.

Adhesives

Broken concrete can be joined by the use of epoxy resin adhesive. The piece to be bonded must be sound concrete, such as that broken off by accidental impact. Precast elements, such as curbings, posts, or traffic markers, and objects of metal may be bonded to concrete with epoxy.

Surfaces to be bonded must be sound and thoroughly cleaned, preferably by sandblasting or by washing with detergent followed by rinsing with water, and then permitted to dry. The mixed adhesive is applied with a trowel or putty knife to both surfaces to be joined, then the piece to be bonded is pressed into place. If necessary because of the location, suitable supports or clamps should be provided until the epoxy cures, usually a matter of 2 to 4 hr, depending on the formulation of the adhesive and the ambient temperature.

REFERENCES

13.1   Concrete Cracking Prevented, *Construction World,* March, 1961, pp. 32–33.
13.2   Recommended Practice for Hot Weather Concreting, Report of ACI Committee 605, *J. Am. Concrete Inst.,* November, 1958.
13.3   Recommended Practice for Winter Concreting, Report of ACI Committee 604, *J. Am. Concrete Inst.,* June, 1956.
13.4   Janney, Jack R., and Richard C. Elstner: Inspection of Prestressed Concrete, *Publication INS* 109–60, Prestressed Concrete Institute, April, 1960.
13.5   Tentative Specifications for Design, Materials, and Construction of Prestressed Concrete Structures, *Bulletin* 554, American Railway Engineering Association.
13.6   Suggested Specification for Single Course Floors on Ground, *Concrete Information Series,* Portland Cement Association, Chicago.
13.7   Tilt-up Construction, Portland Cement Association, Chicago.

13.8   Doggett, John H.: First Slip-formed Apartment Building in the United States, *J. Am. Concrete Inst.*, March, 1958, pp. 767–772.

13.9   Camellerie, J. F.: Slip Form Details and Techniques, *J. Am. Concrete Inst.*, April, 1959, pp. 1131–1140.

13.10 Color in Architectural Concrete by the Aggregate Transfer Method, Portland Cement Association, 1950.

13.11 Valore, R. C., Jr.: Insulating Concretes, *J. Am. Concrete Inst.*, November, 1956, pp. 509–532.

13.12 Specifications for Zonolite Insulating Concrete, The Zonolite Company.

13.13 Fiesenheiser, E. I., and B. A. Wasil, Heavy Steel-Aggregate Concrete, *J. Am. Concrete Inst.*, September, 1955, pp. 73–82.

13.14 Henrie, James O.: Properties of Nuclear Shielding Concrete, *J. Am. Concrete Inst.*, July, 1959, pp. 37–46.

13.15 Maintenance Practices for Concrete Pavement, Portland Cement Association, Chicago, 1956.

13.16 Symposium of Papers on Repair of Concrete, *J. Am. Concrete Inst.*, August, 1960.

CHAPTER 14 *Pavements*

Properly installed, concrete is an unsurpassed material for heavy-duty street, highway, and airport pavement. Basic requirements for a successful concrete pavement are adequate design to carry the expected traffic load, both as to weight and volume, a high-quality riding surface, and durability under the action of the elements to assure a long, trouble-free life.

The initial approval or disapproval by the public is usually based on the smoothness of the riding surface. Of course, continued good service for many years is also expected, but the first impression is of great importance. To obtain a pavement of the required quality, both as to a smooth surface and durability, requires care in all steps from preparation of the subgrade to final curing. It is not the intent of this section to describe in detail how a pavement should be built. Pavements are usually constructed under detailed specifications of the governmental agency supervising the work and the reader is referred to the specifications covering the job at hand. The following suggestions are offered as an aid in obtaining a specification job. A good reference for the inspector is the *Concrete Pavement Inspector's Manual* of the Portland Cement Association.[14.1]* Pavement construction is described in reference 14.2.

Present-day pavement construction is highly automated. As shown in Fig. 14-1, the equipment comprises a train consisting of the spreaders, finishing machines of several types, and other equipment traveling on the side forms which constitute the rails.

14-1. FOUNDATION

The subgrade is the foundation for the surfacing pavement. Compacted subgrade should extend a foot or two beyond the form line and,

* Superscript figures refer to chapter and reference number. The references are found at the end of each chapter.

when compaction has been completed, should be at an elevation slightly above the finish grade and profile. In areas where the subgrade material is a plastic soil, it is customary to make the top 6 in. or so of a nonco-hesive, free-draining material so as to protect the pavement from frost action and pumping. This upper layer of the subgrade is called the base. In fine grading for forms, it is always best to have the compacted

FIG. 14-1. The paving train. Note the two 34-E pavers (mixers). Traveling on the forms are two spreaders, one spreading the first lift ahead of reinforcing steel placing, and the second one spreading the second lift. Following the second spreader are the finishing machine, longitudinal float, mechanical belt, and burlap drag. Between the belt and drag a workman is using the straightedge to check the pavement smooth-ness. After a suitable time, a spray rig will cover the concrete with liquid curing compound, or other curing will be provided. (*Illinois Tollway photo.*)

material slightly above finish grade. Careful excavation of the excess ma-terial enables the forms to be set on well-compacted materials. Prior to final checking, field density tests should be made in the subgrade and base to assure compliance with the specifications. The final opera-tions are removal of excess material, final compaction, and checking with a template.

Traffic should be kept off the finished base, and any low or disturbed spots should be repaired and recompacted before concrete is placed.

14-2. FORMS

It is extremely important that forms be set accurately to line and grade. Besides serving to confine the concrete, they serve as tracks for the spreader, finisher, and the other machines comprising the paving train. The smoothness of the finished pavement depends on the care with which the forms are set.

Specifications are usually very explicit in their requirements for forms, stressing the importance of straightness and rigidity, and the inspector should be governed by the specifications under which he is working. The flange should be straight and not bent up or down, as this causes variations in the concrete surface when the finishing machine rides over the irregularities. Joint locks should be in good condition. All form pins and wedges should be in place. Forms should be supported on a uniformly firm foundation for their entire bearing area. Surface irregularities result if the forms are propped up with stones, wedges, or similar materials.

If forms must be raised, they should be removed and base material tamped in place to the required elevation, unless special tamping tools are available which will permit the fill to be tamped under the form without moving the form. High spots should be carefully and smoothly cut to grade and the form replaced.

Forms should be accurately set to line and grade by instrument and straightedge and a final check of alignment made by sighting along the tops of the forms. Just before concrete is placed, the form should be checked to see that it is clean and oiled.

When the pavement consists of more than one lane, previously placed concrete in the adjacent lane may be used in lieu of forms for supporting finishing equipment provided the concrete has developed sufficient strength to withstand the loadings imposed, and the surface carrying the finishing equipment meets the straightness tolerance specified for forms. The concrete should be protected from damage by construction operations.

14-3. REINFORCEMENT AND JOINT ASSEMBLIES

Usual practice when constructing a reinforced pavement is to spread and strike off a layer of concrete to the depth specified for the reinforcing, place the reinforcing mesh or bar mats on the fresh concrete, then place the second layer of concrete immediately. The fabric or mats should be flat, free from distortion, of the correct size, clean, and free of deep rust. At no time should an attempt be made to place the mesh on the base and pull it up through the concrete, or to force it down from the top.

Dowel bar assemblies should be placed for transverse contraction joints as required in the specifications. The pavement reinforcement should overlap the dowel bars about 6 in. on each side to provide continuous reinforcement throughout the length of the pavement. Dowels should be carefully aligned parallel to the centerline and subgrade (see Fig. 14-2). Alignment of these dowels is especially important as misaligned bars are sure to crack the pavement later on. Workmen should not be permitted to step on the assemblies, and concrete should not be carelessly discharged adjacent to the assemblies. Dowels should be painted as specified and burrs should be ground off the ends.

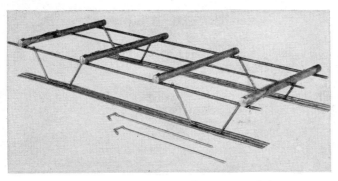

FIG. 14-2. One type of dowel bar assembly. The purpose of the supporting wires is to hold the bars rigidly in place until the concrete hardens. The two pins are driven into the subbase, with the hooked ends over the sand plates. (*Superior Concrete Accessories, Inc.*)

Tie bars for longitudinal hinge joints consist of lengths of reinforcing steel attached to the reinforcing mats or otherwise anchored in place and extending across the longitudinal joints. Their function is to prevent separation of the slabs which, if it occurs, causes weakening of the portion of the slab next to the joint resulting in interior corner breaks. Tie bars should be accurately placed, perpendicular to the joint and parallel to the subgrade. Tie bars at each side of a transverse joint should be not over 15 in. from the transverse joint.

14-4. PLACING CONCRETE

Concrete for pavement is usually discharged from the mixer into a bucket operating on the paver boom. The bucket, in turn, dumps the concrete on to the prepared base. The concrete should be distributed evenly over the base, spread, and struck off to the required depth for placement of the reinforcing. After reinforcing mesh is placed, the second layer of concrete is placed, consolidated and finished. Figure 14-1 shows the "paving train" with two 34-E pavers.

A good paver operator distributes the concrete in a manner that minimizes the amount of spreading required by the concrete spreader, as shown in Fig. 14-3. The concrete should not be dumped in piles along the center of the lane, but individual batches should be distributed so that only a slight excess is carried ahead of the finishing equipment. Height of the mixer boom should be such that the vertical drop of the concrete is a minimum.

As in all concrete, uniformity is essential. Slump should be uniform, and handling methods should be consistent. Concrete should not be

Fig. 14-3. Dumping concrete ahead of the spreader for the second lift. (*Illinois Tollway photo.*)

dumped on joint installations but should be dumped close by and shoveled into place. If there is segregation in a batch as dumped, the stone pockets should be broken up with a shovel and the pieces of gravel scattered, rather than being corrected by adding mortar. Rehandling of the concrete should be kept to a minimum.

If concrete is delivered to the site by truck in ready-mixed batches, the use of chutes should not be permitted. Buckets are the best means of moving the concrete from the trucks to the forms, or a conveyor may be used.

The inspector should be constantly vigilant to see that workmen do not track mud or other materials into the fresh concrete.

Spreading

After the concrete is dumped on the subgrade, a mechanical spreader distributes the concrete between the forms. For a reinforced pavement, the first layer is struck off by the spreader at the proper depth for placing the reinforcing steel. After placement of the reinforcement, the second layer of concrete is placed. Specifications usually limit the delay between layers to not more than 30 min.

Spreaders are equipped with gauges to show the elevation of the strike-off. Being visible to the operator, they enable him to adjust the strike-off for the proper depth to spread concrete before mesh is placed on it, and for the final spreading. Before using a spreader, the gauge should be checked to see that it reads zero when the bottom of the strike-off is even with the top of the forms.

The spreader should be set so as to leave a slight excess of concrete for the finisher.

Consolidation

A thin pavement (8 in. thick or less) may be consolidated by means of the screeds on the finishing machine, provided the slump is about $1\frac{1}{2}$ in. and the mix is properly proportioned. Thicker pavements, up to 12 in. thick, require the use of a vibrating screed or pan surface vibrator, while those pavements exceeding about 12 in. in thickness should be consolidated by means of immersion vibrators. In any event, vibrators are necessary in the vicinity of dowel assemblies and similar installations.

Special equipment is available for consolidating pavements. Vibrating screeds and pans are usually attached to the spreader or finisher. Gang-mounted L-shaped spud vibrators and vibrating tubes, attached to the spreader or finisher, or operating on independent carriages that travel on the forms, are also available.

Concrete must be thoroughly consolidated with just enough mortar brought to the surface to provide for satisfactory finishing without an excess of soupy fines on the surface. The judgment of a competent engineer, familiar with paving techniques, is necessary.

14-5. FINISHING

After the concrete has been spread, it is finished by means of the finishing machine, or finisher. The purpose of the finisher is to consolidate and screed the concrete to the approximate final contour. Two transverse reciprocating screeds remove excess concrete and leave the surface in condition for the longitudinal float.

The proper tilt of the screed aids in consolidating the concrete; this should be about $\frac{1}{8}$ in. for air-entrained concrete. The usual procedure is to adjust the screed for the proper crown, then tilt it the desired amount by means of the bolts provided for that purpose. The rear screed is adjusted with little or no tilt and to the required elevation.

Finishing machines should be checked before they are used, and periodically as the job progresses. The screeds rest on wearing plates which slide on the forms. They should be checked to ensure that the plates have not worn to the extent that the height of the screed is affected. The profile should be checked by means of a wire stretched across the forms, with the screed resting on blocks on the forms, and making measurements between the screed and the wire.

Traction and screed speeds should be adjusted to give the best finish. For air-entrained, low-slump concrete, the screed speed should be relatively fast and the traction slow. About six oscillations of the screed per foot of longitudinal travel of the machine should be satisfactory. If this results in a rough, torn surface, the number of oscillations per foot of travel should be increased. Proper adjustment of the screeds is achieved when the concrete forms a roll, 6 to 8 in. high, ahead of the first screed. This concrete should roll over and over as the screed travels ahead. Loss of the roll indicates a low spot, in which case it is necessary to obtain additional concrete from the paver. The second screed should have a roll about 2 in. high along its entire length.

Two passes of the finisher are required, sometimes more if the concrete surface is not smooth and uniform. On most jobs, it is usual for the second pass to be made by a second machine, although only one machine is sometimes used. The second pass should be made after the concrete has settled slightly. The rolls ahead of the screeds on the second pass are much smaller than they were in the first pass, but their size relationship is about the same.

Longitudinal Float

Following the finishing machine, a longitudinal float shapes and smooths the concrete surface further. The mechanical float consists of a steel float blade several feet long, approximately parallel with the forms. This blade reciprocates in a longitudinal direction as it moves across the slab from one form to the form on the opposite side.

The tracks from which the float is suspended should be adjusted before work begins, and the machine checked to ensure that the bottom of the float is smooth and straight. The manufacturer's instructions should be followed in making these adjustments.

The float should not be permitted to cut into the concrete surface, and a small roll of mortar, tapering from about $1\frac{1}{2}$ in. in diameter at the forward end to nothing about 2 ft from the rear end, should be carried ahead of the blade. Any excess of mortar should be wasted over the edge of the forms. Low spots should be filled with fresh concrete.

A properly floated finish is smooth, with only a slight ripple left by the trailing end of the float.

Timing is very important. Final floating should be delayed as long as possible, consistent with other operations, to allow for initial settlement of the concrete. The delay is less in hot, dry, or windy weather than in damp or cool weather. If mechanical floating is done properly, there should be no need of hand-finishing.

Straightedging

After the longitudinal floating has been completed and the excess water removed, but while the concrete surface is still plastic, the slab surface should be tested for trueness with a straightedge, using a straightedge of specified length (usually 16 ft) swung from handles 3 ft longer than one-half the slab width.

The straightedge should be held in successive positions parallel to the slab center line in contact with the surface and the whole area gone over from one side to the other. Advance along the slab should be in successive stages of about one-half of the length of the straightedge. The straightedge is carefully lifted from each position and slowly lowered into the next position in order to leave a print or mark on the pavement surface. The depth and width of these prints are an indication of the smoothness of the slab. (These prints are removed in subsequent finishing operations.)

Any depressions should be immediately filled with fresh concrete, struck off, consolidated, and refinished. High areas should be cut down and refinished.

This operation requires careful attention by the inspector, not only to see that it is properly done, but to see that the indicated corrections are made.

Belting

Before the concrete becomes nonplastic, the surface of the pavement in short increments of length should be belted with a two-ply canvas or rubber belt having a width of not less than 6 in. and a length at least 2 ft greater than the width of the slab. Hand belts should have suitable handles to permit controlled, uniform manipulation. The belt should be operated with short strokes transverse to the paving strip and with continuous advance longitudinally. The belting should be carefully done so as not to leave disfiguring marks upon the surface and to produce a finished surface having a uniformly fine granular or sandy texture. The belt should be kept clean and oiled at all times.

The proper time for belting is about the time the water sheen disappears from the surface. Care is necessary to produce a uniform surface and to prevent the edges of the belt from gouging the surface.

A belt may be manipulated by hand, with a workman on each side of the slab. The workmen alternately pull the belt toward themselves in a sort of sawing motion as they slowly move it forward. Mechanical belting machines are also available.

Edging

After belting has been completed but before burlap dragging, the edges of slabs along forms should be carefully finished with an edging tool. Corners of edges of slabs which have crumbled and any areas which lack sufficient mortar for proper finishing should be cleaned by removing all loose fragments and soupy mortar and should be solidly filled and finished with a mixture of correct proportions and appropriate consistency. Unnecessary tool marks should be eliminated, and all edges should be smooth and true to line.

Final Finishing

Final finish should be obtained by the use of two separate, double-thickness burlap drags, at least 4 ft wide and 2 ft longer than the width of slab under construction. The burlap should be attached to a bridge riding on the pavement forms and should be kept saturated with water while in use. The burlap should be laid on the pavement surface and dragged in the direction that the pavement is being laid with approximately 2 ft of its width in contact with the pavement surface. The burlap drag should be kept clean and free from hardened concrete.

Time for dragging is critical. If it is done too soon, it will tear the surface by rolling pieces of aggregate along. If it is too late, it will have no effect. The inspector should watch for loose strings on the burlap which trail behind the drag and leave grooves in the concrete. On windy days special care is necessary to keep the burlap wet. Note that this is the only time during the finishing operations that water may be used.

14-6. SPECIAL EQUIPMENT AND METHODS

Equipment developments during the last few years have included a combination spreader-finisher which eliminates the need for part of the equipment in the paving train, and machines for continuous slip-form construction. Slip-form pavers operate on the previously prepared base, without fixed side forms.

Several experimental reaches of continuously reinforced pavement have been laid in the United States, and indications are that more will be used.[14.3] As its name implies, continuously reinforced pavement is pavement without transverse joints, except construction joints at the end of each day's work or at structures. Construction should follow the practices recommended herein, with special emphasis on accurate placement of the reinforcement.

Prestressed concrete has also been used experimentally in some installations.[14.4]

14-7. CURING

There are a number of curing methods available: ponding, wet earth, liquid membrane-forming compound, impermeable paper or plastic sheets, wet straw, and mats of various materials such as cotton, burlap, or jute. All of these have the same two objectives: to prevent loss of moisture present in the concrete at the time it was placed, and to protect the concrete from extremes of temperature, either hot or cold. Reference should be made to the specifications for approved types.

Curing Compound

Liquid membrane-forming compound, commonly called curing compound, consists of waxes and other materials that form an impervious membrane through which the water in the concrete cannot escape, and it is applied in the same manner as paint. The compound should contain a white pigment to reflect a portion of the sun's heat that would otherwise be absorbed by the concrete.

Curing compounds are ready-mixed when they arrive on the job, but need vigorous stirring or agitating before they can be used. Under no circumstances should they be thinned or otherwise altered on the job. Usually, the drums in which sealing compound is shipped are equipped with agitators which should be operated before and during the time the compound is being sprayed.

During cold weather, it may be necessary to heat the compound if it becomes too viscous for application. Heating should be done in a hot water bath, never over an open flame, and the temperature should never exceed 100°F. When being heated, the container should be vented and there should be room in the container for expansion of the solution. The solution should be agitated during heating.

Application is usually done with power-operated equipment which travels on the forms. The spray nozzles move across the pavement in a transverse direction, their speed so regulated as to give a two-coat coverage at the rate of 135 sq ft per gallon. The nozzles should produce a fan-shaped spray, and should be surrounded with a shield to protect them from the wind. Water and oil traps should be installed on compressed air lines. Hand-operated pressure devices should be permitted only in isolated locations, such as along the edges of the pavement after form removal, or in case of breakdown of the machine.

If rain damages the membrane before it hardens, the damaged areas should be resealed by the application of a new coating as soon as possible.

If the compound is applied after the forming of joints, the joints should be protected to prevent the compound from entering, as it will interfere with adhesion of the joint material to the concrete. Protection may be provided by a rope or narrow strip of wood laid on top of the joint ahead of the compound spraying. The rope or wood should remain in place until the required curing period has elapsed. Also available is a narrow tape which is applied to the joint ahead of the compound application. Any of these expedients require considerable care in placing and continual inspection to see that they are performing satisfactorily.

Compound should be applied as soon as the surface moisture has disappeared while the concrete is still damp. This is evidenced when the concrete loses the shine or sheen caused by free water, but before the surface starts to dry out. On pavement edges, compound should be applied as soon as the side forms have been removed. If the surface has dried, it should be well sprinkled with water, and the compound applied as soon as free water has disappeared.

Specifications usually require that the membrane be kept intact for a designated period of time, ordinarily 14 days. Any damaged areas should be repaired immediately by the application of sealing compound. If the concrete has become dry, it may be necessary to soak it with water before applying the membrane.

Paper and Plastic Covering

Paper for the impermeable paper method should preferably be white-coated for heat reflective value. White polyethylene sheeting may also be used. Either material should be laid on the concrete as soon after finishing as possible without marring the surface. This time is best determined by experience, as it depends on weather conditions and is later than the time for applying sealing compound. The concrete surface should be wetted before placing the covering. Adjacent sheets should be lapped, the sheets weighted, and a longitudinal pleat provided. Windrows on laps and edges should be continuous. Workmen should not be permitted to walk on the paper or plastic at any time, as this is apt to make many small holes.

Reused paper or plastic should be examined very closely for holes, as even small pinholes can damage its sealing value. The object of covering is to provide an impervious covering for at least 7 days, and anything less than complete and perfect coverage is not adequate.

Blankets and Mats

Burlap blankets should not be made out of secondhand gunny sacks or similar material. They should be made of at least two layers of new 9-oz or heavier burlap. Burlap that has been used for curing concrete may be used provided it is clean and in good condition.

Mats may be of several materials, such as cotton, sisal, or jute. Their efficiency should be at least equal to that of the burlap blankets, and, like the blankets, they should be kept saturated by frequent sprinkling with water. Some mats have a waterproof covering which is supposed to retain the water underneath. These should be checked periodically to see that the concrete is wet at all times. If the concrete appears to be drying out, additional water should be added immediately.

Care should be taken in placing blankets and mats to ensure that they completely cover the pavement, including the edges, and that they are adequately lapped. In placing new mats, allowance should be made for shrinkage. They should be laid on the pavement as soon as they can without marring the surface. A fine fog spray may be necessary to keep the concrete moist until it has hardened sufficiently to support the mats. Mats should be kept in place for at least 7 days.

Other Methods

In case it is decided to use wet straw for curing, wet burlap blankets should first be placed on the concrete, as described above, unless other methods of keeping the concrete wet for 4 hr are used.

During cold weather, it may be necessary to protect the concrete by means of insulating blankets. They should be applied to the surface as soon as curing material has been applied. In the case of paper or textile pads and blankets, this is immediately after the latter have been put in place and properly wetted. Liquid membranes should be permitted to dry before insulation is applied.

Curing may also be accomplished by ponding the slab, if it is fairly level, or covering it with wet earth. These methods are usually permitted only upon special permission of the engineer in charge of the project.

14-8. JOINTS IN PAVEMENT

Joints in a pavement may be classified into four general categories: contraction, construction, expansion, and hinge or warping joints.

Contraction Joints

These joints are installed for the purpose of permitting shrinkage of the new concrete, and subsequent movement caused by temperature changes, and are generally installed about 50 to 60 ft apart. They are of two types: preformed and sawed.

Preformed joints are made in the fresh concrete ahead of the final burlap dragging by installing a jointmaking device in the surface of the slab. This may be a strip of wood or metal pressed into a slot that was formed by a vibrating bar forced into the concrete. Final finishing leaves a smooth surface over the strip. The strip is removed on the following day and the joint is subsequently filled with a mastic bituminous filling compound. Another type is a strip of shaped sheet metal that is set permanently in place during paving operations. Preformed joints are especially desirable in multiple-lane pavement, as they preclude sympathy cracking—the formation of a crack in the new slab in which joints have not yet been formed, opposite a joint in the old slab.

In installing joint-forming strips, care should be taken to avoid leaving a raised area of concrete adjacent which will cause an undesirable bump in the pavement. The top of the strip should not be permitted to rest below the slab surface, otherwise spalling is apt to occur when the strip is removed. Longitudinal placement should be accurately over the centerline of dowels.

Sawed joints are cut after the concrete has hardened. Their advantage is that there is no disturbance of the fresh concrete, consequently no danger of irregularities in the slab surface.[14.5]

The time for sawing transverse contraction joints in pavements is very critical, as they must be sawed before the concrete shrinks enough to crack. The time varies with different materials, curing, and weather conditions. For this reason, it is not possible to set any definite time for sawing joints. Even on the same job, the time will vary as weather conditions change. With abrasive blades, sawing may be done between 4 and 12 hr after placement of the concrete, and diamond blades may be used any time after 8 hr. These time limits are approximate only. In general, sawing should be done as soon after placing the concrete as possible without causing undue spalling or other damage. It is best done while the concrete is under compression to preclude cracking of the pavement ahead of the saw before the entire joint is cut. If such a crack develops, sawing of the joint should be discontinued. If the crack remains within 3 in. of the center of the dowels, it may be grooved and sealed. If it goes outside these limits, it may require major repair. Special care is necessary to assure that a small triangular plug of uncut concrete is not left at the end of the joint, next to the form. The form should be carefully loosened so the sawblade can reach the pavement edge. Curing precautions must be observed.

Early sawing is especially important in multiple-lane paving, where a lane is being laid adjacent to one already in place, since cracks may occur opposite open joints in the lane already placed. It may be necessary to saw joints at night or during inclement weather. Sawing cannot be delayed for any reason whatsoever after the concrete is ready. Most saws require an ample supply of water to cool and lubricate the blade, especially the diamond saws. However, nylon-reinforced abrasive blades are now available which can cut in the dry. Dry cutting results in a neater job and reduces the raveling that sometimes accompanies early sawing.

Normally, joints should be sawed in the same succession as the concrete was placed. However, under certain circumstances it may be desirable to cut every other one, or some such sequence, sawing the intermediate joints later.

Construction Joints

Transverse construction joints are installed at the end of each day's run, or whenever paving is delayed long enough for the concrete to set. They should be placed if possible, so as to replace a regularly located contraction joint. Any transverse construction joint not intended to serve as a contraction joint should be reinforced by means of deformed tie bars and a keyway. Longitudinal construction joints are formed in the same way and normally function as hinge joints. A longitudinal construction joint exists between adjacent lanes of pavement that were placed at different times.

Edges of all formed grooves and construction joints should be rounded with an edger.

Expansion Joints

Formerly it was common practice to install expansion joints every few hundred feet, but this practice is being abandoned. These joints are now made where the pavement adjoins a structure, such as a bridge, for curbs, sidewalks, and incidental construction, and at intersections.

Expansion joints may be formed in a similar manner as premolded contraction joints, except that a strip of premolded joint filler is placed in the concrete. The filler is a strip of pressed granulated cork, porous fiber (celotex), or similar material, impregnated with bitumen, which will expand and contract as the pavement moves.

The joint material must be perpendicular to the concrete surface, and a metal shield with a cap should be used to hold it in proper alignment during concreting operations. The shield should be removed as soon as possible. Care is necessary during finishing to avoid displacing the filler and to keep it within $\frac{1}{4}$ in. of the surface.

When an expansion joint is to be located at a construction joint, the filler may be attached to the old concrete by means of a bituminous cement, then the new concrete placed against it.

Hinge or Warping Joints

These are longitudinal joints on highway pavement and may be formed by any of the methods used in forming transverse contraction joints, such as installing a strip of shaped sheet metal, sawing, or by installing a metal parting strip ahead of concrete placement. These metal strips are left in place in the concrete.

A longitudinal hinge joint may be sawed at any reasonable time before opening the pavement to traffic. It is best if they are sawed early, the better to control cracking and to make use of the abrasive type blades.

Filling Joints

Joints should be thoroughly cleaned and temporary joint filler, consisting of jute roving, bedded in the freshly sawed groove. An alternative method is to apply an adhesive tape to the pavement surface over the joint.

Final cleaning, after completion of construction operations, should be done by air jets, water, or any means that removes all foreign material from the groove. After the joint is completely dry, sealing compound may be placed in the joint.

If a hot-applied compound is used, it should not be heated above the safe temperature certified by the manufacturer. A jacketed heating kettle should be used for heating this material; otherwise the sealing compound may easily be damaged by excess heat.

A two-component cold-applied material is sometimes used. This compound consists of a dry powder and a liquid which are mixed immediately prior to application to the joint. For either hot-applied compound or the two-component type, pressure equipment should be used, equipped with special nozzles that fill the joint from the bottom up.

14-9. CRACKS AT CONTRACTION JOINTS

Random cracks sometimes occur at dowel assemblies before the joint is sawed. They may occur when the sawing has been delayed too long, or when sawing is commenced when the temperature of the surface concrete is appreciably lower than that of the main mass of concrete. Such a condition would exist in the early morning, after a cool night, before the sun has had time to warm the surface.

If the crack remains within about 3 in. either side of the dowel centerline (as shown by marks placed on the forms when the dowel assembly was placed), the crack should be grooved and filled with sealing compound.

In case the crack deviates appreciably more than 3 in. from the dowel centerline, heroic action is indicated. This includes removal of the dowel assembly and a section of pavement. This was accomplished on the Northern Illinois Tollway by making two deep saw cuts across the slab at right angles to the centerline, one of which was outside of but as near to the ends of the dowels as the damage permitted. The other was at least 10 ft from the first cut and on the other side of the dowel assembly. The section thus severed was broken out and removed, care being exercised not to damage the top edges of the saw-cut faces of the remaining paving. The dowels were replaced by drilling the end section face nearest the original location of the dowel assembly and grouting in new smooth dowels, taking care that the new dowels were parallel to the centerline and to the roadway surface.

The opposite face was drilled and had $\frac{5}{8}$-in. tie rods grouted in to form a construction joint. The base was repaired and recompacted. The slab was then placed in two lifts so the steel mesh could be introduced in the usual way. Eighteen inches of the original mesh were left protruding to lap new mesh.

The joints thus formed should be edged with a tool which will make a groove $\frac{1}{8}$ in. wide by $1\frac{1}{4}$ in. deep to receive joint sealing material as specified and shown on the drawings for all construction joints.

Should this type of break occur in an area of multilane paving where the joint must be continuous, the dowel assembly should be replaced in its original location by making the two saw cuts 5 ft on either side and forming two construction joints. A normal saw cut will be required over the dowels in this event.

Cracks 10 or more ft from a contraction joint where there is slight spalling or other evidence of movement should be grooved and sealed. Evidence of more vigorous action may indicate the need for introducing a load transfer device. Hairline cracks without spalling generally require no repair.

It should be noted that this repair method applies to cracks in new construction.

REFERENCES

14.1 *Concrete Pavement Inspector's Manual,* Portland Cement Association, Chicago, 1959.

14.2 Paving—How to Get the Best Results, *Construction Methods and Equipment,* 1956.

14.3 Cashell, Harry D., and Wilmer E. Teske: Continuous Reinforcement in Concrete Pavements, *Proceedings,* 34th Annual Meeting, Highway Research Board, 1955.

14.4 Prestressed Pavement Makes Debut on Air Base, *Construction Methods,* September, 1959.

14.5 *Sawed Joints in Concrete Pavement,* Portland Cement Association, Chicago, 1957.

PART FOUR

Tests and Control

CHAPTER 15 *Testing of Concrete*

15-1. SAMPLING

Nonrepresentative sampling of concrete can cause gross discrepancies in strength and other properties of specimens. In order to minimize sampling errors, the sample should be obtained from the middle portion of a batch representative of those being used. A sample being taken from a stream discharging from a mixer or similar location should cut across the entire cross section of the stream. The batch from a paver should be dumped, and the sample taken from at least five locations in the pile. Care should be taken to avoid obtaining parts of previous batches. A sample from a truck mixer should be taken at three or more intervals regularly spaced through the batch discharge, avoiding both the first and final portions of the batch. If only a slump test is desired to check on the consistency of the batch in the mixer, a small sample may be taken as soon as the first part of the batch has been discharged. The sample should be thoroughly remixed in a wheelbarrow, large pan, or other clean, damp, nonabsorptive surface.

Test Batch

On a large job where inspectors are stationed both in the batching or proportioning plant and at the mixer, as on a paving job, or at the site where truck mixers are discharging, it is sometimes convenient to use a "test batch." A test batch is simply a normal batch, hauled in a dry-batch truck or in a truck mixer, for which detailed data are obtained and tests made. The following paragraph describes the procedure in a dry-batch plant. If the plant is equipped with an automatic moisture indicator or compensator, no moisture sample is necessary.

After conditions become stabilized for the day, the batch plant inspector takes moisture and grading samples, marks the recorder chart, if any, notes scale readings and time of day, and informs the mixer inspector that a test batch is in a certain batch truck. To do this, he should give a memo to the driver of the truck for delivery to the mixer inspector. Because of lack of interest or forgetfulness on the part of the truck driver, it is suggested that a positive means be provided for identifying the truck. This may take the form of a flag or colored metal disk hung on the truck in some conspicuous place. (Always hang it in the same place, and be sure it is removed as soon as the batch has been delivered.) The mixer inspector notes the amount of water, air-entraining agent, and other admixture added to the batch, notes the time of day, and samples the concrete. After air, water, and concrete temperatures have been taken, the concrete is tested for slump, air content, and unit weight, and cylinders are made. Cylinders should be placed in the protective box immediately after casting and handled as provided in ASTM Designation: C 31.

At a central batching and mixing plant, the procedure is identical with that described above insofar as it is applicable. The amount and temperature of mixing water and the amounts of admixtures are noted. The concrete is sampled upon delivery to the site at the time it is dumped into the forms. Time of day at batching, mixing, and sampling should be noted.

Truck mixer operations are similar to those for a central plant, except that it is more difficult to ascertain the exact amount of water used in the batch.

15-2. CONSISTENCY

Slump

Tests for determination of consistency should be made on samples of concrete taken at the time it is deposited on the subbase or in the forms, following the method of ASTM Designation: C 143. If the concrete contains aggregate larger than 2 in., the pieces larger than 2 in. should be removed by hand picking.

Slump is determined by measuring the vertical subsidence of the sample upon removal of the cone. Measurement is made by placing the slump cone beside the slumped sample and laying the tamping rod across the cone, extending over the specimen, then measuring from the bottom of the rod to the slumped concrete at a point over the original center of the base of the specimen. (Some agencies measure the average subsidence.) After the slump measurement is completed, the side of the concrete frustum should be tapped gently with the tamping rod. The behavior of the concrete under this treatment is a valuable indication of its cohesiveness, workability, and placeability. A well-proportioned, workable mix will slump gradually to lower elevations and retain its original identity, while a poor mix will crumble, segregate, and fall apart.[4.3]

Slump specimens that break or slough off laterally give incorrect results and should be remade with a fresh sample.

Ball Penetration

Concrete consistency may be determined by use of the ball penetration (Kelly ball) method in accordance with ASTM Designation: C 360.[1.1] If this method is used, the ball apparatus should first be calibrated. To calibrate, the values of ball penetration and of slump for each class of concrete should be obtained from the same batches for various mix consistencies and plotted on graph paper. After 10 or more tests have been entered, a straight-line graph can be plotted to obtain a conversion, as shown in the typical curve (Fig. 15-1). Wet mixes as well as dry ones should be checked with the ball and results plotted to widen the range of comparison. Either the graph may be used or a conversion factor may be com-

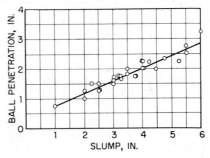

FIG. 15-1. Typical curve of slump-ball penetration relationship.

puted to be used within specified limits of slump. Additional checks should be made and the graph corrected as necessary.

Points to remember when making the penetration test are that the concrete must be unworked and unvibrated except for smoothing off a flat spot on which to make the test. In addition, the concrete must be at least 8 in. thick and must not be confined within a 9-in. radius of the center of the apparatus. The ball must be lowered gently, not dropped. Conversion factors may vary for different mixes.

15-3. AIR CONTENT

Limits and tolerances for entrained air for each class of concrete are given in the specifications. If air-entrained concrete is specified, the air content of fresh concrete should be determined by the pressure (air meter) method each time cylinders are cast and whenever there are significant changes in the weather during the day. During hot- or cold-weather concrete placing, frequent checks should be made, particularly

---

* Superscript figures refer to chapter and reference number. The references are found at the end of each chapter.

when concrete ingredients are heated. If at all possible, every batch of ready-mixed concrete should be checked.

In addition to the pressure test, a gravimetric test for air should be made on each test batch for comparison purposes. Very seldom will the two methods give identical results, but they should agree within 1 per cent. When they do not agree within this tolerance, the testing equipment and procedures should be checked.

The manufacturers of air meters usually provide detailed instructions for calibrating and using their apparatus, and these instructions should be followed. Lacking such instructions, the inspector should be governed by ASTM Designation: C 231. One of the main sources of error, if the meter has been calibrated correctly, is in leveling the concrete in the bowl. Leveling should be carefully done, using a straightedge with a sawing motion to remove the excess concrete, being especially careful to remove mortar that rises behind the straightedge. The edges of the bowl, where the lid gasket fits, should be wiped clean with a rag and the lid carefully seated in place. All valves should be manipulated in accordance with the manufacturer's instructions.

Another test for entrained air is the volumetric test, in which a sample of concrete is placed in a vessel, the lid applied, and the vessel filled with water. After manipulation, the air in the concrete is displaced with water and the per cent air read on a graduated scale. The volumetric method should always be used for lightweight concrete, as the pressure method is subject to considerable error when lightweight concrete is being tested.

The volumetric method, sometimes called the "Roll-a-meter" method, is covered in ASTM Designation: C 173. Concrete used in the air meter (in which water is added to fill the container) should not be used for slump tests or for making cylinders.

15-4. UNIT WEIGHT AND YIELD

Unit Weight

Complete quality control of concrete is not possible without regular determinations of the fresh unit weight of the concrete, as described in ASTM Designation: C 138. The unit weight is required for computing the volume of concrete used and for gravimetric air content, in addition to determination of the yield and actual cement factor.

The ASTM method specifies that the measuring vessel shall have a capacity of either $\frac{1}{2}$ or 1 cu ft, depending upon the maximum size of aggregate in the concrete being tested. It is a good idea, however, to use the bottom part of the air meter as a routine check of unit weight. This check is accomplished by filling the air-meter bowl with concrete in the normal manner, striking off, and weighing. Having predetermined the exact volume of the air-meter bowl, it is a simple calculation to find the concrete unit weight. After weighing the bowl and concrete, the top of the meter is put in place and the concrete air content found in the usual way.

Yield

In ASTM Designation: C 138, *yield* is defined as the cubic feet of concrete produced per sack of cement. However, it is sometimes convenient to express yield as the number of cubic feet in a theoretical cubic yard batch, computed from the relationship:

$$\frac{\text{Total batch wt for nominal 1 cu yd batch}}{\text{Fresh unit wt of concrete}} = \text{actual cu ft per batch}$$

This relationship, called the *return*, is especially useful for field control during construction. For good control, return should not vary more than ± 0.2 cu ft from the theoretical 27 cu ft per batch. Principal causes of variations are changes in percentage of air, water content, cement content, or amount of consolidation of sample in container; poor sample selection; or changes in specific gravity of materials.

The relationships of yield, return, and cement content may be computed from the equations that follow:

Let U = fresh unit weight, pcf
$\quad C$ = cement per batch, lb
$\quad B$ = total batch weight for nominal 1 cu yd batch, lb
$\quad N$ = sacks of cement for nominal 1 cu yd batch
$\quad S$ = actual sacks cement per cu yd
$\quad R$ = return; actual cu ft per nominal 1 cu yd batch
$\quad Y$ = yield (ASTM), cu ft concrete per sack of cement

Then

$$S = \frac{27}{94} \times \frac{UC}{B} = \frac{27\,UN}{B}$$

$$R = \frac{B}{U}$$

$$S = \frac{27N}{R}$$

$$Y = \frac{R}{N} = \frac{B}{UN}$$

$$R = NY$$

Table 15-1 includes values for yield, cement content, and return for mixes most commonly employed. Its use will simplify the computation.

EXAMPLE: Assume that 517 lb (5½ sacks) of cement are batched for a batch of theoretically 1 cu yd or 27 cu ft. Then N, the nominal cement content, is 5½ sacks per cu yd. Field data were:

$$\text{Total batch wt } B \ldots\ldots\ldots\ldots\ldots\ldots \text{ 4,085 lb}$$
$$\text{Fresh unit wt of concrete } U \ldots\ldots\ldots \text{ 152 pcf}$$
$$\text{Then the return } R \ldots\ldots\ldots\ldots\ldots \frac{4,085}{152} = 26.8 \text{ cu ft}$$

From Table 15-1, under a nominal cement content of 5½ sacks per cu yd at a return of 26.8, the actual cement content is found to be 5.54 sacks per cu yd and the yield is 4.87 cu ft per sack.

TABLE 15-1*a*. ACTUAL CEMENT CONTENTS AND YIELDS FOR NOMINAL CEMENT CONTENTS BETWEEN 4 AND 5¾ SACKS PER CUBIC YARD

Return		Nominal cement content, sacks per cu yd (N)							
		4	4.25	4.50	4.75	5	5.25	5.50	5.75
26.0	S	4.15	4.41	4.67	4.93	5.19	5.45	5.71	5.97
	Y	6.50	6.12	5.78	5.47	5.20	4.95	4.73	4.52
26.2	S	4.12	4.38	4.64	4.90	5.15	5.41	5.67	5.92
	Y	6.55	6.16	5.82	5.52	5.24	4.99	4.76	4.56
26.4	S	4.09	4.35	4.60	4.86	5.11	5.37	5.62	5.88
	Y	6.60	6.21	5.87	5.56	5.28	5.03	4.80	4.59
26.6	S	4.06	4.32	4.57	4.82	5.08	5.33	5.58	5.84
	Y	6.65	5.26	5.91	5.60	5.32	5.07	4.84	4.63
26.8	S	4.03	4.28	4.53	4.79	5.04	5.29	5.54	5.79
	Y	6.70	6.30	5.96	5.64	5.36	5.10	4.87	4.66
27.0	S	4.00	4.25	4.50	4.75	5.00	5.25	5.50	5.75
	Y	6.75	6.35	6.00	5.68	5.40	5.14	4.91	4.70
27.2	S	3.97	4.22	4.47	4.71	4.96	5.21	5.46	5.71
	Y	6.80	6.40	6.04	5.73	5.44	5.18	4.95	4.73
27.4	S	3.94	4.19	4.43	4.68	4.93	5.17	5.42	5.67
	Y	6.85	6.44	6.09	5.77	5.48	5.22	4.98	4.76
27.6	S	3.91	4.16	4.40	4.65	4.89	5.14	5.38	5.63
	Y	6.90	6.49	6.13	5.81	5.52	5.26	5.02	4.80
27.8	S	3.88	4.13	4.37	4.61	4.86	5.10	5.34	5.58
	Y	6.95	6.54	6.18	5.85	5.56	5.30	5.05	4.83
28.0	S	3.86	4.10	4.34	4.58	4.82	5.06	5.30	5.54
	Y	7.00	6.59	6.22	5.89	5.60	5.33	5.09	4.87

$$\text{Return} = \frac{\text{total batch weight for nominal 1 cu yd batch}}{\text{fresh unit weight}}$$

$$\text{Yield} = \frac{\text{return}}{\text{nominal sacks per cu yd}}$$

TABLE 15-1*b*. ACTUAL CEMENT CONTENTS AND YIELDS FOR NOMINAL CEMENT CONTENTS BETWEEN 6 AND 8 SACKS PER CUBIC YARD

Return		Nominal cement content, sacks per cu yd (N)								
		6	6.25	6.50	6.75	7	7.25	7.50	7.75	8
26.0	S	6.23	6.49	6.75	7.01	7.27	7.53	7.79	8.05	8.31
	Y	4.33	4.16	4.00	3.85	3.71	3.59	3.47	3.35	3.25
26.2	S	6.18	6.44	6.70	6.96	7.21	7.47	7.73	7.99	8.24
	Y	4.37	4.19	4.03	3.88	3.75	3.61	3.49	3.38	3.28
26.4	S	6.14	6.39	6.65	6.90	7.16	7.41	7.67	7.92	8.18
	Y	4.40	4.22	4.06	3.91	3.77	3.64	3.52	3.41	3.30
26.6	S	6.09	6.35	6.60	6.85	7.11	7.36	7.62	7.87	8.12
	Y	4.43	4.26	4.09	3.94	3.80	3.67	3.55	3.43	3.32
26.8	S	6.04	6.29	6.55	6.80	7.05	7.29	7.55	7.80	8.06
	Y	4.47	4.29	4.12	3.97	3.83	3.70	3.58	3.46	3.35
27.0	S	6.00	6.25	6.50	6.75	7.00	7.25	7.50	7.75	8.00
	Y	4.50	4.32	4.15	4.00	3.86	3.72	3.60	3.48	3.38
27.2	S	5.96	6.20	6.45	6.70	6.94	7.20	7.44	7.69	7.94
	Y	4.53	4.35	4.19	4.03	3.89	3.75	3.63	3.51	3.40
27.4	S	5.91	6.16	6.41	6.65	6.90	7.14	7.39	7.64	7.88
	Y	4.57	4.38	4.23	4.06	3.92	3.78	3.66	3.54	3.42
27.6	S	5.87	6.11	6.36	6.60	6.85	7.09	7.34	7.58	7.83
	Y	4.60	4.42	4.26	4.09	3.95	3.81	3.68	3.56	3.45
27.8	S	5.83	6.07	6.31	6.56	6.80	7.04	7.28	7.53	7.77
	Y	4.63	4.45	4.29	4.12	3.97	3.83	3.71	3.59	3.48
28.0	S	5.79	6.03	6.27	6.51	6.75	6.99	7.23	7.47	7.71
	Y	4.67	4.48	4.32	4.14	4.00	3.86	3.74	3.61	3.50

Cement content may also be computed by means of a nomograph (Fig. 15-2), using measured unit weight of fresh concrete, weight of cement per batch and total weight of all ingredients in the batch. Note that this may be employed for any size of batch. This nomograph is based on the equation:

$$S = \frac{27UN}{B}$$

or (as shown in Fig. 15-2)

$$S = 0.2872 \frac{UC}{B}$$

15-5. ANALYSIS OF FRESH CONCRETE

Some organizations, notably the Bureau of Reclamation, require an analysis of the fresh concrete to determine the efficiency of the mixer. Briefly the test (USBR Designation 26[4.3]) consists in taking two samples of fresh concrete, one from the first of the batch, or front of the mixer, and one from the last of the batch, or rear of the mixer. Unit weight, air content, and the weight retained by washing on a No. 4 sieve are determined for each sample and the variations from averages computed. The unit weight of air-free mortar in the two samples should not vary more than 0.8 per cent from the average of the two mortar weights, and the

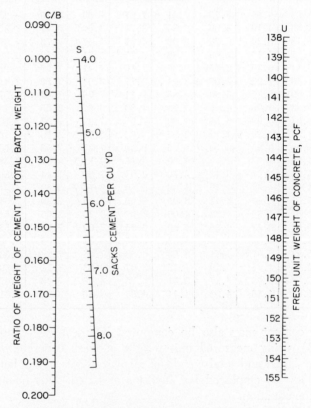

F<small>IG</small>. 15-2. Cement content of fresh concrete: S = sacks of cement per cu yd; U = measured unit wt of concrete, pcf; C = lb cement per batch; B = total batch wt, lb; $S = 0.2872UC/B$.

weight of coarse aggregate (retained on No. 4 sieve) should not vary more than 5 per cent from the average.

A similar test is sometimes referred to as the Dunagan test,[15.1] in which the sample is further treated by washing over a 100-mesh sieve. By the application of a suitable factor, the cement content of the sample is obtained. A further refinement consists of more complicated treatment of the sample by using a flocculant and centrifuging a small sample in a heavy media.[15.2] However, this latter method appears to be too complex for field use, and the Reclamation Bureau method is recommended for mixer-efficiency tests, and the Dunagan method for approximate cement-content determinations.

15-6. STRENGTH

Number of Specimens

The number of test specimens to be made is normally designated in the specifications. Usual practice is to make one set of specimens from each 100 cu yd or fraction thereof, of each class of concrete daily. At least one set of specimens should be made from concrete for each structural element of a building, for example, each major foundation unit or each floor slab. Every mix being used should be sampled each day it is used. For pavements, every 1,000 sq yd should be represented by at least one set of specimens.

Many specifications, especially for buildings, require that each set of cylinders consist of cylinders for standard curing and for field curing (see Sec. 3-10).

The number of specimens in each set depends upon the use to be made of the results, the type of structure, volume of concrete, and the purpose of the tests. If an analysis of within-batch variations is to be made, then at least two 28-day cylinders should be made at each time, otherwise single pairs of specimens (one 7-day and one 28-day) may be made at different times during the placement. At no time should only one specimen be relied upon.

Strength data should be analyzed statistically as described in the ACI Recommended Practice for Evaluation of Compression Test Results of Field Concrete.[15.3] Application of this method is described later in this chapter.

Making Test Specimens

Improperly made specimens will give false information that may have serious consequences. For this reason, if for no other, the technician should diligently follow the standard methods described in ASTM Designation: C 31. The following suggestions apply to making 6 × 12-in. compressive-strength cylinders. Obvious changes can be made when making beams for flexural tests.

In making test specimens, the concrete should be taken from batches spaced throughout the period of concreting operations, not from just one or two batches. The inspector should make the specimens. He may be assisted by a laborer in obtaining the concrete sample and transporting it to the point of casting, but it is the inspector's responsibility to make the specimens and tests.

All testing equipment should be clean, without hardened or dry concrete adhering to it, and free of oil or other dirt. A long-handled scrub brush should be a part of every inspector's set of equipment. As soon as a group of tests has been completed, the equipment should be scrubbed clean, using the brush and plenty of water. A stiff-bristled toilet bowl brush has been found to be especially useful for cleaning slump cones.

Molds for cylinders may be steel, cast iron, paraffin-coated cardboard, or tin cans. Plastic molds have recently been introduced and give every indication of proving quite serviceable.

Molds should be clean and watertight. Metal or plastic molds should be oiled very lightly. Paraffin-coated cardboard or paper molds should have metal bottoms. (Specimens cast in cardboard molds will have strength slightly below those made in steel or cast-iron molds. Tin-can molds will produce specimens of 5 to 10 per cent lower strength.)

Molds should be placed on a smooth, level, firm surface before filling. All molds should be filled one-third full and rodded exactly 25 times with a bullet-pointed rod $\frac{5}{8}$ in. in diameter. The second and third layers are similarly placed. In rodding the first layer, the rod should not come in contact with the bottom of the mold. In rodding subsequent layers, the rod should just penetrate the layer below.

The top layer should have a slight excess of concrete which is struck off with a trowel after rodding has been completed. Excess finishing or working of the top should be avoided. Surface of the concrete should be perpendicular to the sides of the mold.

Some agencies permit cylinders to be consolidated by vibration. In this case the concrete is consolidated in two layers. The U.S. Bureau of Reclamation requires a vibrating element approximately 1 in. in diameter inserted three times in each layer for 3 or 4 sec per insertion. The duration of vibration is longer for stiff, unworkable mixes than it is for fluid or wet ones. The vibrator should not touch the mold. When vibrating the top layer, the vibrator should penetrate the lower layer about 1 in. Mortar should not run over the top of the mold when the vibrator is inserted in the top layer. After vibration has been completed, concrete should be added and worked into the specimen with a trowel, then the top is struck off.

When casting cylinders in tin-can molds, the top of the concrete should be leveled off about $\frac{1}{2}$ in. below the top of the can using a small trowel with a rounded point.

The specimens should be properly identified. Scratching the information on the side of the mold or in the fresh concrete with a nail is not the way to do it. A good way to do this is to use a paper tag which has a wire attached. (A cloth tag is apt to disintegrate in the presence of moisture.) With indelible pencil or ballpoint pen, write specimen number, job identification, and date made, then attach the tag by embedding the wire in the fresh concrete at the edge of the specimen. Additional data will be included on the inspector's report.

Tops of cylinders should be covered with glass plates, wet burlap, or similar material to prevent drying out. A plastic refrigerator-bowl cover with an elastic band makes a good cover. Friction tops for tin-can molds should be carefully and firmly pressed into place.

Care of Specimens

Specimens should immediately be placed where they are out of the way of construction activities and where they can be kept between 60 and 80°F for 24 hr. It is good practice to keep them in a field office where they can be kept warm in winter and cool in summer. Under no circumstances should specimens be moved before 12 hr since they can easily be damaged.

ASTM Designation: C 31 states that cylinders shall be kept in a storage box during the first 24 hr. If this box is out of doors during cold weather, it should be insulated, and a source of heat, such as an electric light bulb or lighted lantern, should be provided in the box. A thermostatically controlled heater of the type used in chicken incubators has been found to be quite useful. Overheating and drying of the specimens should be avoided. The box should be kept in a shady location during warm weather. Evaporation of water from sand, burlap, or other porous surfaces helps to keep the temperature down.

After one day the specimens are sent to the laboratory, where the molds are stripped and the specimens placed in 73°F moist curing. At this time, the identifying data should be marked on the specimen with graphite lumber crayon or with a felt-tip pen using black waterproof ink. If it is necessary to transport them by car or truck they should be placed in boxes padded with sawdust, Celotex, or other material that will protect them from jostling and bumping. They should not be permitted to dry out. Specimens should never be shipped by public carrier unless they are well padded in stout boxes.

Many times, specimens are stored at the job site for several days before they are shipped to the laboratory. This practice is harmless as long as the specimens are stored under conditions of moisture and temperature that meet the requirements of ASTM: C 31. Wet sand, burlap, or water tanks are used.

In the laboratory, specimens are stored under moist conditions at 73.4 ± 3°F until time to cap them for breaking. Storage may be in a 100 per cent relative humidity room or in tanks containing a saturated lime-water solution.

Field-cured specimens should be removed from the molds after 24 hr and stored as nearly as practicable under the same conditions as the portion of the structure they represent. Not more than 1 week before they are to be tested they may be stored (dry) in the laboratory.

Testing Specimens

Capping of specimens is the most serious potential source of error. Inasmuch as the ends of cylinders are never smooth and at right angles to the axis, it is necessary that they be prepared before placing them in the testing machine. (An exception is the bottom of a cylinder cast in a heavy steel or iron mold, the mold being fitted with a heavy machined plate firmly and tightly attached to the mold.)

Some laboratories, especially research laboratories, grind or lap the ends, using special jigs to assure accuracy. The most common method is to cap the cylinder with a fluid or mastic material which, upon hardening in contact with a machined metal plate, forms a smooth and strong bearing surface. Neat portland cement, quick-setting (Lumnite) cement, and plaster of paris have been used for this purpose. Present practice is to use a thermosetting compound that develops its strength in a matter of a half-hour or so. Mixtures of powdered sulfur with an inert filler such as fly ash or fire clay are satisfactory, as are a number of proprietary compounds. Special high-strength compound is available for use in testing specimens with strength exceeding 6,000 psi. A mixture of three parts of sulfur to one of fire clay, by weight, heated to 350 to 400°F is satisfactory. It should be kept in mind that the purpose of capping is not to cover up poor workmanship in making cylinders. The following precautions should be observed:

1. Cylinder ends that are extremely rough or crooked should be smoothed somewhat with a coarse horseshoe rasp or similar tool.

2. Cylinders should be fairly dry and at room temperature.

3. Capping material must be at the proper temperature—neither too cold nor too hot. The wrong temperature will cause spongy caps.

4. A capping jig is necessary to assure smooth and square caps.

5. The caps should be as thin as possible, perpendicular to the cylinder axis, smooth, and parallel with each other.

6. The cap should be permitted to cure for at least 30 min before the specimen is tested.

7. It is not necessary to oil the cylinders before capping, although there is no objection to a very thin oiling with a light oil.

8. There is no objection to salvaging a portion of the used caps, provided that most of the compound in the heating pot is new material.

9. After the cap is affixed, it should be tapped lightly with the handle of a screwdriver or putty knife to locate bubbles. If bubbles are found, the cap should be removed and a new one applied.

Testing of specimens is covered in ASTM Designation: C 39. The specimen should be centered on the platen of the testing machine and the bearing block carefully brought into contact with the specimen. The load is applied at a rate of about 2,000 psi per min. It is permissible to apply the load at a slightly faster rate up to about half of the breaking load. The ASTM method requires that the cylinder be tested in a damp condition.

Dials on testing machines are calibrated in pounds total load. To find the strength of a 6-in.-diameter cylinder, divide the total load by the area of a 6-in. circle, or 28.27 sq in. Table 15-2 shows pounds per square inch for various total loads. For example, if the load on a specimen is 146,500 lb, the strength of the specimen is 5,182 psi. If desired, this may be rounded off to the nearest 5 psi, in this case 5,180 psi.

15-7. ANALYSIS OF STRENGTH-TEST RESULTS

Because of the importance attached to the strength of concrete, the method of applying strength results to the control of concrete assumes great significance. It is quite obvious that a single test result, in itself, is of limited value. When a group of tests is analyzed, however, the value of the group assumes great significance.

Recognizing this fact among many others, Committee 214 of the American Concrete Institute prepared Recommended Practice for Evaluation of Compression Tests Results of Field Concrete.[15.3] The following discussion is based on this recommended practice. The reader is referred to the original report for detailed instructions.

Quality Control

In order to understand the application of statistical methods of analysis to concrete strength, an understanding of the principles of quality control, as applied to construction, is first necessary. Parts of the following discussion are extracted from a paper by the author.[15.4]

Quality control of materials is a relatively old concept as applied to products manufactured at a permanently located factory or mill. In the construction industry, typical examples are control of the manufacture of steel and cement. For these and other such manufactured products, quality control and proper use of materials are essential to ensure that the finished product will conform to established standards.

TABLE 15-2. UNIT LOADS IN PSI FOR 6 × 12-in. CONCRETE CYLINDERS

Load, lb	0	500	1,000	1,500	2,000	2,500	3,000	3,500	4,000	4,500	5,000	5,500	6,000	6,500	7,000	7,500	8,000	8,500	9,000	9,500
0	0	18	35	53	71	88	106	124	142	159	177	194	212	230	248	265	283	301	318	336
10,000	354	372	389	407	425	442	460	478	496	513	531	548	566	584	602	619	637	655	672	690
20,000	707	725	742	760	778	795	813	831	849	866	884	901	919	937	955	972	990	1,008	1,025	1,043
30,000	1,061	1,079	1,096	1,114	1,132	1,149	1,167	1,185	1,203	1,220	1,238	1,255	1,273	1,291	1,309	1,326	1,344	1,362	1,379	1,397
40,000	1,415	1,433	1,450	1,468	1,486	1,503	1,521	1,539	1,557	1,574	1,592	1,609	1,627	1,645	1,663	1,680	1,698	1,716	1,733	1,751
50,000	1,768	1,786	1,803	1,821	1,839	1,856	1,874	1,892	1,910	1,927	1,945	1,962	1,980	1,998	2,016	2,033	2,051	2,069	2,086	2,104
60,000	2,122	2,140	2,157	2,175	2,193	2,210	2,228	2,246	2,264	2,281	2,299	2,316	2,334	2,352	2,370	2,387	2,405	2,423	2,440	2,458
70,000	2,476	2,494	2,511	2,529	2,547	2,564	2,582	2,600	2,618	2,635	2,653	2,670	2,688	2,706	2,724	2,741	2,759	2,777	2,794	2,812
80,000	2,830	2,848	2,865	2,883	2,901	2,918	2,936	2,954	2,972	2,989	3,007	3,024	3,042	3,060	3,078	3,095	3,113	3,131	3,148	3,166
90,000	3,183	3,201	3,218	3,236	3,254	3,271	3,289	3,307	3,325	3,342	3,360	3,377	3,395	3,413	3,431	3,448	3,466	3,484	3,501	3,519
100,000	3,537	3,555	3,572	3,590	3,608	3,625	3,643	3,661	3,679	3,696	3,714	3,731	3,749	3,767	3,785	3,802	3,820	3,838	3,855	3,873
110,000	3,891	3,909	3,926	3,944	3,962	3,979	3,997	4,015	4,033	4,050	4,068	4,085	4,103	4,121	4,139	4,156	4,174	4,192	4,209	4,227
120,000	4,244	4,262	4,279	4,297	4,315	4,332	4,350	4,368	4,386	4,403	4,421	4,438	4,456	4,474	4,492	4,509	4,527	4,545	4,562	4,580
130,000	4,598	4,616	4,633	4,651	4,669	4,686	4,704	4,722	4,740	4,757	4,775	4,792	4,810	4,828	4,846	4,863	4,881	4,899	4,916	4,934
140,000	4,952	4,970	4,987	5,005	5,023	5,040	5,058	5,076	5,094	5,111	5,129	5,146	5,164	5,182	5,200	5,217	5,235	5,253	5,270	5,288
150,000	5,306	5,324	5,341	5,359	5,377	5,394	5,412	5,430	5,448	5,465	5,483	5,500	5,518	5,536	5,554	5,571	5,589	5,607	5,624	5,642
160,000	5,659	5,677	5,694	5,712	5,730	5,747	5,765	5,783	5,801	5,818	5,836	5,853	5,871	5,889	5,907	5,924	5,942	5,960	5,977	5,995
170,000	6,013	6,031	6,048	6,066	6,084	6,101	6,119	6,137	6,155	6,172	6,190	6,207	6,225	6,243	6,261	6,278	6,296	6,314	6,331	6,349
180,000	6,367	6,385	6,402	6,420	6,438	6,455	6,473	6,491	6,509	6,526	6,544	6,561	6,579	6,597	6,615	6,632	6,650	6,668	6,685	6,703
190,000	6,720	6,738	6,755	6,773	6,791	6,808	6,826	6,844	6,862	6,879	6,897	6,914	6,932	6,950	6,968	6,985	7,003	7,021	7,038	7,056
200,000	7,074	7,092	7,109	7,127	7,145	7,162	7,180	7,198	7,216	7,233	7,251	7,268	7,286	7,304	7,322	7,339	7,357	7,375	7,392	7,410
210,000	7,428	7,446	7,463	7,481	7,499	7,516	7,534	7,552	7,570	7,587	7,605	7,622	7,640	7,658	7,676	7,693	7,711	7,729	7,746	7,764
220,000	7,781	7,799	7,816	7,834	7,852	7,869	7,887	7,905	7,923	7,940	7,958	7,975	7,993	8,011	8,029	8,046	8,064	8,082	8,099	8,117
230,000	8,135	8,153	8,170	8,188	8,206	8,223	8,241	8,259	8,277	8,294	8,312	8,329	8,347	8,365	8,383	8,400	8,418	8,436	8,453	8,471
240,000	8,488	8,506	8,523	8,541	8,559	8,576	8,594	8,612	8,630	8,647	8,665	8,682	8,700	8,718	8,736	8,753	8,771	8,789	8,806	8,824
250,000	8,842	8,860	8,877	8,895	8,913	8,930	8,948	8,966	8,984	9,001	9,019	9,036	9,054	9,072	9,090	9,107	9,125	9,143	9,160	9,178
260,000	9,196	9,214	9,231	9,249	9,267	9,284	9,302	9,320	9,338	9,355	9,373	9,390	9,408	9,426	9,444	9,461	9,479	9,497	9,514	9,532
270,000	9,550	9,568	9,585	9,603	9,621	9,638	9,656	9,674	9,692	9,709	9,727	9,744	9,762	9,780	9,798	9,815	9,833	9,851	9,868	9,886
280,000	9,903	9,921	9,938	9,956	9,974	9,991	10,009	10,027	10,045	10,062	10,080	10,097	10,115	10,133	10,151	10,168	10,186	10,204	10,221	10,239
290,000	10,257	10,275	10,292	10,310	10,328	10,345	10,363	10,381	10,399	10,416	10,434	10,451	10,469	10,487	10,505	10,522	10,540	10,558	10,575	10,593
300,000	10,611	10,629	10,646	10,664	10,682	10,699	10,717	10,735	10,753	10,770	10,788	10,805	10,823	10,841	10,859	10,876	10,894	10,912	10,929	10,947

$$\frac{\text{Total load, lb}}{28.2744 \text{ sq in.}} = \text{unit load, psi}$$

Total load on specimen equals left-hand column plus amount shown at the top of any other column. Example: If total load is 146,500 lb, find 140,000 in left-hand column and read across to column 6,500. Answer: 5,182 psi

In the construction industry, quality control is thought of as the means by which materials are evaluated and controlled by scientific methods rather than by chance. Scientific methods of investigating, testing, and analyzing provide criteria by which materials are evaluated and used in construction. Specifications for materials, methods of test, and standards of acceptance are established from these criteria. Construction quality control consists of many individual elements, as shown in Table 15-3. Previous chapters have discussed ways and means of achieving quality in construction by means of investigation, inspection, and testing. Only the statistical analysis of data, as applied to concrete strength tests, is discussed in this chapter.

In general, strength is a good index of concrete quality, as most desirable properties are dependent on or related to strength. The magnitude of variations in strength of concrete test specimens depends upon

TABLE 15-3. QUALITY CONTROL OF CONSTRUCTION MATERIALS

A. Preliminary Investigations
    1. Preparation of specifications
    2. Adaptation of standard methods of testing
    3. Establishment of standards for acceptance and control
    4. Development of special test procedures
    5. Investigation, evaluation, and establishment of sources of supply
    6. Arrangement for both offsite and onsite inspection
    7. Preparation of manuals
B. Construction Inspection and Control
    1. Study of service records of materials or combinations of materials
    2. Inspection and testing of materials
    3. Evaluation of test results and determination of suitability of materials
    4. Decision relative to disposition of borderline materials
    5. Control of materials made at the site, such as concrete and bituminous mixtures
    6. Training of testing and control personnel
    7. Supervision of testing and control personnel
    8. Reports
    9. Statistical analysis of data
C. Special Problems
    1. Troubleshooting for architects and engineers, producers, or manufacturers
    2. Consultation on special problems concerning construction materials
    3. Research and development of new methods and equipment

how well the materials, concrete manufacture, and tests are controlled. To obtain maximum information, a sufficient number of tests should be made to be representative of the concrete produced, and appropriate statistical methods should be used to interpret the results. Statistical methods provide the best basis for analyzing these results for determining potential quality and strength of concrete in a structure and expressing results in the most useful form.

Concrete strength test results fall into the familiar pattern of the frequency distribution curve, as shown in Fig. 15-3.

Specifications

Most present-day specifications set forth a minimum strength which all specimens are required to exceed. This is an unrealistic requirement because the likelihood is that no absolute strength requirement will be met 100 per cent of the time.

If all the cylinders reported from a job reached or exceeded the specified minimum, it would indicate that either the average strength was

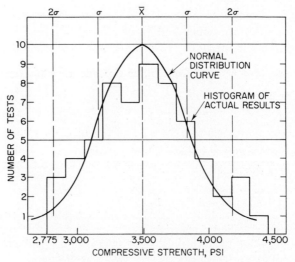

Fig. 15-3. Frequency distribution curve.

unnecessarily high or that the low ones were thrown out as being "non-representative." In either case, an unsatisfactory condition exists which calls for corrective action. One of the first steps is a realistic approach to specifying strength. Knowing that concrete is a variable material, the only realistic approach is to recognize that some cylinders are going to show unusually high strengths and some will show unusually low strengths.

In designing specifications then, it is more realistic to take a calculated risk, basing the probabilities on statistical methods and permitting a certain percentage of strength tests lower than specified design strength. Variations exist, and a certain percentage of low strengths exist, depending on the average strength level and the quality of control. Recognizing this basic fact does not jeopardize construction quality. On the contrary, it gives the engineer a tool which permits him to hold to a standard that can be attained.

Control Charts

Analysis of strength tests is accomplished by means of simplified control charts. While these do not contain all the features of formal control charts, they do accomplish their intended purpose. Figure 15-4 is a portion of a control chart for 3,000-psi structural concrete showing individual compressive strength of specimens for 7 days and 28 days. These curves show how many cylinders are below specified strength, and therefore whether or not specification requirements are being met. From the 7-day strengths, it is possible, after experience with a given set of materials, to determine whether 28-day strengths are likely to meet specifications.

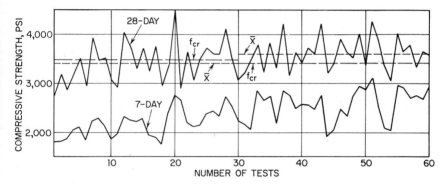

Fig. 15-4. Control chart for concrete strength. For the first 30 tests, $\bar{x}$ = 3,408 psi, f_{cr} = 3,470 psi, σ = 352 psi, and V = 10.3 per cent. For the second 30 tests, $\bar{x}$ = 3,600 psi, f_{cr} = 3,410 psi, σ = 324 psi, and V = 9.0 per cent.

Daily plotting of strength values enables the engineer to analyze trends and develop a course of action, if necessary. Such action might be a change in cement content of the concrete, or a study of job conditions to locate irregularities of operations or materials. This action is sometimes made on the basis of 7-day tests, if the need for it is clearly demonstrated at that time.

After results of 30 sets have been plotted, the average standard deviation and coefficient of variation are computed. Next the required average strength is computed for this same 30 sets. Based on this analysis, further adjustments to field operations are usually necessary. Thirty specimens are the minimum for a good statistical group.

Let $\bar{X}$ = average 28-day strength of all specimens in group

$$= \frac{X_1 + X_2 + X_3 + \cdots X_n}{n}$$

where X_1, X_2, . . . , X_n are strengths of individual tests and n is the total number of tests

$$\sigma = \text{standard deviation}$$

$$= \sqrt{\frac{(X_1 - \bar{X})^2 + (X_2 - \bar{X})^2 + \cdots (X_n - \bar{X})^2}{n}}$$

$$V = \text{coefficient of variation}$$

$$= \frac{\sigma}{\bar{X}}$$

$$f_{cr} = \text{required average strength}$$
$$f_c' = \text{specified design strength}$$
$$t = \text{a constant from Table 15-4}$$

$$f_{cr} = \frac{f_c'}{1 - tV}$$

The value of t depends upon the number of samples (or tests) used in the analysis and the number of tests that are allowed to fall below f_c'. For structural concrete, 90 per cent of the tests are usually required to equal or exceed f_c' (1 in 10 is allowed to fall below the lower limit). Thus f_c' is the lower limit, and, for all practical purposes, the upper limit is not important.

The coefficient of variation V, usually expressed as a percentage, indicates the dispersion of strength results, thus providing a numerical measure of variability of control, a smaller coefficient indicating better uniformity. In the field control of concrete, a coefficient of 10 per cent indicates good control, 15 per cent is fair, and anything over 15 per cent is poor.

In setting up data for a computation of this type, arrange them in columns, as shown in Table 15-5.

An analysis of the data for the first 30 tests in Fig. 15-4 shows that the number of failures (6) is excessive, as only 10 per cent of 30, or 3, are permitted. This is confirmed because the average strength, 3,408 psi, is smaller than the average required (3,470 psi) for the variation coefficient, 10.3 per cent, attained.

In this case, the first few 7-day tests indicated a borderline condition at best, hence an increase was made in the cement content which was reflected in a satisfactory condition for the second 30 tests. The low variation coefficients shown by these test results indicate a good job of field control, somewhat better than average.

By improving the job control, thereby decreasing the coefficient of variation, the number of low strengths can be decreased at the same average strength, thus demonstrating the desirability of maintaining the entire operation under efficient control.

TABLE 15-4. VALUES OF t

No. of tests	Percentage of tests falling within the limits $\bar{X} \pm t\sigma$		
	60	80	90
	Chances of falling below lower limit		
	2 in 10	1 in 10	1 in 20
2	1.376	3.078	6.314
3	1.061	1.886	2.920
4	0.978	1.638	2.353
5	0.941	1.533	2.132
10	0.883	1.383	1.833
20	0.861	1.320	1.728
30	0.854	1.310	1.697
Over 30.....	0.842	1.282	1.645

TABLE 15-5. SAMPLE CALCULATIONS

Test no.	X 28-day strength	$X - \bar{X}$	$(X - \bar{X})^2$
1	2,780	628	394,384
2	3,180	228	51,984
3	2,830	578	334,884
...	....	...	....
30	3,510	102	10,404
Σ30	102,250	...	3,748,656

$$\bar{X} = \frac{102,250}{30} = 3,408 \text{ psi}$$

$$\sigma = \sqrt{\frac{3,748,656}{30}} = 352 \text{ psi}$$

$$V = \frac{352}{3,408} = 0.103, \text{ or } 10.3\%$$

$f_c' = 3,000$ psi, from design data

$t = 1.31$ from Table 15-4, for 1 test in 10 below f_c'

$$f_{cr} = \frac{3,000}{1 - (1.31 \times 0.103)} = \frac{3,000}{0.865} = 3,470 \text{ psi}$$

Frequency Distribution Curve

Although not an essential part of control, the frequency distribution curve (Fig. 15-3) is valuable as a matter of record, and, when data are plotted as a histogram with the normal curve superimposed, an indication is given of the skewness of the data, that is, whether the plotted results follow the normal distribution or whether they are influenced by some assignable cause other than normal probability.

To make the histogram, the range in strength of all results under consideration is divided into a number of groups, or cells. The minimum number of cells should be about 11 or 12 in order to obtain a good grouping. Cell boundaries should be selected so no strength value falls on a cell boundary. For example, if strength is shown to the nearest 5 psi, then cell boundaries should fall between 0 and 5, or 5 and 10, that is, at 2,873 psi, 3,517 psi, or similar figures. The number of strengths within each cell is plotted at the midpoint of the cell and a horizontal line drawn between the cell boundaries at this number. The horizontal lines are then connected by vertical lines on the cell boundaries.

In making the histogram in Fig. 15-3, the cell boundaries were selected to fall on values ending in 5, inasmuch as the strengths were rounded off to the nearest 10 psi. Twelve cells were used, each with a range of 140 psi, starting at 2,775 psi (low enough to include the lowest value, 2,780 psi in this case) and ending at 4,455 psi, which is higher than the highest strength, 4,430 psi in the group.

It is a good idea to tabulate the cell boundaries vertically, leaving spaces between them to tally the specimen strength values falling in each cell, as shown in Fig. 15-5.

CELL BOUNDRY		TOTAL NUMBER
2775		
	///	3
2915		
	////	4
3055		
	JHT	5
3195		
	JHT ///	8
3335		
	JHT //	7
3475		
	JHT ////	9
3615		
	JHT ///	8
3755		
	JHT /	6
3895		
	////	4
4035		
	//	2
4175		
	///	3
4315		
	/	1
4455		

FIG. 15-5. Method of tallying strength values for histogram construction.

The normal curve is plotted by computing the ordinates at $\bar{X}$, at $\bar{X} \pm \sigma$, and at $\bar{X} \pm 2\sigma$ and drawing a smooth curve through these points with the points of inflection at $\bar{X} \pm \sigma$. Ordinates are computed as follows:

	Equation	*Example*
At $\bar{X}$:	$y = 0.3989 \dfrac{nc}{\sigma}$	9.9
At $\bar{X} \pm \sigma$:	$y = 0.242 \dfrac{nc}{\sigma}$	6.0
At $\bar{X} \pm 2\sigma$:	$y = 0.054 \dfrac{nc}{\sigma}$	1.33

where $\bar{X}$ = average strength   3,504 psi
    n = number of specimens   60
    σ = standard deviation   339 psi
    c = cell size, or range in strength
        encompassed by each cell   140 psi

In applying statistical control to concrete strength, a separate chart should be kept for each class or type of concrete. In a ready-mix plant, this may mean a separate chart for each specified strength or cement content, regardless of where it is used. On a job, it may mean a chart for each class of structural concrete, or for paving concrete.

A book of squares and square roots, such as Barlow's,[15.5] is of great value when one is making these statistical computations.

15-8. MODULUS OF ELASTICITY

By proper instrumentation, the compressive-strength test can be enlarged to include measurement of the elastic modulus. Two metal rings are clamped to the specimen, one near the top and one near the bottom, a measured distance apart. Two dial gauge extensometers are placed between the rings, diametrically opposite each other. As the load is applied to the specimen, the gauges measure the compression of the specimen. Normal practice is to remove the gauges after about half of the expected load has been applied, to avoid damaging them when the specimen fails. The stress-strain measurements thus obtained provide data for computing the elastic modulus.

Sonic and electrical methods are also available. The procedure is described in ASTM Designation: C 215.

15-9. TESTS OF HARDENED CONCRETE

Cores are taken from concrete pavements as a routine check on the thickness of the slab. Cores are also useful for the determination of strength of concrete in a structure, for examining construction joints, for examining the depth of surface deterioration, and other information.

Only experienced drillers should be employed, as the diamond drill bits may be damaged by improper usage. The driller should be instructed to determine the core location by measurement to columns, bench marks, or other features of known location and elevation.

If used for a strength test, the core should have a length as near as possible to twice its diameter, and the diameter should be at least three times the maximum size of aggregates in the concrete. Obvious defects, rock pockets, and joints should be avoided for strength specimens. Cores from slabs on the ground and long cores must be sawed to eliminate extreme end roughness or to obtain the proper length. Specimens should be ground or capped to provide proper surfaces for testing.

Samples of hardened concrete are sometimes tested for absorption, unit weight, and cement content. Specifications for pipe and masonry require absorption tests. Core samples can easily be measured and weighed for density determination. The chemical test for cement content of hardened concrete requires the facilities of a chemical laboratory (ASTM Designation: C 85). Certain aggregates and admixtures liberate soluble silica during the test and nullify the test values. For this reason, such tests should be performed only by experienced technicians and evaluated with considerable caution.

15-10. OTHER TESTS

Bond with reinforcing steel, volume change, resistance to freezing and thawing, fire tests, and structural load tests are tests that are sometimes performed under certain conditions. Descriptions of these tests may be found in various ASTM Designations or the ACI Building Code.[15.6]

REFERENCES

15.1   Proposed Method of Test for the Field Determination of the Constituents of Fresh Concrete, *ASTM Proc.*, vol. 31, part 1, pp. 383–385, 1931.
15.2   Hime, W. G., and R. A. Willis: A Method for the Determination of the Cement Content of Plastic Concrete, *ASTM Bull.*, no. 209, October, 1955.
15.3   Recommended Practice for Evaluation of Compression Test Results of Field Concrete, Report of ACI Committee 214, *J. Am. Concrete Inst.*, July, 1957, pp. 1–19.
15.4   Waddell, Joseph J.: Quality Control in the Construction Industry, *Industrial Quality Control*, January, 1961.
15.5   Barlow's Tables of Squares, Cubes, etc., E. & F. N. Spon, Ltd., 57 Haymarket, London S.W.1, England.
15.6   Building Code Requirements for Reinforced Concrete, Report of ACI Committee 318, *J. Am. Concrete Inst.*, May, 1956.

16-1. MIX PROPORTIONING

There are a number of different ways to proportion concrete mixes, some of which are rather complex and cumbersome, and others that are based on a degree of refinement that is never attained under field conditions. In this chapter, the ACI method as described in the report of ACI Committee 613[16.1]* is used. This method is simple, accurate, and rapid.

Requirements and Specifications

Mixes should be proportioned so as to make best use of available materials and to produce concrete possessing suitable workability, which, upon hardening, will develop the required degree of strength, durability, and other features. The properties of the aggregates and cement have a pronounced effect upon the workability and quality of hardened concrete, hence any method of proportioning mixes must, of necessity, be based upon average conditions and further, must be adjustable to make it fit specific conditions and materials.

Nearly all specifications for concrete specify a strength, usually a minimum below which no tests may fall. (This minimum strength requirement has its drawbacks, as discussed in Sec. 15-7.) Further specification requirements are generally a minimum cement content, maximum water-cement ratio, range in slump, and range in entrained-air content. Some recent architectural specifications have required that the average strength shall be 15 per cent higher than the design strength f_c'.

Specifications may be divided into two general types: One type is a performance specification, in which certain minimum requirements are set forth in the specifications, and the contractor is charged with the

* Superscript figures refer to chapter and reference number. The references are found at the end of each chapter.

responsibility of providing concrete that meets these requirements. Requirements may include a minimum strength (either compressive or flexural), maximum slump, or range in slump, maximum water-cement ratio, minimum cement content, and range in entrained-air content. Locations in which each class of concrete is to be used are specified, and the contractor is required to employ a commercial inspection agency, approved by the architect, to proportion mixes and test the concrete.

The second type of specification, sometimes called a "prescription" specification, is one in which the architect or engineer assumes responsibility for the mixes. Mixes are proportioned by the engineer, and adjustments or changes during construction are made at the discretion of the engineer. Equipment and methods may be specified in considerable detail. The sources or types of some of the materials may be specified. This type of specification is more apt to be used by a governmental agency rather than a private engineer or architect, although the latter sometimes use it, especially on a large project. Sometimes the actual testing and inspection work is performed by a commercial inspection agency under direction of the engineer or architect.

Under either type of specification, certain quality standards for materials are specified, either directly or by reference to ASTM or similar standards. Usually the maximum size of aggregate for the several features of the work is specified.

Required Data

The information required for proportioning a mix includes type and brand of cement, type and brand of air-entraining agent or other admixture, if any, type and size of coarse aggregate, sand grading, cement content, slump range, water-cement ratio, and air content. Some of this information will be found in the specifications, some by previous knowledge, and some by laboratory tests.

Tables in ACI Standard 613 should be used, following the examples shown in that report. Volumes of coarse aggregate from ACI Table 6 (Table 16-1), based on average values, are apt to result in mixtures with somewhat more than the necessary amount of sand, especially in mixes with smaller maximum size of coarse aggregates. Tabular values should be used, however, in the beginning, unless laboratory or field experience with the proposed materials indicates otherwise.

There has been some confusion in the past as to what specific gravity to use in making mix computations. ACI Standard 613 uses dry aggregate as a basis for calculations; that is, bulk specific gravity based on oven-dry weight. When the bulk specific gravity of a concrete aggregate is mentioned, it therefore refers to bulk specific gravity on an oven-dry basis.

TABLE 16-1. VOLUME OF COARSE AGGREGATE PER UNIT OF VOLUME OF CONCRETE*

Maximum size of aggregate, in.	Volume of dry-rodded coarse aggregate per unit volume of concrete for different fineness moduli of sand			
	2.40	2.60	2.80	3.00
⅜	0.46	0.44	0.42	0.40
½	0.55	0.53	0.51	0.49
¾	0.65	0.63	0.61	0.59
1	0.70	0.68	0.66	0.64
1½	0.76	0.74	0.72	0.70
2	0.79	0.77	0.75	0.73
3	0.84	0.82	0.80	0.78
6	0.90	0.88	0.86	0.84

* Volumes are based on aggregates in dry-rodded condition as described in Method of Test for Unit Weight of Aggregate (ASTM Designation: C 29).

These volumes are selected from empirical relationships to produce concrete with a degree of workability suitable for usual reinforced construction. For less workable concrete, such as required for concrete pavement construction, they may be increased about 10 per cent.

SOURCE: From Table 6, ACI Standard: ACI 613-54.

Specific gravity should be determined by the method of ASTM:C 127 for coarse aggregate and C 128 for fine aggregate.

The relationship between bulk specific gravities is expressed by the equation:

Bulk sp gr SSD (saturated surface dry) basis = bulk sp gr dry
basis × (1 + decimal absorption)

Within the range of values normally encountered, it is sufficiently accurate to add a constant to bulk dry specific gravity to obtain bulk SSD specific gravity as follows:

Per cent absorption	*Constant to add to bulk dry sp gr to obtain bulk SSD sp gr*
0.5	0.01
1.0	0.03
1.5	0.04
2.0	0.05

For example, if bulk dry specific gravity is 2.60, then bulk SSD specific gravity, of aggregate with 1 per cent absorption, is 2.63. These constants permit use of the flask method of determining fine aggregate

TABLE 16-2a. PER CENT MOISTURE IN SAND

Volume	Bulk specific gravity, SS dry basis										
	2.55	2.56	2.57	2.58	2.59	2.60	2.61	2.62	2.63	2.64	2.65
382											
383											
384											
385											
386											
387											
388											
389											0.1
390									0	0.2	0.4
391							0	0	0.3	0.5	0.7
392						0	0.1	0.4	0.6	0.8	1.1
393				0	0	0.2	0.5	0.7	0.9	1.2	1.4
394			0	0.1	0.3	0.6	0.8	1.0	1.3	1.5	1.7
395		0	0.1	0.4	0.6	0.9	1.1	1.4	1.6	1.8	2.1
396	0	0.2	0.5	0.7	1.0	1.2	1.5	1.7	1.9	2.2	2.4
397	0.3	0.6	0.8	1.1	1.3	1.5	1.8	2.0	2.3	2.5	2.7
398	0.7	0.9	1.1	1.4	1.6	1.9	2.1	2.4	2.6	2.8	3.1
399	1.0	1.2	1.5	1.7	2.0	2.2	2.5	2.7	2.9	3.2	3.4
400	1.3	1.6	1.8	2.1	2.3	2.6	2.8	3.0	3.3	3.6	3.8
401	1.7	1.9	2.2	2.4	2.6	2.9	3.1	3.4	3.7	3.9	4.2
402	2.0	2.2	2.5	2.7	3.0	3.2	3.5	3.8	4.0	4.3	4.5
403	2.4	2.6	2.8	3.1	3.3	3.6	3.9	4.1	4.4	4.6	4.8
404	2.7	2.9	3.2	3.4	3.7	4.0	4.2	4.5	4.7	4.9	5.2
405	3.0	3.3	3.5	3.8	4.0	4.3	4.6	4.8	5.1	5.3	5.5
406	3.4	3.6	3.9	4.2	4.4	4.7	4.9	5.2	5.4	5.7	5.9
407	3.8	4.0	4.2	4.5	4.8	5.0	5.3	5.5	5.8	6.0	6.3
408	4.1	4.3	4.6	4.9	5.1	5.4	5.6	5.9	6.1	6.4	6.7
409	4.4	4.7	5.0	5.2	5.5	5.7	6.0	6.3	6.5	6.8	7.0
410	4.8	5.1	5.3	5.6	5.8	6.1	6.4	6.6	6.9	7.1	7.4
411	5.2	5.4	5.7	6.0	6.2	6.5	6.7	7.0	7.2	7.5	7.8
412	5.6	5.8	6.1	6.3	6.6	6.8	7.1	7.4	7.6	7.9	8.1
413	5.9	6.2	6.4	6.7	7.0	7.2	7.5	7.7	8.0	8.3	8.5
414	6.3	6.5	6.8	7.1	7.3	7.6	7.8	8.1	8.4	8.7	8.8
415	6.7	6.9	7.2	7.4	7.7	8.0	8.2	8.5	8.8	9.0	9.2
416	7.0	7.3	7.6	7.8	8.1	8.4	8.6	8.9	9.1	9.4	9.6
417	7.4	7.7	7.9	8.2	8.5	8.7	9.0	9.2			
418	7.8	8.0	8.3	8.6	8.8	9.1	9.4				
419	8.2	8.4	8.7	9.0	9.2	9.5					
420	8.6	8.8	9.1	9.4							
421	8.9	9.2									
422	9.3										

TABLE 16-2b. PER CENT MOISTURE IN SAND

Volume	Bulk specific gravity, SS dry basis									
	2.66	2.67	2.68	2.69	2.70	2.71	2.72	2.73	2.74	2.75
382										0.1
383									0.2	0.4
384							0.1	0.3	0.5	0.7
385						0.2	0.4	0.6	0.8	1.0
386				0	0.3	0.5	0.7	0.9	1.1	1.3
387			0.1	0.4	0.6	0.8	1.0	1.3	1.5	1.7
388	0	0.2	0.4	0.7	0.9	1.1	1.4	1.6	1.8	2.0
389	0.3	0.5	0.8	1.0	1.2	1.5	1.7	1.9	2.1	2.3
390	0.6	0.9	1.1	1.3	1.6	1.8	2.0	2.2	2.4	2.6
391	1.0	1.2	1.4	1.7	1.9	2.1	2.3	2.5	2.7	3.0
392	1.3	1.5	1.8	2.0	2.2	2.5	2.6	2.8	3.1	3.3
393	1.6	1.9	2.1	2.3	2.6	2.8	3.0	3.2	3.4	3.7
394	2.0	2.2	2.4	2.7	2.9	3.1	3.3	3.5	3.8	4.0
395	2.3	2.5	2.8	3.0	3.3	3.4	3.7	3.9	4.1	4.3
396	2.6	2.9	3.1	3.4	3.6	3.8	4.0	4.2	4.4	4.7
397	3.0	3.2	3.5	3.7	4.0	4.1	4.3	4.6	4.8	5.0
398	3.3	3.6	3.8	4.1	4.3	4.5	4.7	4.9	5.1	5.4
399	3.7	3.9	4.2	4.4	4.6	4.8	5.0	5.3	5.5	5.7
400	4.0	4.3	4.5	4.7	4.9	5.2	5.4	5.6	5.8	6.1
401	4.4	4.6	4.8	5.1	5.3	5.5	5.8	6.0	6.2	6.4
402	4.7	5.0	5.2	5.5	5.7	5.9	6.1	6.3	6.5	6.8
403	5.1	5.3	5.6	5.8	6.0	6.2	6.5	6.7	6.9	7.1
404	5.4	5.7	5.9	6.2	6.4	6.6	6.8	7.0	7.3	7.5
405	5.8	6.0	6.3	6.5	6.7	7.0	7.2	7.4	7.7	7.9
406	6.1	6.4	6.6	6.9	7.1	7.3	7.5	7.8	8.0	8.2
407	6.6	6.7	7.0	7.2	7.5	7.7	7.9	8.1	8.4	8.6
408	6.9	7.1	7.3	7.6	7.8	8.1	8.3	8.5	8.7	9.0
409	7.3	7.5	7.7	8.0	8.2	8.4	8.6	8.9	9.1	
410	7.7	7.8	8.1	8.3	8.6	8.8	9.0	9.3		
411	8.0	8.2	8.5	8.7	8.9	9.2				
412	8.3	8.6	8.8	9.1	9.3					
413	8.7	9.0	9.2							
414	9.1									
415	9.5									

$$\text{Per cent moisture} = \frac{V - (500/\text{sp gr}) - 200}{200 + 500 - V}$$

where V = flask reading

sp gr = bulk specific gravity, SS dry basis

See USBR Manual, 6th ed., p. 416.

moisture using Table 16-2 based on Reclamation Bureau Designation 11B.

For field control, it is simpler to use the specific gravity based on a saturated surface dry condition. Aggregates are nearly always batched in a wet or damp condition, and the use of the saturated surface dry specific gravity eliminates the necessity of considering aggregate absorption when making adjustments to the mix under operating conditions.

Procedure

The following outline should assist in using tables in this chapter to implement the method of ACI Standard 613.

1. It is assumed that materials have been investigated as to quality, availability, etc. A satisfactory history of use in the area, based on a careful inspection and evaluation of existing structures known to have been constructed with the proposed materials, may serve as the basis for acceptance. Laboratory tests may also serve as a basis for evaluation.

Unless otherwise specified by job specifications, materials should conform to the following standard specifications:

Cement	ASTM Designation: C 150
Aggregates	ASTM Designation: C 33
Water	AASHO Designation: T 26
Air-entraining agent	ASTM Designation: C 260

The amount of preliminary investigative work done depends on the size and importance of the project and the service conditions to which it will be exposed. However, it should be remembered that a small yardage of concrete does not necessarily mean that it is unimportant.

2. Cement content, slump, water-cement ratio, and maximum size of aggregate will be either designated by the specifications or computed from tables in ACI Standard 613.

For example, assume that the following values were specified for structural concrete exposed in a moderate section to severe exposure in air:

Strength, average	3,200 psi + 15 per cent
Slump	3 in. max
Size of coarse aggregate	1½ in.
Total air content	4.5 per cent ± 1 per cent
Water-cement ratio	5.5 gal per sack max

From Table 16-3, the water-cement ratio required for a strength of 3,685 psi (3,200 + 15 per cent) for air-entrained concrete is about 5½ gal per sack of cement (the same as specified). This is safe for the expected exposure, as shown in Table 16-4. From Table 16-5, the water re-

TABLE 16-3. COMPRESSIVE STRENGTH OF CONCRETE FOR
VARIOUS WATER-CEMENT RATIOS

Water-cement ratio, gal per sack of cement	Probable compressive strength at 28 days, psi	
	Non-air-entrained concrete	Air-entrained concrete
4	6,000	4,800
5	5,000	4,000
6	4,000	3,200
7	3,200	2,600
8	2,500	2,000
9	2,000	1,600

These average strengths are for concretes containing not more than the percentages of entrained and/or entrapped air shown in Table 16-5. For a constant water-cement ratio, the strength of the concrete is reduced as the air content is increased. For air contents higher than those listed in Table 16-5, the strengths will be proportionately less than those listed in this table.

Strengths are based on 6 × 12-in. cylinders moist-cured under standard conditions for 28 days. See ASTM Designation: C 31.

SOURCE: From Table 5, ACI Standard: ACI 613-54.

quired for 1½ in. maximum aggregate concrete and 3-in. slump (air-entrained) is 32 gal per cu yd.

$$\frac{32 \text{ gal per cu yd}}{5\frac{1}{2} \text{ gal per sack}} = 5.82 \text{ sacks of cement per cu yd}$$

Assume that the first trial mix will be made with 6 sacks, subject to adjustment if subsequent tests indicate the feasibility.

3. Make sieve analysis of all aggregates, using the methods of ASTM: C 136. At this time, determine whether the aggregates, both sand and gravel, meet required gradations given in the specifications.

Aggregates for trial mixes should fall near the middle of the specification range. In case they do not, they should be adjusted to meet this condition. If necessary, blend more than one sand or gravel until required gradations are obtained. If coarse aggregate consists of two sizes of material, the coarser fraction should be at least 50 per cent by weight of total coarse aggregate. In the example being

TABLE 16-4. MAXIMUM PERMISSIBLE WATER-CEMENT RATIOS (GAL PER SACK) FOR DIFFERENT TYPES OF STRUCTURES AND DEGREES OF EXPOSURE

Type of structure	Exposure conditions*					
	Severe wide range in temperature, or frequent alternations of freezing and thawing (air-entrained concrete only)			Mild temperature rarely below freezing, or rainy, or arid		
	In air	At the water line or within the range of fluctuating water level or spray		In air	At the water line or within the range of fluctuating water level or spray	
		In fresh water	In sea water or in contact with sulfates†		In fresh water	In sea water or in contact with sulfates†
Thin sections, such as railings, curbs, sills, ledges, ornamental or architectural concrete, reinforced piles, pipe, and all sections with less than 1 in. concrete cover over reinforcing...............	5.5	5.0	4.5‡	6	5.5	4.5‡
Moderate sections, such as retaining walls, abutments, piers, girders, beams......	6.0	5.5	5.0‡	§	6.0	5.0‡
Exterior portions of heavy (mass) sections............................	6.5	5.5	5.0‡	§	6.0	5.0‡
Concrete deposited by tremie under water............................		5.0	5.0		5.0	5.0
Concrete slabs laid on the ground.......	6.0			§		
Concrete protected from the weather, interiors of buildings, concrete below ground..............................	§			§		
Concrete which will later be protected by enclosure or backfill but which may be exposed to freezing and thawing for several years before such protection is offered..............................	6.0			§		

*Air-entrained concrete should be used under all conditions involving severe exposure and may be used under mild exposure conditions to improve workability of the mixture.

† Soil or ground water containing sulfate concentrations of more than 0.2 per cent.

‡ When sulfate resisting cement is used, maximum water-cement ratio may be increased by 0.5 gal per sack.

§ Water-cement ratio should be selected on basis of strength and workability requirements.

SOURCE: From Table 4, ACI Standard: ACI 613-54.

computed, assume the fineness modulus of the sand was found to be 2.60.

4. Determine specific gravity, absorption, and moisture content of aggregates, using the methods of ASTM: C 70, C 127, and C 128, and USBR 11B.

TABLE 16-5. APPROXIMATE MIXING WATER REQUIREMENTS FOR DIFFERENT SLUMPS AND MAXIMUM SIZES OF AGGREGATES*

Slump, in.	Water, gal per cu yd of concrete for indicated maximum sizes of aggregate							
	⅜ in.	½ in.	¾ in.	1 in.	1½ in.	2 in.	3 in.	6 in.
Non-air-entrained concrete								
1–2	42	40	37	36	33	31	29	25
3–4	46	44	41	39	36	34	32	28
6–7	49	46	43	41	38	36	34	30
Approximate amount of entrapped air in non-air-entrained concrete, per cent..............	3	2.5	2	1.5	1	0.5	0.3	0.2
Air-entrained concrete								
1–2	37	36	33	31	29	27	25	22
3–4	41	39	36	34	32	30	28	24
6–7	43	41	38	36	34	32	30	26
Recommended average total air content, per cent..............	8	7	6	5	4.5	4	3.5	3

* These quantities of mixing water are for use in computing cement factors for trial batches. They are maxima for reasonably well-shaped angular coarse aggregates graded within limits of accepted specifications.

If more water is required than shown, the cement factor, estimated from these quantities, should be increased to maintain desired water-cement ratio, except as otherwise indicated by laboratory tests for strength.

If less water is required than shown, the cement factor, estimated from these quantities, should not be decreased except as indicated by laboratory tests for strength.

SOURCE: From Table 3, ACI Standard: ACI 613-54.

There are several different methods of obtaining the moisture content of aggregates, any of which is acceptable.

Drying in an oven or over a hot plate is a common method. It is suggested that the sample be dried bone-dry, and a correction made for absorption.

$$\text{Per cent moisture} = \frac{\text{wet wt} - \text{bone-dry wt}}{\text{bone-dry wt}} \times 100 - \% \text{ absorption}$$

A slight error is introduced by using bone-dry weight in the denominator, instead of saturated surface dry weight, but it is not significant. Figure 16-1 is based on this formula, corrected for surface dry weight and absorption, and will save computing each time. All that is necessary is to obtain a sample of 400 g wet weight, dry and weigh it, and read the per cent moisture from the curve for the correct absorption.

Where no oven or hot plate is available, the aggregate may be dried by the alcohol method. The wet sample is weighed in a large flat pan (cake pan), and 1 or 2 oz of denatured alcohol mixed with it. The alcohol is ignited and allowed to burn off while the aggregate is stirred

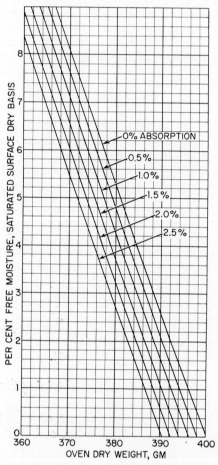

Fig. 16-1. Chart for determining moisture content of aggregate. (1) Use 400 g wet sample. (2) Dry to oven dryness. (3) Enter chart at dry weight, intersect curve for correct absorption, and read per cent moisture on scale at left.

$$\text{Per cent } M = 100 \frac{400 - A(1 + X)}{A(1 + X)}$$

where A = oven-dry wt
      X = absorption expressed as a decimal

occasionally. If necessary, repeat. A little practice enables one to estimate the amount of alcohol to use. This should be done in a well-ventilated place, where there is no danger of fire. This method may be used
for both fine and coarse aggregate.

Pycnometers and flasks may also be used. An easy-to-use device consists of a pint or quart fruit jar (mason jar) with the top edge ground to
a true plane surface, and a small square of glass or clear plastic to rest
on the top. This is calibrated and used in the same way as the pycnometer (ASTM Designation: C 70) except that the jar is filled with water
until the water surface, supported by surface tension, is slightly above
the edge of the top. The glass or plastic plate is carefully placed over
the top by sliding it from one side, taking care to avoid inclusion of air
bubbles underneath, and making uniform contact with the top of the
jar. Computations and other details are the same as for the pycnometer.
This method can be used for fine aggregate and, with care, for the finer
fractions of coarse aggregate.

There are several patented devices on the market that give varying
qualities of performance. One is a pressure vessel similar to a bomb
calorimeter, in which the reaction between sand moisture and calcium
carbide produces acetylene gas. The pressure created by the acetylene
is a measure of the moisture in the aggregate.

In yet another method, after determination of the bulk, saturated-
surface dry specific gravity of the sand, the moisture content can be read
direct from Table 16-2. The procedure, based on U.S. Bureau of Reclamation Designation: 11B, is as follows:

Apparatus:

A standardized volumetric flask of 500-milliliter capacity calibrated to 0.15
milliliters.
Balance having a capacity of 2 kilograms and sensitive to 0.1 grams.
A pipette, ¼-inch-diameter glass tube of sufficient length to be used to adjust the water level in the flask.

Procedure:

The flask is filled with water at room temperature to just above the calibrated 200-milliliter mark. The level of water is then lowered by means of the
pipette until the lower part of the water surface coincides with the 200 mil-
liliter mark.

From a representative sample of approximately 1,000 g of sand from
the batcher, 500 g is introduced into the flask and the combined volume
of water and fine aggregate read directly from the graduated scale.

The percentage of moisture can then be read directly from the table. Continuing the hypothetical example, assume the following values were found:

	Specific gravity	Absorption, %	Moisture content, %
Sand..................	2.64	1.0	3.0
Coarse aggregate......	2.67	0.5	1.0

5. Determine unit weight of coarse aggregate (U) using ASTM: C 29. Note that C 29 requires that aggregate be in "room dry" condition. EXAMPLE: Value of $U = 100$ pcf
6. Compute weight of coarse aggregate. This equals V from Table 16-1 multiplied by 27, multiplied by U dry-rodded unit weight, or

$$W = 27VU$$

EXAMPLE: From Table 16-1, $V = 0.74$ for 1½-in. maximum aggregate and sand FM of 2.60

$$W = 27 \times 0.74 \times 100 = 2{,}000 \text{ lb}$$

7. Compute solid volume V_s of coarse aggregate. Use Table 16-6 in this chapter to simplify the computation.

$$V_s = W \times \frac{1}{\text{density}}$$

Sp gr of coarse aggregate [from (4)] = 2.67

$$V_s = 2{,}000 \times 0.006012 = 12.02 \text{ cu ft}$$

8. Compute solid volume and weight of cement per cubic yard of concrete.
For a 6-sack mix, Table 16-7 gives the following values:

$$\text{Wt cement} = 564 \text{ lb}$$
$$\text{Vol cement} = 2.87 \text{ cu ft}$$

9. Compute volume and weight of water per cubic yard of concrete.

Max gal per sack [from (2)] = 5.5
Sacks per yard [from (2)]   = 6.0
$6.0 \times 5.5 = 33$ gal per yd allowed

TABLE 16-6. DENSITY AND VOLUME RELATIONSHIPS

Table for unit weight

Specific gravity (S)	Density (D)	$\dfrac{1}{\text{Density}}$
2.45	152.64	0.006552
2.46	153.26	0.006525
2.47	153.88	0.006498
2.48	154.50	0.006472
2.49	155.13	0.006446
2.50	155.75	0.006420
2.51	156.37	0.006395
2.52	157.00	0.006370
2.53	157.62	0.006344
2.54	158.24	0.006319
2.55	158.86	0.006295
2.56	159.49	0.006270
2.57	160.11	0.006246
2.58	160.73	0.006222
2.59	161.36	0.006197
2.60	161.98	0.006174
2.61	162.60	0.006150
2.62	163.23	0.006126
2.63	163.85	0.006103
2.64	164.47	0.006080
2.65	165.10	0.006057
2.66	165.72	0.006034
2.67	166.34	0.006012
2.68	166.96	0.005989
2.69	167.57	0.005967
2.70	168.21	0.005945
2.71	168.83	0.005923
2.72	169.46	0.005901
2.73	170.08	0.005880
2.74	170.70	0.005858
2.75	171.33	0.005837
3.10	193.13	0.005178
3.15	196.24	0.005096
3.20	199.36	0.005016

Notation

S = specific gravity
D = density, pcf
W = weight, lb
V = volume, cu ft

BASIC FORMULAS

Weight of water is 62.3 pcf
$D = 62.3S$
$W = DV$
$\quad = 62.3SV$
$V = \dfrac{W}{62.3S} = W \times \dfrac{1}{\text{density}}$

TABLE 16-7. CEMENT CONVERSION FACTORS
(Weight and solid volume equivalents
per sack from 0.1 to 10.9 sacks)

Sacks		Weight and solid volume, cu ft											
		0	0.1	0.2	0.25	0.3	0.4	0.5	0.6	0.7	0.75	0.8	0.9
0	Wt	0	9.4	18.8	23.5	28.2	37.6	47.0	56.4	65.8	70.5	75.2	84.6
	Vol	0	0.048	0.096	0.120	0.144	0.192	0.240	0.287	0.335	0.359	0.383	0.431
1	Wt	94	103.4	112.8	117.5	122.2	131.6	141.0	150.4	159.8	164.5	169.2	178.6
	Vol	0.479	0.527	0.575	0.599	0.623	0.671	0.719	0.766	0.814	0.838	0.862	0.910
2	Wt	188	197.4	206.8	211.5	216.2	225.6	235.0	244.4	253.8	258.5	263.2	272.6
	Vol	0.958	1.006	1.054	1.078	1.102	1.150	1.198	1.245	1.293	1.317	1.341	1.389
3	Wt	282	291.4	300.8	305.5	310.2	319.6	329.0	338.4	347.8	352.5	357.2	366.6
	Vol	1.437	1.485	1.533	1.557	1.581	1.629	1.677	1.724	1.772	1.796	1.820	1.868
4	Wt	376	385.4	394.8	399.5	404.2	413.6	423.0	432.4	441.8	446.5	451.2	460.6
	Vol	1.916	1.964	2.012	2.036	2.060	2.108	2.156	2.203	2.251	2.275	2.299	2.347
5	Wt	470	479.4	488.8	493.5	498.2	507.6	517.0	526.4	535.8	540.5	545.2	554.6
	Vol	2.395	2.443	2.491	2.515	2.539	2.587	2.635	2.682	2.730	2.755	2.778	2.826
6	Wt	564	573.4	582.8	587.5	592.2	601.6	611.0	620.4	629.8	634.5	639.2	648.6
	Vol	2.874	2.922	2.970	2.994	3.018	3.066	3.114	3.161	3.209	3.234	3.257	3.305
7	Wt	658	667.4	676.8	681.5	686.2	695.6	705.0	714.4	723.8	728.5	733.2	742.6
	Vol	3.353	3.401	3.449	3.473	3.497	3.545	3.593	3.640	3.688	3.713	3.736	3.784
8	Wt	752	761.4	770.8	775.5	780.2	789.6	799.0	808.4	817.8	822.5	827.2	836.6
	Vol	3.832	3.880	3.928	3.952	3.976	4.024	4.072	4.119	4.167	4.192	4.215	4.263
9	Wt	846	855.4	864.8	869.5	874.2	883.6	893.0	902.4	911.8	916.5	921.2	930.6
	Vol	4.311	4.359	4.407	4.431	4.455	4.503	4.551	4.598	4.646	4.671	4.694	4.742
10	Wt	940	949.4	958.8	963.5	968.2	977.6	987.0	996.4	1005.8	1010.5	1015.2	1024.6
	Vol	4.790	4.838	4.886	4.910	4.934	4.982	5.030	5.077	5.125	5.150	5.173	5.221

Weight = 94 × sacks
Volume = weight × 0.00509567, based on specific gravity of 3.15
1 bbl = 4 sacks = 376 lb = 1.916 cu ft

However, from Table 16-5, for air-entrained 1½-in. concrete at 3-in. slump, the required water is 32 gal per cu yd.

Equivalent weight and volume for 32 gal, obtained from Table 16-8, are 267 lb and 4.28 cu ft.

10. Compute volume of air.

$$\text{Per cent air [from (2)]} = 4.5\%$$
$$0.045 \times 27 \qquad\qquad = 1.22 \text{ cu ft}$$

TABLE 16-8. WATER CONVERSION FACTORS

Gal	Lb	Cu ft
0.12	1.0	0.01607
1.0	8.33	0.1338
7.48	62.3	1.0
26.0	216.67	3.48
26.5	220.83	3.54
27.0	225.00	3.61
27.5	229.17	3.68
28.0	233.33	3.75
28.5	237.50	3.81
29.0	241.67	3.88
29.5	245.83	3.95
30.0	250.00	4.01
30.5	254.17	4.08
31.0	258.33	4.15
31.5	262.50	4.21
32.0	266.67	4.28
32.5	270.83	4.35
33.0	275.00	4.41
33.5	279.17	4.48
34.0	283.33	4.55
34.5	287.50	4.61
35.0	291.67	4.68
35.5	295.83	4.75
36.0	300.00	4.82
36.5	304.17	4.88
37.0	308.33	4.95
37.5	312.50	5.02
38.0	316.67	5.08
38.5	320.83	5.15
39.0	325.00	5.22
39.5	329.17	5.28
40.0	333.33	5.35

11. Add together volumes computed in (7), (8), (9), and (10), and subtract from 27. Remainder is solid volume of sand.

	Weight, lb	Volume, cu ft
Cement, 6 sacks..............	564	2.87
Coarse aggregate.............	2,000	12.02
Water, 32 gal...............	267	4.28
Air.......................		1.22
Total....................	2,831	20.39

Solid volume sand equals 27.00 − 20.39 = 6.61 cu ft.

12. Compute weight per cubic yard for sand. Weight of sand equals density times solid volume per cubic yard.

Sp gr sand [from (4)] =   2.64
Density (Table 16-6)   = 164.47
Solid vol sand [from (11)] =   6.61
Wt = 164.47 × 6.61 = 1,087 lb

Summary of preliminary trial mix:

	Weight, lb	Volume, cu ft
Cement, 6 sacks..............	564	2.87
Water, 32 gal.............	267	4.28
Coarse aggregate.............	2,000	12.02
Fine aggregate...............	1,087	6.61
Entrained air, 4.5%..........		1.22
Total.....................	3,918	27.0

Air-entraining agent: Use amount recommended by manufacturer to entrain the required percentage of air.

$$\text{Theoretical unit wt:} \frac{3,918}{27} = 145.1 \text{ pcf}$$

When proportioning non-air-entrained concrete, assume 1 per cent voids.

13. Design a batch of 2 cu ft (use 3 cu ft when beams in addition to cylinders are to be made) for mixing in the laboratory by multiplying each of the weights per cubic yard of the ingredients by $\frac{2}{27}$ to obtain batch weights for a 2 cu-ft batch.

14. Aggregate design batch weights should be corrected for free moisture by adding more aggregate in an amount to compensate for the moisture. That is;

Batch wt = computed dry wt × $(1 + M)$

where M is net moisture content expressed as a decimal. Moisture content may be computed from Fig. 16-1 or Table 16-2. The weight of water in aggregates must be considered as part of the mixing water, so the design water weight should be corrected for aggregate moisture.

Batch wt water = computed wt − $(S + A)$

where S = wet batch wt sand minus saturated surface dry batch wt sand

A = wet batch wt coarse aggregate minus saturated surface dry batch wt coarse aggregate

Example continued:

	Wt per cu yd (item 12)	Wt per batch (item 13)	% moisture (item 4)	Water in aggregate	Corrected batch wt
Cement..........	564	41.8 lb			41.8
Water...........	267	19.8		(3.9)	15.9
Coarse aggregate..	2,000	148.3	1.0	1.5	149.8
Fine aggregate....	1,087	81.5	3.0	2.4	83.9
Total..........	3,918	291.4 lb		3.9	291.4

Air-entraining agent should be proportioned in the same manner; that is, take $\frac{2}{27}$ of the recommended amount per cubic yard.

15. Batching: exact quantities of cement and aggregates are batched by weight; water may be weighed or measured by volume in a graduated container. The aggregates are weighed cumulatively, beginning with the smallest size, on a scale accurate to 0.03 lb, or ½ oz. A container of sufficient size to hold either a half batch or a full batch is placed on the scales, tare correction made, and the aggregates weighed. Cement is weighed separately. Aggregates should be moist when weighed and should be at room temperature (65 to 75°F) before being mixed. In batching water, a quantity greater than computed requirement is measured. Air-entraining agent is added to a portion of this water, and this portion of water is the first part to be added to the batch in the mixer. Water from the weighed container is then added until the concrete has the required slump. After the concrete reaches this slump, water remaining is measured, this amount subtracted from the total measured, and net water which has been added is computed.

EXAMPLE:

> Estimated water requirement (item 14) = 15.9 lb
> Total wt water plus container   = 24.8 lb

An estimated 10 or 11 lb of water is poured from this container into a bucket, the total AEA added to the bucket, and this mixture poured into the materials already in the mixer. More water is added from the weighed container to obtain the 3-in. slump.

> Wt container plus water   = 24.8 lb
> Final wt container plus remaining water = 10.6
> Total water used for 3-in. slump   = 14.2 lb

16. Mixing: Capacity of the mixer should equal or slightly exceed batch size. Before a trial batch is placed in the mixer, the mixer should be primed by mixing a small partial batch (one-half of normal batch, or less), of approximately the same composition as the trial batch, or by mixing a small amount of mortar of the same composition as mortar of the batch. This priming batch is discharged and wasted, leaving a coating of mortar on the mixer interior. Place dry ingredients in the mixer and add about two-thirds of expected water, including all the air-entraining agent. Allow it to mix about ½ min, then add clean water from the remaining measured amount until the desired slump is attained, as judged by appearance of the concrete in the mixer.

Mix the batch for a total of 3 min. Dump the concrete into a watertight and nonabsorptive receptacle of such size and shape that the concrete can be turned over with a shovel to eliminate segregation. A clean, damp concrete floor is satisfactory.

17. Tests: Immediately after the concrete is dumped from the mixer, the following tests are made:

1. Slump	ASTM Designation: C 143
2. Air content (pressure method)	ASTM Designation: C 231
3. Unit wt, yield, and air content (gravimetric)	ASTM Designation: C 138
4. Casting and testing cylinders and beams	ASTM Designation: C 192

Concrete used in determining air content by the pressure method should be wasted. Concrete used in unit weight tests and slump can be recombined with the concrete remaining in the pan for making six 6 × 12-in. cylinders and two 6 × 6 × 24-in. beams for flexure test where the latter are required.

18. Computations and retests: In all probability the amount of water actually used is not the same as the preliminary amount computed beforehand, and it is necessary to adjust mix proportions to compensate for the difference in volume of water. This is most easily accomplished by increasing or decreasing aggregate volume by a quantity equal to the decrease or increase in water volume, keeping cement and air volumes constant. Making an adjustment in this manner introduces a slight error in the amount of water required in the new batch, but the error is not significant, if estimated water requirement of the first trial batch was reasonably close to actual.

EXAMPLE:

Estimated water requirement (item 14) = 15.9 lb
Actual water used (item 15)   = 14.2
Difference   = 1.7 lb

1.7 × 0.01607 = 0.027 cu ft less water used (Table 16-8)

Make the volume correction in the coarse aggregate:

Sp gr coarse aggregate (item 4) = 2.67
Density from Table 16-6 = 166.34
0.027 × 166.34 = 4.5 lb to be added to coarse aggregate

New trial mix proportions:

	Batch wt, lb
Cement	41.8
Water	14.2
Coarse aggregate	154.3
Fine aggregate	83.9
Total	294.2

At this point, characteristics of the proposed materials have been well enough established to permit making a group of mixes to determine the effect of water-cement ratio on the concrete strength. A series of mixes is made at different cement contents and constant slump. Total water per cubic yard will be almost constant for these mixes. Information from each mix includes mix number, gallons water per sack of cement, total water per cubic yard, barrels (or sacks) cement per cubic yard, yield, return, slump, unit weight, per cent air, fine-aggregate content, coarse-aggregate content, and notes about the workability of the batch. Subsequently, results of strength tests are included. Figure 16-2 shows the results of a group of mixes made with crushed-limestone coarse aggregate. This particular series of mixes contained a water-reducing retarder.

All cylinders and beams should be cured in accordance with ASTM: C 192. Two cylinders will be broken at 7 days, two at 14 days, and two at 28 days. One beam will be broken at 7 days and one at 14 days.

Cylinder numbers, markings, transmittal forms, and reports should indicate clearly that the cylinders were cast from trial mixes.

Final adjustments of the proposed mix should be made under full-batch field-operating conditions at the beginning of concreting operations. Table 16-9 is useful for making weight and volume conversions for any amount of water normally encountered in the field.

As an alternative procedure, instead of mixing small batches in the laboratory it is sometimes possible to mix full-size batches in the ready-

TABLE 16-9. CONVERSION—GALLONS TO POUNDS

Gal	\<Tenths of gal\>									
	0	0.1	0.2	0.3	0.4	0.5	0.6	0.7	0.8	0.9
	\<Lb\>									
0	0	0.83	1.67	2.50	3.33	4.17	5.00	5.83	6.67	7.50
1	8.33	9.17	10.00	10.83	11.67	12.50	13.33	14.17	15.00	15.83
2	16.67	17.50	18.33	19.17	20.00	20.83	21.67	22.50	23.33	24.17
3	25.00	25.83	26.67	27.50	28.33	29.17	30.00	30.83	31.67	32.50
4	33.33	34.17	35.00	35.83	36.67	37.50	38.33	39.17	40.00	40.83
5	41.67	42.50	43.33	44.17	45.00	45.83	46.67	47.50	48.33	49.17
6	50.00	50.83	51.67	52.50	53.33	54.17	55.00	55.83	56.67	57.50
7	58.33	59.17	60.00	60.83	61.67	62.50	63.33	64.17	65.00	65.83
8	66.67	67.50	68.33	69.17	70.00	70.83	71.67	72.50	73.33	74.17
9	75.00	75.83	76.67	77.50	78.33	79.17	80.00	80.83	81.67	82.50
10	83.33	84.17	85.00	85.83	86.67	87.50	88.33	89.17	90.00	90.83
11	91.67	92.50	93.33	94.17	95.00	95.83	96.67	97.50	98.33	99.17
12	100.00	100.83	101.67	102.50	103.33	104.17	105.00	105.83	106.67	107.50
13	108.33	109.17	110.00	110.83	111.67	112.50	113.33	114.17	115.00	115.83
14	116.67	117.50	118.33	119.17	120.00	120.83	121.67	122.50	123.33	124.17
15	125.00	125.83	126.67	127.50	128.33	129.17	130.00	130.83	131.67	132.50
16	133.33	134.17	135.00	135.83	136.67	137.50	138.33	139.17	140.00	140.83
17	141.67	142.50	143.33	144.17	145.00	145.83	146.67	147.50	148.33	149.17
18	150.00	150.83	151.67	152.50	153.33	154.17	155.00	155.83	156.67	157.50
19	158.33	159.17	160.00	160.83	161.67	162.50	163.33	164.17	165.00	165.83
20	166.67	167.50	168.33	169.17	170.00	170.83	171.67	172.50	173.33	174.17
21	175.00	175.83	176.67	177.50	178.33	179.17	180.00	180.83	181.67	182.50
22	183.33	184.17	185.00	185.83	186.67	187.50	188.33	189.17	190.00	190.83
23	191.67	192.50	193.33	194.17	195.00	195.83	196.67	197.50	198.33	199.17
24	200.00	200.83	201.67	202.50	203.33	204.17	205.00	205.83	206.67	207.50
25	208.33	209.17	210.00	210.83	211.67	212.50	213.33	214.17	215.00	215.83
26	216.67	217.50	218.33	219.17	220.00	220.83	221.67	222.50	223.33	224.17
27	225.00	225.83	226.67	227.50	228.33	229.17	230.00	230.83	231.67	232.50
28	233.33	234.17	235.00	235.83	236.67	237.50	238.33	239.17	240.00	240.83
29	241.67	242.50	243.33	244.17	245.00	245.83	246.67	247.50	248.33	249.17
30	250.00	250.83	251.67	252.50	253.33	254.17	255.00	255.83	256.67	257.50
31	258.33	259.17	260.00	260.83	261.67	262.50	263.33	264.17	265.00	265.83
32	266.67	267.50	268.33	269.17	270.00	270.83	271.67	272.50	273.33	274.17
33	275.00	275.83	276.67	277.50	278.33	279.17	280.00	280.83	281.67	282.50
34	283.33	284.17	285.00	285.83	286.67	287.50	288.33	289.17	290.00	290.83
35	291.67	292.50	293.33	294.17	295.00	295.83	296.67	297.50	298.33	299.17
36	300.00	300.83	301.67	302.50	303.33	304.17	305.00	305.83	306.67	307.50
37	308.33	309.17	310.00	310.83	311.67	312.50	313.33	314.17	315.00	315.83
38	316.67	317.50	318.33	319.17	320.00	320.83	321.67	322.50	323.33	324.17
39	325.00	325.83	326.67	327.50	328.33	329.17	330.00	330.83	331.67	332.50
40	333.33	334.17	335.00	335.83	336.67	337.50	338.33	339.17	340.00	340.83

mix concrete plant, provided the proper materials are available as required by the specifications and job conditions. The procedure is identical through step 12. Normally 1 cu yd batches are made. Corrections must be made for moisture in the aggregates. A series of mixes should be made in order that a curve similar to Fig. 16-2 may be made.

The foregoing procedure should always be followed when proportioning mixes using materials from a new source, not previously used for concrete. On the other hand, in urban areas, where ready-mixed-concrete

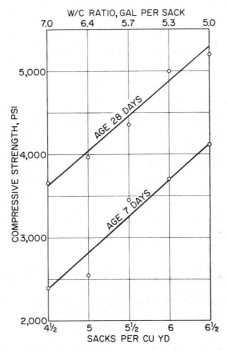

FIG. 16-2. Typical strength curves for trial mixes.

plants have been established, it is possible to use existing mixes as a basis for new mixes for any specific job. Usually the commercial mixes commonly in use will have to be adjusted in some way to make them acceptable for a specification job, but the existence of these mixes and the knowledge of their characteristics and properties greatly simplify the work of proportioning new mixes. A pair of curves similar to those in Fig. 16-2 should be prepared. Curves of this type may be prepared for the commercial mixes from a ready-mix plant and will be useful in selecting mixes for those jobs for which commercial mixes are suitable. Different curves are necessary for different maximum sizes of aggregate in the mixes, and for different admixtures.

Mix Adjustments

Rarely will a laboratory mix be entirely suitable under field conditions. Adjustments to the amount of water or admixtures are commonly required. Certain rules of thumb are useful under these circumstances. Lean mixes require more sand than rich mixes. Once the optimum amount of sand has been found for a certain mix, the water-cement ratio may be adjusted by interchanging equal absolute volumes of sand and cement. This will affect the strength but will have little effect on slump and water content.

A change of approximately 3 per cent in total water will change slump by about 1 in. (Fig. 16-3). Changing the ratio of fine to coarse aggregate

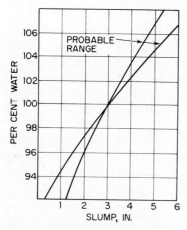

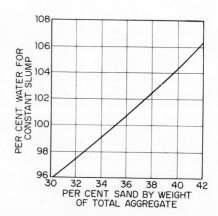

Fig. 16-3. Relation of slump to water requirement.

Fig. 16-4. Relation of sand percentage to water requirement at constant cement content 1½-in. aggregate.

affects the amount of water for constant slump (Fig. 16-4). Under field conditions, fluctuations in temperature, aggregate gradation, and other factors cause changes in the amount of water required for constant slump, hence variations of water-cement ratio of ±0.02 by weight, or ¼ gal per sack by volume, may be considered normal and do not require that the mix be adjusted. However, if the water-cement ratio is consistently high, an adjustment should be made to bring it down. If it is consistently low, it may be raised if strength of the concrete is adequate. Steps that aid in reducing the water-cement ratio include reducing the percentage of sand in the mix, improvement in sand grading, use of a larger size of coarse aggregate, use of a water-reducing admixture, or use of an air-entraining agent. Improvement in handling and placing procedures which permit the use of lower-slump concrete is sometimes effective.

Sometimes, during concreting operations, the technician may receive complaints of harshness of the concrete. If there has been an actual change in workability of the concrete, it is nearly always caused by a change in aggregate grading, either the fine or the coarse, or both. Correction may be made by adjusting the aggregate percentages. For example, an increase of 0.10 in the sand-fineness modulus may be partially offset by a decrease of about 25 lb of coarse aggregate per cubic yard of concrete, with a corresponding increase of an equal solid volume of sand. Changes in coarse-aggregate grading may affect the percentage of voids and therefore the rodded unit weight of the aggregate, which is reflected in a change in the amount of sand required.

Factors influencing workability of concrete are discussed in Chap. 2.

Lightweight Concrete

In proportioning lightweight concrete, use is made of the cement content rather than the water-cement ratio. By using the methods of ACI Standard 613-A, it is not necessary to know the values of absorption and specific gravity of the aggregate, yet this method enables one to proportion and control lightweight concrete with the same degree of precision as normal-weight concrete, provided certain precautions are observed.

Following the suggestions in ACI 613-A, a trial batch is first made, based on dry, loose unit weights of the aggregates and their moisture contents. The first trial batch is made with estimated amounts of the several materials, with sufficient water to produce the required slump. Fine and coarse aggregates should be proportioned in equal volumes, assuming about 32 cu ft of dry loose aggregates are required per cubic yard of concrete.

After the first trial batch has been made, corrected quantities per cubic yard are determined, and the "specific gravity factor" for each aggregate is computed. The specific gravity factor expresses the relationship between the dry weight of the aggregate and the space it occupies, assuming that no water is absorbed during mixing. That is, it equals

$$\frac{\text{wt of aggregate}}{62.3 \times \text{vol occupied in batch}}$$

The volume of aggregate is the difference between 27 cu ft and the sum of the volumes of cement, water, and air in a 1 cu yd batch. Subsequent batches are then proportioned at different cement contents.

When lightweight concrete is being used, frequent checks should be made of the slump, air content, and unit weight. Cement content and volume of dry aggregate per cubic yard of concrete should be kept constant. If the unit weight changes, a check of the entrained air content will reveal whether the change is caused by a change in entrained air or a change in grading, moisture content, or density of the aggregate. Most frequent aggregate change is due to a change in moisture content, and the aggregate weight on the scales is adjusted to keep the aggregate dry weight constant. An actual change in density should be compensated for by keeping the volume of dry aggregate constant (see discussion in Sec. 13-11).

Nailing Concrete

Sometimes it is desirable to make a concrete into which nails can be driven. For example, it may be necessary to attach roofing or flashing to a concrete structure. Actually, present-day construction practices and materials have nearly eliminated the need for nailing concrete, but there may be occasions when the engineer will find such material desirable.

Most of the lightweight concretes discussed in Sec. 13-11 are nailable under most conditions, but tests should be made prior to actual construction since proportions and timing are critical for successful nailing.

A type of concrete especially proportioned to receive nails is composed of cement, sand, and sawdust mixed in more or less equal parts by volume with sufficient water to produce a slump of about 2 in. A plastering sand, passing the No. 16 sieve, gives best results. Sawdust should be pine, rather coarse, but containing no chips larger than about ¼ in., and should be soaked for 24 hr before use. Some woods, especially the hardwoods, cedar, and Douglas fir, are entirely unsuitable. Trials should be made before materials and proportions are decided upon. Twenty-eight-day compressive strength may be expected to reach 1,200 to 2,000 psi.

16-2. ADMIXTURES

Air-entraining Agents

When converting a non-air-entrained mix to an air-entrained one, the cement content should be held the same and advantage taken of the lower water requirement in order to minimize any reduction in strength. Only in the rich mixes, over 6 sacks of cement per cu yd, is the strength difference significant.

The recommended amounts of air for concrete of different maximum sizes of coarse aggregate are as follows:

Maximum aggregate, in.	Total % air
½	7 ± 1
¾	6 ± 1
1½	5 ± 1
3	4 ± 1
6	3 ± 1

As compared with similar, non-air-entrained concrete, air-entrained concrete has the following properties:

1. Greatly improved resistance to weathering damage from cycles of freezing and thawing.

2. Greatly improved resistance of pavements to scaling by de-icing salts.

3. Greatly improved workability of the fresh concrete.

4. At the same water-cement ratio, compressive strength of the concrete is reduced by 4 to 6 per cent for each 1 per cent of entrained air. However, strength of lean mixes may be increased.

5. Resistance to attack by most chemicals is increased slightly.

6. Elasticity and erosion resistance follow strength.

7. Drying shrinkage increases as amount of air increases, but this is offset by lower water requirement, hence a negligible effect.

8. Reduction in permeability.

9. Only minor reduction in susceptibility to alkali-aggregate reaction.

10. Unit weight of concrete reduced in direct proportion to the amount of entrained air.

11. Reduced rate of bleeding.

The amount of air is affected by many variables other than the amount of agent used. An *increase* in any of the following has the indicated effect on the amount of entrained air:

Increase	*% air is*
Slump	Increased
W/C ratio	Increased
Per cent sand	Increased
Fines in sand	Decreased
Cement content	Decreased
Temperature	Decreased
Mixing time	Decreased
Cement fineness	Decreased

If the concrete mixer is overloaded, the blades worn, or the mixer operating at the wrong speed, the batch may not be mixed vigorously enough to make efficient use of the air-entraining agent. Changing from hard water to soft, or vice versa, may affect the amount of entrained air. Air-entraining agents are not permanently damaged by freezing, but stratification in the tank will result, requiring energetic remixing. During cold weather when using calcium chloride in the concrete, the air-entraining agent and chloride must be admitted to the batch in the mixer separately because the chloride tends to prevent entrainment of air. One expedient is to introduce the chloride in the mixing water and the air-entraining agent in the sand.

In certain areas known to exist in parts of Canada, Washington, and the Middle West, some sands contain organic material that acts as a foaming agent, entraining air in the concrete. This entrained air is unstable in the fresh concrete, and the remaining voids are poorly spaced and of the wrong size to be of any value in improving durability. When this condition is encountered, a minute amount of isopropyl alcohol will act as a defoaming agent. Sometimes an excess of air-entraining agent is effective in removing this "organic air" as it is sometimes called.

The air-entraining agent may be introduced into the concrete as a separate ingredient which may be added at the batch proportioning plant by means of a dispensing device, or it may be interground with the cement, reaching the concrete by way of the cement. Best control of the amount of entrained air is obtainable when the AEA is batched separately, as the amount can be varied in accordance with results of tests made on the concrete. However, for the job being done under minimum or partial inspection, it is best to use air-entraining cement, as this will assure at least a minimum amount of air in every batch. If concrete is being truck-mixed in transit, it is recommended that air-entraining cement be used, with additional AEA added to each batch at the proportioning plant, as required to maintain the proper percentage of air in the concrete.

Accelerators

Calcium chloride may be added to normal concrete mixes without further adjustments to the mix, except that a small reduction of mixing water may be possible. The amount of calcium chloride should not exceed 2 per cent by weight of the cement; usually, less is adequate.

When used in the proper amount, calcium chloride causes rapid strength gain during the first few days. As compared with plain concrete, concrete with the accelerator may be as much as 400 psi stronger at 1 day, 1,000 psi at 3 days, and 900 psi at 7 days. At 28 days the effect is still pronounced, and even at 1 year there may still be an effect. Actual effects will vary appreciably with different cements and temperature conditions. Other effects of the use of chloride are acceleration of the setting time, increased early heat development (but no effect on total heat of hydration), and a slight improvement of workability of the fresh concrete. Calcium chloride increases drying shrinkage, reduces bleeding, and increases expansion under moist curing; it does not cause rusting of reinforcing steel; it lowers the resistance to sulfate attack but increases the resistance to abrasion and erosion.

Calcium chloride should always be added to the batch in solution: to add it in flake or pellet form may result in stains or popouts where undissolved chloride concentrates in lumps. A good solution is one in which 1 qt of solution contains 1 lb of chloride. This solution is measured into the mixing water as it flows into the mixer by means of a mechanical dispensing device. Commercial calcium chloride for making the solution may be either the pellet form which contains about 95 per cent $CaCl_2$ or flake calcium chloride containing about 80 per cent $CaCl_2$. The amount of solution should be considered as part of the mixing water when computing the water-cement ratio.

Retarders

In the summer when air temperatures are high, cement sets or hydrates more rapidly than it does during cool weather. For this reason, it is often desirable to use a retarder during hot weather to lengthen the time the concete is plastic and workable. This retardation is especially desirable when placing conditions are such that the concrete has to be placed slowly in small increments such as would exist when concrete is placed through a small opening.

Under proper control, the use of a retarder is of great benefit in placing the concrete deck on a multispan continuous bridge. Formerly, practice was to place the deck in relatively short sections, alternating from end to end of the structure on different days, the reason being to permit beam deflections to take place before the deck concrete had set or after it had gained sufficient strength to resist. With the controlled use of a retarder regulated so as to provide much retardation to the first concrete placed and none to the last placed, it is possible to place a deck in a continuous operation, from one end of the structure to the other, without danger of cracking the first span when concrete is placed in the second, and so forth. As pointed out, this must be done under careful engineering supervision.

The several manufacturers of retarders furnish automatic dispensers for their products, and a dispenser should always be used. A laborer with a coffee can or pop bottle cannot be considered an automatic dispenser, although this procedure has been used. Even under careful control, there may be occasions when a double dose of admixture gets into the mixer. This need not be cause for alarm, as the affected concrete will develop full strength under adequate curing (see Sec. 3-5).

The method of evaluating retarders is briefly discussed in Sec. 10-8. This test evaluates the retarder as such, but when a retarder is used, trial mixes should be made in the field, with the equipment that will be used for mixing on the job. This is because small laboratory batches may not give the same results as job batches.

Temperature is important, not only as the admixture is affected by temperature, but also as the amount of retardation desired depends upon temperature. In ordinary concrete placements, no retardation is required at temperatures below 75°F. As the temperature rises, the amount of retarder is increased to maintain a constant period of workability.

Water Reducers

It sometimes happens that the combination of materials in use on a job just will not produce concrete of adequate workability and consistency without exceeding the specified water-cement ratio unless the cement content is excessive. A situation of this nature calls for the use of a water reducer. Concrete of very high strength, such as that specified for prestressed concrete, is more possible to attain, usually with less cement, if a water reducer is used in the concrete.

Inasmuch as strength increases and durability improves as the water-cement ratio goes down, other things being the same, it may be seen that it is advantageous to make use of a water reducer to aid in keeping the water-cement ratio as low as possible, within reasonable limits.

A water-reducer should be used only after field tests have demonstrated its effect on mix proportions, entrained air, and other properties of the concrete. Trials should be made with varying amounts of admixture, starting with a relatively small amount. The amount used should be the minimum to give the desired results, taking into account the varying effects of temperature, mix proportions, and placing conditions.

Gas-forming Agents

Shrinkage and bleeding of fresh concrete in difficult placements in which a fluid consistency is required are apt to result in voids under forms, embedded items, or machinery, causing a loss of bond and reduction in watertightness. This shrinkage can be prevented by the proper use of a material that reacts with the cement to produce an expansive gas. Unpolished aluminum powder is commonly used for this purpose in an amount equal to about 1 teaspoonful to a sack of cement (see Sec. 4-1).

The action of aluminum powder is a reaction with the hydroxides in the hydrating cement, producing minute hydrogen bubbles in the cement paste. Besides the fineness of aluminum powder used, the type of aluminum powder, temperature, cement composition and fineness, and mix proportions all affect the speed and amount of reaction.

During cold weather, the reaction is slowed considerably, and the desired result may not be obtained because the cement sets before the expansive action takes place. On the other hand, during hot weather, the reaction may occur so rapidly that no benefit results because the concrete may shrink normally after the gas generation reaction has ceased. The reaction starts when the materials come in contact and at normal temperatures may last for 1 to 3 hr.

The effect on strength of concrete depends upon whether or not the concrete is restrained from expanding. If it is restrained, the effect is negligible, but without restraint, the loss may be considerable.

Because of the very small quantity of aluminum used, it is usually mixed with 1 or 2 lb of dry sand per sack of cement before adding to the batch in the mixer.

The gas-forming technique is used for making lightweight concrete of very low density, as described in Chapter 13.

Pozzolans

Pozzolans are used in large massive structures where it is desirable to keep the heat of hydration as low as possible, in concrete exposed to sea water or sulfate attack, and as alkali-aggregate inhibitors. In those areas where the cost of a pozzolan is appreciably less than the cost of portland cement, proper use of the pozzolan as a replacement for part of the cement results in a saving in cost per cubic yard of concrete. However, no pozzolan should be used without complete understanding of its character, nor without trials with the materials proposed for the project, including strength and durability tests of the concrete. The amount varies with the type of pozzolan, mix, exposure, and other factors, ranging from 10 to 30 per cent replacement of the cement.

A pozzolan is usually proportioned in the batch as a replacement for part of the cement. When used in this way, it reduces water permeability, especially for lean mixes, and improves resistance to aggressive solutions such as sea water and sulfate or acid waters. Briefly, effects are as follows:

Heat generation in mass concrete is lessened because of the lower cement content. Because pozzolans are usually used in lean mixes, there is an improvement in workability, with a reduction in segregation and bleeding tendencies. The effect on mixing water requirement is variable. Fly-ash mixes require less water than plain concrete for the same consistency. Water requirements may be higher for some pozzolans, although the use of air-entrainment tends to counterbalance this.

In general, the cracking tendency of the hardened concrete is lessened, although drying shrinkage is increased with most pozzolans. Fly ash, however, appears to lessen shrinkage. The effect on strength is quite variable, depending on the type of pozzolan used. It is usually improved for lean mixes. Strength gain is slow, hence longer curing is necessary. With some pozzolans, strength after 1 yr is higher than for plain concrete. Fly ash gives flexural and compressive strengths equal or superior to plain concrete after a year.

Durability effects are variable. In general, the effect of pozzolans is to improve durability, especially if entrained air is used. However, there may be a reduction for some mixes and materials.

Most pozzolans have an inhibiting action on the alkali-aggregate reaction. Those high in opal are most effective, fly ash is least effective.

Probably one of the most important uses of pozzolans is for the enhanced resistance to moderate sulfate attack imparted to concrete by most pozzolans, especially those high in silica. However, Type V cement should be used in a severe sulfate exposure. Whether to use Type V cement or a pozzolan depends upon economic considerations and the results of laboratory tests.

When a pozzolan is added to concrete, as an addition to the cement, most of the above effects result, especially if the original concrete contained insufficient fines. Durability of mixes with adequate fines is affected adversely, and the shrinkage is increased. Strength is usually reduced, but the strength of lean mixes is increased.

16-3. CONCRETE OF A REQUIRED DENSITY

In making concrete for such an installation as a counterweight for a lift bridge, it is sometimes necessary to proportion and maintain the concrete at a certain high density within rather close tolerances.

To determine quantities of materials for a concrete of specified cement content and water-cement ratio required to have a high density, the first step is to determine weights and volumes per cubic yard of cement, water, voids, total aggregates, and sand. Then determine weight and volume of total coarse aggregate per cubic yard, and finally, determine weight and volume per cubic yard, of normal coarse aggregate and of the heavy aggregate.

EXAMPLE: A concrete is required to have a density of 156 pcf, using the following materials:

Material	Specific gravity	Density, pcf
Cement....................	3.15	196.24
Sand.....................	2.62	163.23
Gravel...................	2.55	158.87
Barites coarse aggregate.....	4.30	267.89

Specified values are:

Cement content: 5½ sacks per cu yd
Water: 6 gal per sack
Sand: 36 per cent by weight of total aggregate

Computed quantities per cu yd:

	Lb	Cu ft
Cement: 5.5 sacks..............	517.0	2.63
		from Table 16-7
Water: 6 × 5.5 = 33 gal.........	275	4.41
		from Table 16-8
Voids, 1% assumed		0.27
	792	7.31

Total wt: 27 × 156 = 4,212
Vol aggregate = 27 − 7.31 = 19.69 cu ft
Wt aggregate = 4,212 − 792 = 3,420 lb
Sand: 3,420 × 0.36 = 1,231 lb
1,231 × 0.006126 = 7.54 cu ft from Table 16-6.

Coarse Aggregate

$$3,420 - 1,231 = 2,189 \text{ lb}$$
$$19.69 - 7.54 = 12.15 \text{ cu ft}$$

Let G = wt gravel
B = wt barites

Then
$$12.15 = \frac{G}{158.87} + \frac{B}{267.89}$$

or
$$267.89G + 158.87B = 517,100.16$$

But
$$G + B = 2,189$$

Substituting and simplifying:

$$G = 1,552 \text{ lb}$$
$$B = 2,189 - 1,552 = 637 \text{ lb}$$

Vol gravel = 1,552 × .006294 = 9.77 cu ft, from Table 16-6

Vol barites = $637 \times \dfrac{1}{267.89}$ = 2.38 cu ft

The required mix: quantities per cu yd

Material	Weight, lb	Volume, cu ft
Cement.........	517	2.63
Water..........	275	4.41
Sand...........	1,231	7.54
Gravel.........	1,552	9.77
Barites.........	637	2.38
Voids..........		0.27
Total.........	4,212	27.00

If it is necessary to adjust the amount of water, proportions of all materials will have to be adjusted as above in order to maintain correct unit weight of concrete.

16-4. TEMPERATURE OF CONCRETE

The approximate temperature of concrete can be calculated from the temperatures of its ingredients by use of the following formula:

$$T = \frac{S(T_aW_a + T_cW_c) + T_fW_f + T_mW_m}{S(W_a + W_c) + W_f + W_m}$$

where T = temperature of concrete
S = 0.20, assumed specific heat of dry materials

	Weight symbol	Temperature symbol
Aggregates (surface dry)..........	W_a	T_a
Cement........................	W_c	T_c
Mixing water...................	W_m	T_m
Free moisture in aggregate........	W_f	T_f

Reference 4.3, Designation 35.

16-5. MISCELLANEOUS TABLES AND CHARTS

The following tables and charts will assist the technician in making certain computations in connection with concrete control.

Table 16-10: Water-Cement Ratio Conversions

Some agencies report water-cement ratios by volume, i.e., gallons of water per sack of cement; others report them by weight, i.e., pounds of water per pound of cement. Table 16-10 makes the conversion from one to the other for all values normally found in concrete work.

TABLE 16-10. CONVERSION OF WATER-CEMENT RATIO BY WEIGHT TO GALLONS PER SACK (GALLONS PER SACK = W/C BY WEIGHT × 11.28)

Lb water per lb cement	Lb water per lb cement									
	0	0.01	0.02	0.03	0.04	0.05	0.06	0.07	0.08	0.09
0.20	2.2560	2.3688	2.4816	2.5944	2.7072	2.8200	2.9328	3.0456	3.1584	3.2712
0.30	3.3840	3.4968	3.6096	3.7224	3.8352	3.9480	4.0608	4.1736	4.2864	4.3992
0.40	4.5120	4.6248	4.7376	4.8504	4.9632	5.0760	5.1888	5.3016	5.4144	5.5272
0.50	5.6400	5.7528	5.8656	5.9784	6.0912	6.2040	6.3168	6.4296	6.5424	6.6552
0.60	6.7680	6.8808	6.9936	7.1064	7.2192	7.3320	7.4448	7.5576	7.6704	7.7832
0.70	7.8960	8.0088	8.1216	8.2344	8.3472	8.4600	8.5728	8.6856	8.7984	8.9112
0.80	9.0240	9.1368	9.2496	9.3624	9.4752	9.5880	9.7008	9.8136	9.9264	10.0392
0.90	10.1520	10.2648	10.3776	10.4904	10.6032	10.7160	10.8288	10.9416	11.0544	11.1672

Note: Water-cement ratio by weight equals pounds of water per pound of cement.
EXAMPLE: A W/C of 0.55 by weight equals 6.2 gal per sack. Six gal per sack equals 0.532 by weight.

Table 16-11: Density of Concrete

This table is useful for determining the density of concrete from measurements of 6 × 12-in. cylinders. Note that this applies to specimens of exactly 6 in. diameter and lengths of 11¾, 11⅞, 12, and 12⅛ in. Length should be measured in four places and the diameter checked with calipers.

TABLE 16-11a. DENSITY OF CONCRETE
(From 6-in.-diameter cylinders)

Cylinder weight, lb	Length of cylinder, in.				Cylinder weight, lb	Length of cylinder, in.			
	11¾	11⅞	12	12⅛		11¾	11⅞	12	12⅛
19.00	98.8	97.8	96.8	95.8	22.00	114.4	113.2	112.1	110.9
19.10	99.3	98.3	97.3	96.3	22.10	114.9	113.7	112.6	111.4
19.20	99.9	98.8	97.8	96.8	22.20	115.5	114.2	113.1	111.9
19.30	100.4	99.3	98.4	97.3	22.30	116.0	114.7	113.6	112.4
19.40	100.9	99.8	98.9	97.8	22.40	116.5	115.2	114.1	112.9
19.50	101.4	100.4	99.4	98.3	22.50	117.0	115.8	114.6	113.4
19.60	101.9	100.9	99.9	98.8	22.60	117.5	116.3	115.1	113.9
19.70	102.5	101.4	100.4	99.3	22.70	118.1	116.8	115.6	114.4
19.80	103.0	101.9	100.9	99.8	22.80	118.6	117.3	116.1	114.9
19.90	103.5	102.4	101.4	100.3	22.90	119.1	117.8	116.6	115.4
20.00	104.0	102.9	101.9	100.8	23.00	119.6	118.4	117.1	115.9
20.10	104.5	103.4	102.4	101.3	23.10	120.1	118.9	117.7	116.4
20.20	105.1	103.9	102.9	101.8	23.20	120.7	119.4	118.2	116.9
20.30	105.6	104.4	103.4	102.3	23.30	121.2	119.9	118.7	117.4
20.40	106.1	104.9	104.0	102.8	23.40	121.7	120.4	119.2	118.0
20.50	106.6	105.5	104.5	103.3	23.50	122.2	120.9	119.7	118.5
20.60	107.1	106.0	105.0	103.8	23.60	122.7	121.5	120.2	119.0
20.70	107.7	106.5	105.5	104.3	23.70	123.3	122.0	120.7	119.5
20.80	108.2	107.0	106.0	104.8	23.80	123.8	122.5	121.2	120.0
20.90	108.7	107.5	106.5	105.3	23.90	124.3	123.0	121.7	120.5
21.00	109.2	108.1	107.0	105.9	24.00	124.8	123.5	122.2	121.0
21.10	109.7	108.6	107.5	106.4	24.10	125.3	124.1	122.7	121.5
21.20	110.3	109.1	108.0	106.9	24.20	125.9	124.6	123.2	122.0
21.30	110.8	109.6	108.5	107.4	24.30	126.4	125.1	123.7	122.5
21.40	111.3	110.1	109.0	107.9	24.40	126.9	125.6	124.2	123.0
21.50	111.8	110.7	109.6	108.4	24.50	127.4	126.2	124.7	123.5
21.60	112.3	111.2	110.1	108.9	24.60	127.9	126.7	125.2	124.0
21.70	112.9	111.7	110.6	109.4	24.70	128.5	127.2	125.7	124.5
21.80	113.4	112.2	111.1	109.9	24.80	129.0	127.7	126.3	125.0
21.90	113.9	112.7	111.6	110.4	24.90	129.5	128.2	126.8	125.5

TABLE 16-11*b*. DENSITY OF CONCRETE

(From 6-in.-diameter cylinders)

Cylinder weight, lb	Length of cylinder, in.				Cylinder weight, lb	Length of cylinder, in.			
	$11\frac{3}{4}$	$11\frac{7}{8}$	12	$12\frac{1}{8}$		$11\frac{3}{4}$	$11\frac{7}{8}$	12	$12\frac{1}{8}$
25.00	130.0	128.7	127.3	126.0	28.00	145.6	144.1	142.6	141.1
25.10	130.5	129.2	127.8	126.5	28.10	146.2	144.6	143.1	141.6
25.20	131.1	129.7	128.3	127.0	28.20	146.7	145.1	143.6	142.1
25.30	131.6	130.2	128.8	127.5	28.30	147.2	145.6	144.1	142.6
25.40	132.1	130.8	129.3	128.1	28.40	147.7	146.2	144.6	143.1
25.50	132.6	131.3	129.8	128.6	28.50	148.2	146.7	145.1	143.7
25.60	133.1	131.8	130.3	129.1	28.60	148.8	147.2	145.7	144.2
25.70	133.7	132.3	130.8	129.6	28.70	149.3	147.7	146.2	144.7
25.80	134.2	132.8	131.3	130.1	28.80	149.8	148.2	146.7	145.2
25.90	134.7	133.4	131.8	130.6	28.90	150.3	148.7	147.2	145.7
26.00	135.2	133.9	132.4	131.1	29.00	150.8	149.3	147.7	146.2
26.10	135.7	134.4	132.9	131.6	29.10	151.4	149.8	148.2	146.7
26.20	136.3	134.9	133.4	132.1	29.20	151.9	150.3	148.7	147.2
26.30	136.8	135.4	133.9	132.6	29.30	152.4	150.8	149.2	147.7
26.40	137.3	136.0	134.4	133.1	29.40	152.9	151.3	149.7	148.2
26.50	137.8	136.5	134.9	133.6	29.50	153.4	151.8	150.2	148.7
26.60	138.3	137.0	135.4	134.1	29.60	154.0	152.3	150.8	149.2
26.70	138.9	137.5	135.9	134.6	29.70	154.5	152.9	151.3	149.7
26.80	139.4	138.0	136.4	135.1	29.80	155.0	153.4	151.8	150.2
26.90	139.9	138.5	136.9	135.6	29.90	155.5	153.9	152.3	150.7
27.00	140.4	139.0	137.5	136.1	30.00	156.0	154.4	152.8	151.2
27.10	140.9	139.5	138.0	136.6	30.10	156.6	154.9	153.3	151.7
27.20	141.5	140.0	138.5	137.1	30.20	157.1	155.4	153.8	152.2
27.30	142.0	140.5	139.0	137.6	30.30	157.6	155.9	154.3	152.7
27.40	142.5	141.0	139.5	138.1	30.40	158.1	156.5	154.8	153.2
27.50	143.0	141.6	140.0	138.6	30.50	158.6	157.0	155.3	153.7
27.60	143.5	142.1	140.5	139.1	30.60	159.2	157.5	155.8	154.2
27.70	144.1	142.6	141.0	139.6	30.70	159.7	158.0	156.4	154.7
27.80	144.6	143.1	141.5	140.1					
27.90	145.1	143.6	142.1	140.6					

16-6. REPORTS

Most of the information in concrete control activities can be reported in form reports rather than in narrative reports. Forms may vary from job to job, depending upon the type of work and the personal preferences of engineers and architects.

Figure 16-5 is a typical daily report for a field concrete inspector, showing the type of information required. This form was found to be suitable

SOIL TESTING SERVICES, INC.

Project No. __2365__

STS Job No. __6198 A__

Date __March 19, 1962__

Report No. __12__

Quality Control Section:

DAILY INSPECTION OF CONCRETE

Architect Engineer __Simpson-Peck, Inc__ Contractor __Turner Construction Co__

Structure __Apartment Bldg__ Location __6700 S. Oglesby__ Portion __Fuel Oil Tank__

PRODUCERS: Concrete __M S Co.__ Fine Agg. __Romeo Blend__ Co. Agg. __Romeo Stone__

CEMENT: Brand & Type __Universal Type I__ Admixtures AEA __None__ Other __None__

MIXER: Make __Smith__ Type __Truck__ Capacity __7½ cu yd__

Class of Concrete __3000 psi__ Mix. No. __1A__ Weather __Cloudy__

HOURS OF OPERATION From __10 a m__ To __2:30 p m__ Total __4½ hr__ Source of Water __City__

COARSE AGGREGATE SIZE RANGE: Small: __No. 4__ To __3/4 in__; Large: __--__ To __--__

Time	% Moisture Sand	Coa.	Coa.	Scale Settings Cement	Sand	Coarse	Coarse	Water	Water In Agg.	Total Water	Gal./ Sack
10:30	5	1		1939	5020	7460	--	780	315	1095	6.5
Design Mix per cu yd				517	1275	1970	--	35 gal			

FIELD DATA

Time	Slump in.	Unit Wt. lbs./c. ft.	Air %	Temperature °F Air	Conc.	Cylinder or Beam No.	Location	Temperature °F Water	Cement	Sand
11:15	3½	150.5	0.5	38	74	OT-7 to OT-12	Tank footing	100	58	40

	Return c.f./cu. yd.	Cement Factor Sks./Cu. yd.	AEA oz.	Admixture oz. or lb.	CaCl₂ %
	26.9	5.52	0	0	0

Size Batch __7½ cy__ No. of Batches __11__

Cu. Yds. Rejected __0__

Cu. Yds. Placed __82.2__

Cu. Yds. Previous __895.0__

Cu. Yds. to Date __977.2__

Remarks: Scale settings shown for ½ batch.
Full batch made in two dumps.

__B. LaRue__
Inspector

Form M-1

FIG. 16-5. A typical concrete inspector's daily report.

where inspection was being performed for many different types of jobs. In addition to this report, the inspector was required to file a strength test report for each group of strength specimens. (The strength report was completed in the laboratory at the time the specimens were tested.) If aggregate tests were made during the day, they were reported on a special report form.

The importance of accurate and complete reports cannot be stressed too strongly. Whenever a situation arises, weeks or months—even years— after the concrete was placed, requiring an examination of the inspector's reports, the value of good reports is forcibly demonstrated.

REFERENCES

16.1   Recommended Practice for Selecting Proportions for Concrete (ACI 613), American Concrete Institute, Detroit, September, 1954.

Glossary

Accelerator: An admixture which, when added to a batch of concrete, accelerates cement hydration, thus causing the concrete to develop strength more rapidly than concrete without the accelerator.

Admixture: A substance, other than cement, water, or aggregate, added to a batch of fresh concrete in the mixer for the purpose of altering any of the properties of the concrete—includes pozzolans.

AEA: Air-entraining agent, which see.

Agitator: A vehicle for transporting concrete, in which premixed concrete is slowly mixed or agitated en route to the jobsite. Specifically, a rotary drum mixer mounted on a motor truck. See *Truck mixer.*

Air-entrained Concrete: Concrete containing purposefully entrained air. Principal advantage is improved durability.

Air-entraining Agent: An admixture that forms numerous microscopic air bubbles or spheroids in concrete. See *Entrained air.*

Alkali-Aggregate Reaction: A detrimental reaction which can occur in hardened concrete between certain siliceous portions of the aggregates and the alkalies in cement.

Architectural Concrete: Exposed concrete on a building, either exterior or interior, required to have an especially high-quality finish free from blemishes.

Autogenous Healing: Self-healing of cracks under favorable conditions of temperature, moisture, and lack of movement.

Bank Run: See *Pit run.*

Bar Mat: Reinforcing steel bars preassembled into a mat for installation in a slab, usually a paving slab.

Barrel: A unit of measure of cement, equal to 376 lb or 4 sacks.

Base: The compacted earth or granular material on which a paving slab is placed.

Batch Truck: A dump truck with the body divided into transverse compartments by partitions, for hauling weighed batches of cement and aggregate from the proportioning (batching) plant to the mixer.

Batching Sequence: Any sequence of introducing the ingredients of concrete into the mixer.

Belting: A finishing operation for pavement in which a wide belt is dragged back and forth across the fresh slab as it is advanced along the slab.

Beneficiation: Any process that beneficiates, or improves the quality of, aggregate by removal of soft or lightweight particles.

Bleeding: Water gain. Sedimentation. The appearance of free water on the surface of fresh concrete resulting from settlement of solid particles and consequent relative upward movement of water.

Blending Sand: A sand added to the normal available sand for improvement of gradation.

Blockout: An opening or cavity formed in concrete to facilitate subsequent construction on a structure. Example, a blockout in a wall for installation of a pipe. Blockouts are usually filled with concrete or mortar upon completion of construction.

Blowup: Buckling and cracking of a paving slab caused by abnormal expansion of the concrete.

Bond: Adhesion of cement paste to aggregate particles, or of concrete or mortar to reinforcing steel, or of concrete to previously hardened concrete on a construction joint or in a patch.

Bonding Agent: (1) An admixture for improving bond, especially in mortar or concrete for a patch. (2) A paint or coating applied to hardened concrete to facilitate bonding of new concrete or mortar.

Bug Holes: Small pits, bubbles, or voids, in the surface of formed concrete.

Bull Float: A float with a handle several feet long which enables the finisher to float a slab from outside the edges of the slab.

Cage: A prefabricated assembly of reinforcing mesh or bars, especially for pipe or piling.

Cage Mill Disintegrator: See *Impact crusher.*

Cap: The act of preparing a strength specimen for testing, in which a fluid or mastic material is applied to the specimen ends to be in contact with the testing machine. Hardening of the capping compound against a machined steel plate provides a smooth surface. Also, the hardened material after application to the specimen.

Capillarity: Flow of water through minute pores and voids in concrete, resulting from capillary action instituted when a constant supply of water is in contact with one surface of the concrete, and evaporation occurs on the other side.

Cast Stone: A high-quality precast concrete of architectural quality used for such items as sills and copings.

Cavitation: Wearing away of concrete exposed to high-velocity, turbulent flow of water, resulting in a rough, pockmarked surface.

Cement Content: The amount of cement in 1 cu yd of concrete, expressed either in pounds, sacks, or barrels.

Cement Factor: Cement content.

Central-mixed Concrete: Concrete that is mixed in a stationary mixer and hauled to the jobsite in agitators. See *Ready-mixed concrete.*

Centrifugal Pipe: Concrete pipe manufactured by spinning a horizontal form, the concrete being forced against the rotating form by centrifugal force.

Classification: The process of improving or changing the gradation of aggregate by means of screening or other sorting equipment.

Cleanup: The act of preparing a construction joint or rock foundation to receive concrete, in which the surface is scrubbed or sandblasted for removal of dirt, laitance, oil, and other foreign material.

Coarse Aggregate: The aggregate particles retained on a ³⁄₁₆-in. sieve.

Cobble Mix: Mass concrete containing coarse aggregate up to 6 in. in diameter (rarely larger).

Coefficient of Expansion: The rate at which concrete changes volume with changes in temperature. For concrete, the coefficient of linear expansion is 0.0000055 in./(in.)(°F).

Cohesiveness: The element of workability that governs the extent of harshness or stickiness.

Cold Joint: The surface between two successive runs of concrete, in which the first concrete placed has passed its final set and can no longer be blended into the second run.

Concrete Products: Precast concrete, especially brick, block, pipe, sills, etc., produced at a central manufacturing plant for many users.

Conductivity: The rate at which concrete conducts heat.

Consistency: A measure of the fluidity, softness, or wetness of fresh concrete, determined by measuring the number of inches a specific sample slumps or subsides when a conical form is removed from the sample. The greater the number of inches of subsidence, the "higher" the slump, and the wetter or softer the concrete.

Consolidate: To make concrete into a solid, uniform mass, without voids or rock pockets, usually accomplished by the application of vibration, occasionally by hand spading or tamping. Sometimes called "compact."

Construction Joint: A plane surface between two increments of concrete, the second increment having been placed on or against the first after the first had hardened.

Contraction: Reduction in volume of hardened concrete due to drying after wetting, or temperature reduction. See *Expansion.*

Contraction Joint: A groove formed in the fresh concrete, or sawed in the hardened concrete, to create a plane of weakness in a slab or panel so as to cause the concrete, during drying shrinkage, to crack at the weakened plane rather than at random.

Control Chart: A chronological graph of concrete strength for control and analysis of concrete strength.

Control Joint: A contraction joint or expansion joint.

Crazing: Hair cracking. A pattern of fine hairlike cracks caused by shrinkage of the surface of concrete relative to the interior (see Fig. 7-2).

Creep: Plastic flow. Deformation of concrete under sustained load.

Cumulative Weighing: Weighing of materials successively on the same scale, the weight of each material being cumulative or added to the previous ones in the batch.

Curing: Protection of concrete for a specified period of time after placement to provide moisture for hydration of the cement, to provide proper temperature, and to protect the concrete from damage by loading or mechanical disturbance.

Curing Blanket: A curing mat.

Curing Compound: Sealing compound. Liquid sprayed on the surface of fresh concrete to seal against loss of moisture.

Curing Mat: A mat or pad of jute, sisal, or cotton moistened and laid on a fresh concrete slab to provide curing moisture. Also, a mat, kept dry, to insulate a green slab during cold weather.

D-line Crack: Weathering crack, occurring as many fine, closely spaced cracks more or less parallel to edges of affected member, filled with a deposit of calcium carbonate and dirt (see Fig. 5-4).

Dampproofer: A substance, added to a batch of concrete as an admixture or applied to the hardened concrete as a paint or coating, which decreases capillarity.

Darby: A special finishing tool (see Fig. 13-13).

Deformed Bar: A steel bar or rod for reinforcing concrete, which is covered with a pattern of ribs or ridges (deformations) to enhance its bond with the concrete.

Diatomaceous Earth: Fine-grained, chalky appearing material consisting of shells of diatoms (microscopic one-celled organisms) occurring in siliceous sedimentary deposits. Used as a pozzolan.

Diffusivity: A measure of the capability of concrete to undergo temperature changes.

Dowel: A smooth metal bar extending across a joint in concrete to transfer the applied loading, and to prevent vertical misalignment at the joint. See *Load transfer device.*

Dowel Assembly: Dowel basket. An assembly of dowels and supporting framework for holding the dowels in place during concrete placing, especially in pavement construction.

Dropchute: Elephant trunk. A series of conical sections of sheet steel pipe that forms a flexible downspout for confining concrete during a vertical fall. Each section is about 3 ft long, 12 in. in diameter at the large end and 10 in. in diameter at the small, or lower, end.

Dry: Stiff, nonplastic consistency of fresh concrete with low slump, as opposed to soft or wet consistency.

Dry Pack: To patch with dry pack mortar. A mixture of cement and sand with just sufficient water to make it moist, used for patching deep, narrow cavities.

Dry Process: To process aggregate without the use of water. Also, a process for manufacturing portland cement.

Dry Shake: Dust coat. A dry mixture of cement and special fine aggregate broadcast on a floor slab before final finishing to provide a wear-resistant surface.

Drying Shrinkage: Reduction in volume of hardened concrete as it dries out after placing.

Dual Drum Mixer: A mixer consisting of a long drum divided into two separate compartments by a bulkhead with a swinging chute extending through it.

Dummy Joint: A preformed contraction joint.

Durability: Resistance of hardened concrete to forces or substances attempting to destroy it; especially, resistance to weathering.

Dust Coat: See *Dry shake.*

Dusting: Wearing away of a concrete surface, especially a floor of inferior hardness, under traffic.

Efflorescence: Crystalline salts deposited on a concrete surface by movement of water from the interior of the mass and subsequent evaporation.

Elastic Deformation: Deformation of concrete under load which disappears upon removal of the load.

Elastic Fractionation: Removal of soft aggregate particles based on the principle that hard particles will rebound off a steel plate farther than soft, friable ones.

Elephant Trunk: See *Dropchute.*

Entrained Air: Minute bubbles or spheroids of air formed in concrete by the introduction of an air-entraining agent.

Entrapped Air: Air voids larger than 0.05 in. in diameter mechanically entrapped in concrete.

Erosion: Wearing away of concrete by water containing suspended solids.

Expansion: Increase in volume of concrete caused by wetting or rise in temperature. See *Contraction.*

Expansion Joint: A joint in concrete that allows the concrete to contract and expand without damaging the structure or introducing excessive stresses.

Exposed Aggregate: Any process of finishing or surface treatment that results in clean aggregate particles being exposed on the surface for special architectural effect.

FM: Fineness modulus.

False Set: Gum set. Rubber set. Premature stiffening. Erratic, abnormal quick setting of cement in concrete, caused by unstable gypsum in the cement. Subsequent working of the concrete "breaks down" false set.

Fat: (Applied to a concrete mix.) Rich, cohesive, plastic. Opposite of harsh.

Field-cured Specimen: Strength specimen cured at the structure site supposedly under the same conditions as the structural concrete.

Fill Plane: A construction joint.

Filler, Joint: See *Joint filler.*

Final Set: The time in the course of hardening of cement beyond which the concrete can no longer be made plastic. See *Setting time.*

Fine Aggregate: Sand. That portion of the aggregate passing a No. 4 (¾₁₆ in.) sieve.

Fines: In aggregate processing, sand. Undersize. In concrete finishing, silt and clay material mixed with cement and water. Laitance.

Finish Screen: A screen at the batching plant for final removal of undersize and dirt from coarse aggregate just before it enters the plant bins.

Flash Set: Quick setting of cement caused by the use of excessively hot water and aggregates, or similar causes. A flash set is permanent. See *False set.*

Flatwork: Sidewalks, floors, any flat slab work on the ground.

Float: A finishing tool used after screeding and before troweling. The act of floating.

Floor Topping: A thin (1 in. or less) layer of high-strength, high-quality concrete applied to a slab to provide a finish floor.

Fluidity: An element of workability. Consistency. The wetness or softness of fresh concrete.

Fly Ash: Precipitator ash. Fine residue in flue gas from furnaces burning powdered coal. Particles are usually smaller than about 10 μ. Used as a pozzolan.

Form Oil: Any liquid material applied to forms to prevent concrete from sticking. Some form oils remain liquid, others (lacquer) harden before concrete is placed.

Foundation Seal: Sand slab. A slab of concrete placed in the bottom of a wet excavation to seal the bottom and facilitate subsequent work.

Fresh Concrete: Concrete that has not reached its initial set.

Gel: An amorphous material formed during the hardening or setting of cement, composed of water and the dissolved constituents of the cement. Also, an amorphous, gelatinous exudation resulting from the alkali-aggregate reaction.

Gradation: Grading. Mechanical analysis. Sieve analysis. The distribution of particle sizes of an aggregate on several specified sizes of sieves. Expressed either as individual or cumulative per cents, either retained or passing.

Grading: See *Gradation.*

Green Concrete: An indefinite term applied to concrete that has passed initial set, or final set, but has not yet gained appreciable strength.

Green Cracks: Preset or plastic cracks. Cracking that occurs in concrete while in the green state.

Grout: 1. A fluid mixture of cement and water, sometimes with an admixture and sometimes containing sand, forced under pressure into voids such as may exist between concrete and rock in tunnel lining, or into cracks in rock foundations, or into joints in massive concrete structures. 2. Mortar, especially mortar spread on a construction joint or rock foundation ahead of concrete placing. Neat grout is composed of cement and water only.

Gum Set: See *False set.*

Gunite: Shotcrete.

Hair Cracks: See *Crazing.*

Harsh: Harshness. Applied to a concrete mix: unworkable, lacking plasticity, noncohesive, tending to segregate easily. Opposite of fat.

Heat of Hydration: The heat liberated during the hydration or setting of cement.

Heavy Aggregate: Special aggregate of high specific gravity such as barite, magnetite or steel punchings, for producing high-density concrete for radiation shielding and counterweights.

Heavy Concrete: High-density concrete for radiation shielding or counterweights. Density may exceed twice that of ordinary concrete.

Heavy Media: A high-density fluid for removing aggregate particles of low specific gravity by means of flotation. Usually a suspension of magnetite and ferrosilicon in water.

Hindered Settlement: A classifying process for fine aggregate in which aggregate is fed into a rising current of water. Fine material rises with the water and coarse material settles to the bottom. See *Jigging.*

Hinge Joint: A joint in pavement that permits movement of adjacent slabs.

Honeycomb Rock pockets. Voids in concrete resulting from incomplete consolidation.

Hydration: The chemical process of hardening of cement paste.

Hydraulic Structure: Any structure used for conveying water, or exposed to water, such as a sea wall or canal structure.

Impact Crusher: A machine for beneficiating coarse aggregate, in which high-speed rotating vanes break up the soft particles by impact.

Initial Set: See *Setting time.*

Insulating Concrete: Lightweight concrete with density of 90 pcf or less, used for thermal insulation in roofs, etc., and for fire protection of structural elements in buildings.

Integral Waterproofer: An admixture which reduces flow or capillarity of water through concrete. See *Dampproofer* and *Waterproofer.*

Jigging: A process of aggregate beneficiation, based on the hindered settlement principle, in which aggregate is passed over a perforated plate in a tank of water which is subjected to vertical pulsations either by air jets or vibrating diaphragms. Lightweight material floats off to waste.

Job-cured Specimen: See *Field-cured specimen.*

Joint: See type of joint referred to: cold joint; construction joint; contraction joint; control joint; dummy joint; expansion joint; hinge joint; warping joint; weakened plane joint.

Joint Assembly: See *Dowel assembly.*

Joint Filler: A material for filling or sealing joints in concrete, at the same time allowing movement of the joint. Contraction joint filler is usually a heavy mastic composed of bituminous material and a filler. Expansion joint filler is usually a preformed strip of compressible material, such as self-expanding cork, or a felt or fibre saturated with bituminous material.

Key: An elevation or depression formed in a concrete joint surface for providing shear strength across the joint. See *Load transfer device.*

Laitance: A weak, light-gray substance consisting of cement, water, and silt or clay from the aggregates, appearing on the top surface of concrete during and immediately after consolidation.

Leach: To wash out by the passage of water through a material.

Lead: In batching concrete, to commence the introduction of a material into the mixer ahead of another material.

Lean Mix: A concrete low in cement content. Opposite of rich mix.

Lift: A layer. The depth of concrete placed at one time.

Lift Slab Construction: A method in which floor slabs are cast on the ground floor and raised to final position by means of jacks on top of the building columns.

Lightweight Concrete: Any concrete made with special low-density aggregate. Lightweight structural concrete has a density of approximately 100 pcf. Lightweight insulating concrete has a density between 15 and 90 pcf.

Load Transfer Device: Any device, such as a dowel or key, for transferring live load across a joint. See *Key.*

Los Angeles Abrasion: A method for testing aggregates for hardness and abrasion resistance by tumbling a standard sample in a standard ball mill for a certain number of revolutions. See ASTM Designation: C 131.

Map Cracking: A random distribution of cracks on the surface of concrete, sometimes in a roughly hexagonal or square pattern. May be quite fine, or deep and serious. Evidence of surface shrinkage or internal expansion.

Mass Concrete: Concrete placed in large masses, such as in a dam or large footing. It is lean concrete, containing aggregate as large as 6 in. and usually containing a pozzolan.

Mechanical Analysis: See *Gradation.*

Membrane Curing: The method of curing concrete by the application of a curing compound. See *Curing compound.*

Membrane Waterproofing: A method of waterproofing concrete below grade in which alternate layers of bituminous material (usually hot) and felt or fabric are applied to the concrete surface.

Mix: Fresh concrete. The mixture of aggregates, cement, water, and admixtures.

Mix Proportions: 1. The ratio by weight of the several constituents of concrete. 2. The actual amounts of the constituents, usually in 1 cu yd of concrete.

Mixture: See *Mix.*

Mobility: An element of workability of concrete, best described as the ease with which the concrete can be moved about while in the plastic state.

368 *Practical Quality Control for Concrete*

Mud Jacking: The act of raising a slab-on-ground, most commonly a paving slab, by pumping a cement-soil-water slurry under pressure through holes drilled through the slab.

Nailing Concrete: Any concrete proportioned to receive nails, such as for a roof flashing. A lightweight or sawdust concrete.

Neat Grout: A grout consisting of cement and water. See *Grout.*

Oversanded: Applied to a concrete mix; containing an excess of fine aggregate.

Oversize: In aggregate, the material retained on the maximum specified sieve. For example, in ¾ × 1½ in. aggregate, the portion retained on 1½-in. sieve.

Packerhead: A machine for making concrete pipe in which a revolving packerhead or shoe compacts the concrete against a stationary outside vertical mold.

PAM: Pneumatically applied mortar. See *Shotcrete.*

Paste: The cementing medium in concrete, consisting of cement and water.

Pattern Cracking: See *Map cracking.*

Paving Train: The lineup of equipment on a road-paving job consisting of such machines as the spreader, finisher, longitudinal float, burlap drag, etc.

Permeability: The property of concrete which allows water, under a hydrostatic head, to flow through interstices or channels in the concrete.

Pit Run: Bank run. Applied to aggregates; the condition of the raw aggregate as it is excavated from the bank or pit.

Place: To deposit concrete in the forms or on the subgrade.

Plastic Cracks: See *Green cracks.*

Plastic Flow: See *Creep.*

Plastic Shrinkage: Shrinkage of paste occurring while the concrete is still plastic, or after the concrete has become rigid but has not developed appreciable strength.

Plasticity: An element of workability. The property of fresh concrete to change shape under the application of an external force.

Pneumatically Applied Mortar: See *Shotcrete.*

Popout: A blemish on the surface of concrete consisting of a conical piece of concrete, with the base on the surface of the concrete, pushed out by the expansion of an aggregate particle at the apex of the cone.

Posttensioned: Prestressed by the application of tensile load to the prestressing tendons after the concrete has gained the required strength.

Pour: To place concrete. The amount of concrete placed during one continuous placement. A colloquialism.

Pozzolan: As defined in ASTM Designation: C 219: A pozzolan is "a siliceous or siliceous and aluminous material, which in itself possesses little or no cementitious value but will, in finely divided form and in the presence of moisture, chemically react with calcium hydroxide at ordinary temperatures to form compounds possessing cementitious properties."

Precast Concrete: Any concrete that is cast in molds or forms at a location other than its final location in the structure. Especially concrete products.

Premature Stiffening: See *False set.*

Preset Cracks: See *Green cracks.*

Prestressed Concrete: Concrete in which a compressive load is applied during the manufacturing process by means of the application of a tensile load to steel strands, wires, or rods in the concrete. The load is transferred as a compressive load in the concrete by means of bond with the steel or special fixtures where the tendons emerge from the concrete.

Pretensioned: Prestressed by first tensioning the steel tendons, then placing the concrete about them. After the concrete reaches the required strength, stress is transferred to the concrete by releasing the anchorages holding the strands at the ends of the casting bed.

Pumpcrete: Trade name for a machine for pumping fresh concrete through a pipeline.

Pumping: In a pavement, loss of fines from the subgrade through cracks or joints in the pavement under action of traffic. Fines are carried through the crack by water forced through the crack when a vehicle depresses the slab slightly on a fine-grained, nondraining base or foundation.

Quarter: To divide an aggregate sample into quarter parts for the purpose of reducing the sample quantity to a size suitable for testing.

Random Cracks: See *Map cracking.*

Reactive Aggregate: An aggregate that undergoes a destructive reaction after its inclusion in concrete. Specifically, certain siliceous minerals and rocks that react with cement alkalies, causing a destructive internal expansion of hardened concrete.

Ready-mixed Concrete: Concrete that is mixed before delivery to the jobsite. It may be mixed in a central plant and hauled to the jobsite in truck hauling units (agitating or nonagitating), or it may be batched into a mixer mounted on a truck and mixed en route to the site, or a combination of partial mixing in the central plant and mixing en route in a truck mixer.

Rebar: A concrete reinforcing bar.

Resteel: Reinforcing steel.

Retarder: An admixture that slows or retards the setting of cement, but has little or no effect on strength gain of the paste after initial set.

Return: The actual number of cubic feet of concrete in a designed or theoretical 1-cu-yd batch, based on tests of the fresh concrete.

Ribbon Feed: A batching sequence in which all materials are fed into the mixer practically simultaneously.

Rich: A mix high in cement content. Opposite of lean.

Rock Ladder: A series of inclined steps, arranged in a vertical column, to break up the vertical drop of coarse aggregate as it is discharged from a belt or chute, for the purpose of minimizing breakage of the aggregate.

Rock Pocket: See *Honeycomb.*

Rubbed Surface: A formed concrete surface modified by rubbing with a carborundum stone, or with burlap and mortar, to improve the appearance.

Rubber Set: See *False set.*

Rustication Strip: A strip of wood or other material attached inside the form, for forming a groove in the concrete at a construction joint or panel joint.

Sack: (1) A unit of measure of cement, ¼ bbl or 94 lb. (2) To rub a concrete surface with burlap and mortar.

Sand: Fine aggregate. That portion of aggregate passing a No. 4 (³⁄₁₆-in. mesh) sieve.

Sand Slab: See *Foundation seal.*

Sand Streak: A blemish on a formed concrete surface resulting from loss of mortar or grout through cracks in the forms, or resulting from failure to consolidate the concrete. See *Honeycomb.*

Sawdust Concrete: Concrete of low strength containing sawdust as "aggregate," used for lightweight nailing concrete for roof flashings and similar construction.

Scale: To come off the surface by peeling or flaking; especially as applied to pavements, to peel or flake under the influence of de-icing agents.

Scalp: To remove certain portions of pit-run aggregate, either fine or coarse, in a preliminary screening operation.

Screed: Any of several guides or tools for making the first strike-off of the surface of concrete; especially (1) one of a pair of temporary pipes or strips of wood set accurately to grade, on which the strike-off board slides while removing excess concrete; and (2) the strike-off board itself.

Scrubber: A machine for cleaning coarse aggregate consisting of a horizontal rotating cylinder containing blades that lift and tumble the aggregate, usually in the presence of water, to remove soft particles and coatings.

Sealing Compound: (1) A bituminous material for filling or sealing joints and cracks. (2) Curing compound.

Sedimentation: See *Bleeding.*

Segregation: In aggregate, separation of the fine portion of the material from the coarser portion. In concrete, separation of coarse aggregate from the mortar, or main mass of the concrete.

Setting Time: The period of time elapsed between the mixing of water with cement, and certain arbitrary points in the hydration or setting process. It is determined by the penetration of a standard needle into a sample of cement paste in a specified period of time. "Initial set" and "final set" are arbitrary values of penetration, indicating respectively the time when the paste (and consequently the concrete) starts to lose plasticity, and the time the paste or concrete starts to become rigid. See ASTM Designation: C 191, C 266, and C 403.

Settlement Crack: A crack in the soffit of a beam, or top of a wall or column, where it joins a slab, resulting from continuous placing of concrete in the beam, wall or column, and the slab. Shrinkage and restraint at the juncture between the structural elements cause a green crack.

Shotcrete: A mixture of cement, sand, and water, applied by shooting into place with compressed air. Also gunite, or pneumatically applied mortar.

Shrink-mixed Concrete: A form of ready-mixed concrete, in which the ingredients are combined in a stationery mixer (shrunk), then dumped into a truck mixer, where mixing is completed in transit. See *Transit-mixed concrete.*

Shrinkage: See *Plastic shrinkage.*

Shrinkage Cracks: Any cracking that results from shrinkage of the concrete.

Sieve Analysis: See *Gradation.*

Slag: A nonmetallic by-product of steel blast furnaces, crushed and sized for concrete aggregate. When quenched in water, a lightweight aggregate is produced.

Slip Form: A sliding form that produces a continuous placement of concrete as the form is moved along, either vertically, as for a silo, or horizontally, as for a canal lining.

Slump: See *Consistency.*

Slurry: Neat Grout. A thin mixture of cement and water.

Spall: To crumble at a joint or along an edge. Also, a fragment of concrete broken off in this manner.

Split: To divide a sample into smaller parts. See *Quarter.*

Spreader: (1) A machine for distributing or spreading concrete on a pavement base ahead of the finisher. (2) A metal rod or piece of wood temporarily inserted in a form to hold the form in alignment until concrete is placed.

Sticky: Applied to a concrete mix; fat, rich-appearing, plastic, opposite of harsh.

Stiff: Applied to a concrete mix; dry, lacking plasticity, low slump.

Stone: To rub a concrete surface with a carborundum stone. See *Rubbed surface.*

Strand: A group of wires twisted into a cable for use in prestressed concrete. A tendon.

Subbase: The layer of compacted, selected material placed on the subgrade to support the base. Some pavements have both a base and a subbase.

Subgrade: The foundation on which a pavement is constructed.

Suction: Absorption into the pores of a concrete surface. Customarily used in connection with the absorption of paint.

Tamped Pipe: Concrete pipe made by tamping a dry, no-slump mix into a rotating vertical mold.

Tendon: A wire, group of wires, or strand, for applying prestress to concrete.

Terrazzo: A floor finish obtained by embedding special aggregate in the fresh concrete, followed by grinding and polishing of the hardened concrete. Colored mortars are usually used.

Test Batch: A routine, normal batch of concrete from which samples are taken for routine-job quality-control tests, such as slump, air content, yield, and strength.

Thermal Incompatibility: A condition in which part of the aggregate has such different values of thermal properties, especially coefficient of expansion, when compared with other portions of the aggregate or the cement paste in any given concrete, as to cause damage or distress to the hardened concrete.

Tilt-up: A method of building construction in which wall panels are precast in a horizontal position, usually on the floor slab of the building, and subsequently tilted into vertical position, after the concrete has developed sufficient strength.

Time of Set: See *Setting time.*

Topping: See *Dust coat.* See *Floor topping.*

Tramp Iron: A piece of iron or steel that finds its way into bulk material, especially cement. It may be a bolt or similar item from some piece of machinery.

Transit-mixed Concrete: Concrete that is mixed in a truck mixer en route from the proportioning plant to the jobsite. See *Ready-mixed concrete.*

Tremie: A pipe, at least 10 in. in diameter, consisting of sections joined together with flanged and gasketed couplings, with a funnel-shaped section at the top to receive concrete for placing under water.

Tremie Seal: A foundation seal placed under water by means of a tremie, usually within an area enclosed by sheet piling. See *Foundation seal.*

Trial Mix: A preliminary batch of concrete mixed in the laboratory to determine the proportions of materials to produce concrete having certain specified properties.

Truck-mixed Concrete: Transit-mixed concrete.

Truck Mixer: A mixer mounted on a motor truck for mixing concrete while in transit from the proportioning plant to the jobsite. See *Transit-mixed concrete.*

Undersanded: The condition of concrete in which it appears to contain insufficient fine aggregate.

Undersize: In aggregate, the material passing the minimum specified sieve size. For example, in ¾ × 1½-in. aggregate, it is the portion passing the ¾-in. sieve.

Vacuum Concrete: Concrete that has been subjected to a vacuum, applied by means of mats placed on the surface of a slab, or by means of special form panels, for the purpose of removing water and entrapped air from the surface layer of concrete to improve durability, strength, and hardness of the surface.

Vibration: The act of rendering fresh concrete into a quasi-liquid state by the application of high-frequency vibratory impulses for the purpose of consolidation in the forms.

Vibration Limit: A limiting point in the hardening or setting time of concrete, determined by the penetration needle, beyond which the concrete can no longer be made plastic by vibration. See ASTM Designation: C 403. See *Setting time.*

Vibrocast Pipe: Concrete pipe made by placing concrete in a stationary vertical mold or form, and applying vibration, either internally or externally.

Volume Change: Expansion and contraction of hardened concrete resulting from wetting and drying or temperature variations.[4.3]

Warping Joint: See *Hinge joint.*

Wash Water: Water carried on a truck mixer or agitator for washing out the mixer drum after discharge of the batch.

Waste Mold: A mold or form made of plaster which, after the concrete placed therein has hardened, is removed piecemeal, being wasted or destroyed in the process.

Water-Cement Ratio: (1) The ratio of the weight of total water to the weight of cement in a batch of concrete. (2) The number of gallons of water per sack of cement in a batch of concrete. The amount of free water (but not absorbed water) in the aggregate is included in either case.

Water Gain: See *Bleeding.*

Water Reducer: An admixture that reduces the amount of mixing water required per batch of concrete, at the same time maintaining equal or superior workability and slump.

Waterproofer: A substance, added to a batch of concrete as an admixture, or applied to the hardened concrete as a paint or coating, which decreases permeability.

Weakened Plane Joint: See *Contraction joint.*

Weathering: Deterioration or decay of concrete under the influence of freezing and thawing, wetting and drying, and temperature changes.

Wet: As applied to consistency of fresh concrete: high slump, fluid, soft, opposite of dry.

Workability: The ease with which a given set of materials can be mixed into concrete and subsequently handled, transported, and placed with minimum loss of homogeneity.[2.1]

Workability Agent: An admixture added to concrete for the purpose of improving workability.

Yield: The number of cubic feet of concrete produced per sack of cement. Equals total volume per batch divided by the number of sacks per batch.

Specifications and Test Methods

List of principal specifications and test methods appertaining to concrete and concrete materials.

Note: This list includes only those methods and specifications that are apt to be used or referred to by the field engineer or inspector. It is suggested that the user contact the appropriate organization shown in Appendix B for standards not listed here.

Cement

ASTM C 150	Specifications for Portland Cement
ASTM C 175	Specifications for Air-Entraining Cement
ASTM C 205	Specifications for Portland–Blast-Furnace Slag Cement
ASTM C 340	Specifications for Portland-Pozzolan Cement
ASTM C 358	Specifications for Slag Cement
ASTM C 183	Method of Sampling Hydraulic Cement
SS-C-192	Federal Specifications for Cements, Portland
SS-C-158	Federal Specifications for Cements, Hydraulic, General Specifications (methods for sampling, inspection, and testing)

Aggregates

ASTM C 33	Specifications for Concrete Aggregates
ASTM C 330	Specifications for Lightweight Aggregate for Structural Concrete
ASTM C 332	Specifications for Lightweight Aggregates for Insulating Concrete
ASTM C 29	Test for Unit Weight of Aggregate
ASTM C 30	Test for Voids in Aggregate for Concrete
ASTM C 40	Test for Organic Impurities in Sands for Concrete
ASTM C 58	Definition of Terms Relating to Aggregate
ASTM C 70	Test for Surface Moisture in Fine Aggregate
ASTM C 87	Test for Mortar-Making Properties of Fine Aggregate
ASTM C 88	Test for Soundness of Aggregates by Use of Sodium or Magnesium Sulfate
ASTM C 117	Test for Materials Finer Than No. 200 Sieve in Mineral Aggregates by Washing
ASTM C 123	Test for Lightweight Pieces in Aggregate

ASTM C 125	Definition of Terms Relating to Concrete and Concrete Aggregates
ASTM C 127	Test for Specific Gravity and Absorption of Coarse Aggregate
ASTM C 128	Test for Specific Gravity and Absorption of Fine Aggregate
ASTM C 131	Test for Abrasion of Coarse Aggregate by Use of the Los Angeles Machine
ASTM C 136	Test for Sieve Analysis of Fine and Coarse Aggregate
ASTM C 142	Test for Clay Lumps in Natural Aggregates
ASTM C 227	Test for Potential Alkali Reactivity of Cement-Aggregate Combinations (Mortar Bar Method)
ASTM C 235	Test for Scratch Hardness of Coarse Aggregate Particles
ASTM C 289	Test for Potential Reactivity of Aggregates (Chemical Method)
ASTM C 294	Descriptive Nomenclature of Constituents of Natural Mineral Aggregates
ASTM C 342	Test for Volume Change, Potential, of Cement-Aggregate Combinations
ASTM D 3	Test for Toughness of Rock
ASTM D 75	Method of Sampling Stone, Slag, Gravel, Sand, and Stone Block for Use as Highway Materials
ASTM C 295	Recommended Practice for Petrographic Examination of Aggregates for Concrete
ASTM E 11	Specifications for Sieves for Testing Purposes
AASHO T 10	Test for Percentage of Shale in Aggregate
AASHO T 103	Test for Soundness of Aggregates by Freezing and Thawing

Concrete

ASTM C 94	Specifications for Ready-Mixed Concrete
ASTM C 260	Specifications for Air-Entraining Admixture for Concrete
ASTM C 350	Specifications for Fly Ash for Use as an Admixture in Portland Cement Concrete
ASTM C 387	Specifications for Dry Packaged Materials for Mortar and Concrete
ASTM C 402	Specifications for Pozzolans, Natural, Raw, or Calcined for Use as Admixtures in Portland Cement Concrete
ASTM C 470	Specifications for Single-Use Molds for Forming 6 by 12-in. Concrete Compression Test Cylinders
ASTM C 31	Concrete Compression and Flexure Test Specimens, Making and Curing in the Field
ASTM C 39	Compressive Strength of Molded Concrete Cylinders
ASTM C 42	Securing, Preparing, and Testing Specimens from Hardened Concrete for Compressive and Flexural Strengths
ASTM C 78	Flexural Strength of Concrete (Using Simple Beam with Third-Point Loading)
ASTM C 85	Cement Content of Hardened Portland Cement Concrete
ASTM C 116	Compressive Strength of Concrete Using Portions of Beams Broken in Flexure (Modified-Cube Method)
ASTM C 124	Flow of Portland Cement Concrete by Use of the Flow Table

ASTM C 138	Weight per Cubic Foot, Yield, and Air Content (Gravimetric) of Concrete
ASTM C 143	Slump of Portland Cement Concrete
ASTM C 157	Volume Change of Cement Mortar and Concrete
ASTM C 172	Sampling Fresh Concrete
ASTM C 173	Air Content of Freshly Mixed Concrete by the Volumetric Method
ASTM C 174	Measuring the Length of Drilled Concrete Cores
ASTM C 192	Making and Curing Concrete Compression and Flexure Specimens in the Laboratory
ASTM C 215	Fundamental Transverse, Longitudinal, and Torsional Frequencies of Concrete Specimens
ASTM C 231	Air Content of Freshly Mixed Concrete by the Pressure Method
ASTM C 232	Bleeding of Concrete
ASTM C 233	Testing Air-Entraining Admixtures for Concrete
ASTM C 234	Comparing Concretes on the Basis of Bond Developed with Reinforcing Steel
ASTM C 290	Resistance of Concrete Specimens to Rapid Freezing and Thawing in Water
ASTM C 291	Resistance of Concrete Specimens to Rapid Freezing in Air and Thawing in Water
ASTM C 292	Resistance of Concrete Specimens to Slow Freezing and Thawing in Water or Brine
ASTM C 293	Flexural Strength of Concrete (Using Simple Beam with Center Point Loading)
ASTM C 310	Resistance of Concrete Specimens to Slow Freezing in Air and Thawing in Water
ASTM C 311	Sampling and Testing Fly Ash for Use as an Admixture in Portland Cement Concrete
ASTM C 403	Time of Setting of Concrete Mixtures Using Proctor Penetration Resistance Needles
ASTM C 441	Testing Effectiveness of Mineral Admixtures in Preventing Excessive Expansion of Concrete Due to Alkali-Aggregate Reaction
ASTM C 469	Determination of Static, Young's Modulus of Elasticity and Poisson's Ratio in Compression of Cylindrical Concrete Specimens
USCE CRD-C6	Test for Workability of Concrete (Remolding Test)
USBR 26	Test for Variability of Mortar in Concrete (a Test of Mixer Performance)
USCE CRD-C53	Calculation of Amount of Ice Needed to Produce Mixed Concrete of a Specified Temperature

Curing Materials and Joint Fillers

ASTM C 156	Test for Water Retention Efficiency of Liquid Membrane Forming Compounds and Impermeable Sheet Materials for Curing Concrete
ASTM C 171	Specifications for Waterproof Paper for Curing Concrete
ASTM C 309	Specifications for Liquid Membrane-Forming Compounds for Curing Concrete
ASTM C 440	Specifications for Cotton Mats for Curing Concrete

ASTM D 98	Specifications for Calcium Chloride
ASTM D 345	Sampling and Testing Calcium Chloride
ASTM D 545	Testing of Preformed Expansion Joint Fillers for Concrete
ASTM D 632	Specifications for Sodium Chloride
ASTM D 994	Specifications for Preformed Expansion Joint Filler for Concrete
ASTM D 1190	Specifications for Hot-Poured Elastic Concrete Joint Filler
ASTM D 1191	Testing Concrete Joint Sealers
ASTM D 1751	Specifications for Preformed Expansion Joint Fillers for Concrete Paving and Structural Construction (Nonextruding and Resilient Bituminous Types)
ASTM D 1752	Specifications for Preformed Expansion Joint Fillers for Concrete Paving and Structural Construction (Nonextruding and Resilient Nonbituminous Types)
ASTM D 1850	Specifications for Cold-Applied Concrete Joint Sealer
ASTM D 1851	Testing of Cold-Applied Concrete Joint Sealer
ASTM D 1852	Specifications for Jet-Fuel-Resistant, Cold Applied Concrete Joint Sealer
ASTM D 1853	Testing of Jet-Fuel-Resistant, Cold-Applied Concrete Joint Sealer
ASTM D 1854	Specifications for Jet-Fuel-Resistant, Hot-Poured Elastic Concrete Joint Sealer
ASTM D 1855	Testing of Jet-Fuel-Resistant, Hot-Poured Elastic Concrete Joint Sealer
AASHO M 74	Specifications for Subgrade Paper
AASHO T 26	Test for Quality of Water to Be Used in Concrete

Reinforcing Steel

ASTM A 15	Specifications for Billet-Steel Bars for Concrete Reinforcement
ASTM A 16	Specifications for Rail-Steel Bars for Concrete Reinforcement
ASTM A 82	Specifications for Cold-Drawn Steel Wire for Concrete Reinforcement
ASTM A 160	Specifications for Axle-Steel Bars for Concrete Reinforcement
ASTM A 184	Specifications for Fabricated Steel Bar or Rod Mats for Concrete Reinforcement
ASTM A 185	Specifications for Welded Steel Wire Fabric for Concrete Reinforcement
ASTM A 305	Minimum Requirements for the Deformations of Deformed Steel Bars for Concrete Reinforcement
ASTM A 408	Specifications for Special Large-Size Deformed Billet-Steel Bars for Concrete Reinforcement
ASTM A 416	Specifications for Uncoated, Seven-Wire Stress-Relieved Strand for Prestressed Concrete
ASTM A 421	Specifications for Uncoated, Stress-Relieved Wire for Prestressed Concrete
ASTM A 431	Specifications for High-Strength Billet-Steel Bars for Concrete Reinforcement
ASTM A 432	Specifications for Deformed Billet-Steel Bars, with 60,000 psi Minimum Yield Point for Concrete Reinforcement

Precast Concrete

ASTM Various	Specifications for Masonry Units: C 55, C 90, C 129, C 139, C 145
ASTM C 140	Methods of Sampling and Testing Concrete Masonry Units
ASTM Various	Specifications for Concrete Pipe: C 76, C 118, C 361, C 444
AASHO T 33	Methods of Testing Culvert Pipe, Sewer Pipe, and Drain Tile

Miscellaneous

ASTM Various	Specifications for Membrane Waterproofing Materials; Primers D 41, D 43; Asphalts D 449, D 491; Coal Tar Pitch D 450; Bituminous Grouts D 170, D 171; Felts and Fabrics D 173, D 226, D 227, D 250, D 1327, D 1668

APPENDIX B *Sources of Information*

The following listed professional, technical, and other organizations publish standards, recommended practices, and other publications in the field of concrete and related materials.

AASHO
American Association of State Highway Officials
917 National Press Building
Washington 4, D.C.

ACI
American Concrete Institute
P.O. Box 4754, Redford Station
Detroit 19, Mich.

ACPA
American Concrete Pipe Association
228 North LaSalle Street
Chicago, Ill.

AGC
Associated General Contractors of America
20th and E Street, N.W.
Washington 6, D.C.

AIA
American Institute of Architects
1735 New York Avenue, N.W.
Washington 6, D.C.

APWA
American Public Works Association
1313 E. 60th Street
Chicago 37, Ill.

ARBA
American Road Builders Association
1319 F Street, N.W.
Washington 4, D.C.

AREA
American Railway Engineering Association
59 E. Van Buren Street
Chicago, Ill.

ASCE
American Society of Civil Engineers
33 West 39th Street
New York 18, N.Y.

ASTM
American Society for Testing and Materials
1916 Race Street
Philadelphia 3, Pa.

BOCA
Building Officials Conference of America, Inc.
1525 E. 53d Street
Chicago 15, Ill.

BPR	Bureau of Public Roads U.S. Department of Commerce Washington 25, D.C.
BRC	Building Research Council See National Academy of Sciences
CCI	Calcium Chloride Institute 1200 18th Street, N.W. Washington 6, D.C.
CJI	Concrete Joint Institute 360 N. Michigan Ave. Chicago 1, Ill.
CRSI	Concrete Reinforcing Steel Institute 38 S. Dearborn Street Chicago 3, Ill.
CSI	Construction Specifications Institute 632 DuPont Circle Building Washington 6, D.C.
ECSA	Expanded Clay and Shale Association P.O. Box 94 Alpena, Mich.
EJMA	Expansion Joint Manufacturers Association 53 Park Place New York 7, N.Y.
HRB	Highway Research Board See National Academy of Sciences
MMB	Mixer Manufacturers Bureau 20th and E Street, N.W. Washington 6, D.C.
NAS	National Academy of Sciences 2101 Constitution Avenue Washington 25, D.C.
NBS	National Bureau of Standards U.S. Department of Commerce Washington 25, D.C.
NCMA	National Concrete Masonry Association 1015 Wisconsin Avenue, N.W. Washington 6, D.C.
NCSA	National Crushed Stone Association 1415 Elliot Place, N.W. Washington 7, D.C.
NRMCA	National Ready Mixed Concrete Association 1411 K Street, N.W. Washington 5, D.C.
NRS	National Research Council See National Academy of Sciences
NSA	National Slag Association 613 Perpetual Building Washington 4, D.C.
NSGA	National Sand and Gravel Association 1411 K Street, N.W. Washington 5, D.C.

NTMA	National Terrazzo and Mosaic Association 2000 K Street, N.W. Washington 6, D.C.
PCA	Portland Cement Association 33 West Grand Avenue Chicago 10, Ill.
PCI	Prestressed Concrete Institute 205 West Wacker Drive Chicago 6, Ill.
PI	Perlite Institute, Inc. 45 West 45th Street New York 36, N.Y.
RSBA	Rail Steel Bar Association 38 South Dearborn Street Chicago 3, Ill.
US	U.S. Government Printing Office Washington 25, D.C.
USBR	U.S. Bureau of Reclamation Denver Federal Center Denver 2, Colo.
USCE	Corps of Engineers, U.S. Army Waterways Experiment Station Vicksburg, Miss.
VI	Vermiculite Institute 208 S. LaSalle Street Chicago 4, Ill.
WRI	Wire Reinforcing Institute, Inc. National Press Building Washington 4, D.C.

Index

Abrasion of aggregate, effect on concrete strength, 27
Absorption of aggregate, 27, 44, 91, 98, 327
Accelerator, 33, 350, 351
  calcium chloride (*see* Calcium chloride admixture)
  types, 139
ACI Building Code, 324
  Committee 212, 138
  Committee 214, 311, 315
  Committee 604, 33, 237
  Committee 609, 218
  Committee 613, 325–345
  Committee 613A, 347
  Committee 622, 203
  Committee 505, 79
Acids, effect on concrete, 7
  organic, sources of, 7, 64
  (*See also* type of acid)
Adhesive, 103, 150, 256
  uses, 282
Admixture, batching, 177, 179, 189
  for dampproofing and waterproofing, 83, 84
  definition of, 138
  effect, on compressive strength, 33
    on workability, 20
  evaluation of, 138
  in hot weather, 230, 231
  inspection of, 187, 304
  overdose, effect of, 139
  sampling, 138–142, 187
Aggregate, absorption, and shrinkage of concrete, 27, 44, 91, 98, 327
  batching, 177–182, 191
  beneficiation, 54, 108, 159–162
  coatings on, 28, 55, 173
    removal of, 157
  contaminants in, 55, 153, 187
  crushed material in, 170
  deleterious particles in, 92, 173
  deposit, evaluation of, 151, 152
    preliminary approval of, 151, 152
  effect, on cracking, 90, 92, 94

Aggregate, effect, on creep, 49
  on durability, 48, 54, 55, 64, 95–97, 107
  on shrinkage, 44
  on stains, 110
  on strength, 24, 27, 28
  on thermal properties, 47
  on workability, 4, 11, 18, 19, 27, 347
  expansion of, 92, 97
  frozen, 234
  grading of, 4, 18–20, 27, 44, 90, 157, 171–173, 326, 331, 347
  lightweight, 154, 155
  moisture content, determination of, 179, 188, 327–334
    uniformity of, 12, 29, 188
    variations, causes, 188
  production, 155–165
  reactive, 67, 92, 95–97, 175
  sampling, 153, 166–170, 187
    precautions in, 187
    schedule for, 168
  segregation of (*see* Segregation of aggregate)
  stockpiles, 162–165
    capacity of, 174, 175
    contamination, 163, 186
  surface of, 10, 55
  tests, 9
    methods, 170–175
    for preliminary approval, 152
    for trial batch, 331
  undersize, 19, 187
  unsound, 67
    causes popouts, 107, 159
Agitator, 197, 199
Air content, measuring, 305
    errors in, 306
    gravimetric, 306
    pressure, 305
    volumetric, 306
      for lightweight concrete, 306
    recommended amount, 66, 348
      for floor, 248

381